STUDIES IN ROMANCE LANGUAGES: 27
John E. Keller, *Editor*

THE BOOK OF THE
KNIGHT ZIFAR

A Translation of
El Libro del Cavallero Zifar

CHARLES L. NELSON

THE UNIVERSITY PRESS OF KENTUCKY

Library of Congress Cataloging in Publication Data

Libro del cavallero Zifar. English.
    The book of the knight Zifar.

    (Studies in Romance languages ; 27)
    Includes bibliographical references.
    I. Nelson, Charles L. II. Title. III. Series.
PQ6388.C2E5   1982   863'.1   82-21940
ISBN 0-8131-1478-0

Contents

Introduction

I have felt for a long time that an English version of the *Book of the Knight Zifar* should be available to more than just the limited number of persons interested in medieval Spanish, that it should be in reach of the many readers who are intrigued by the novels of chivalry and their origins. Since this famous novel appeared in Spain more than three hundred years before the world-renowned and much translated masterpiece *Don Quixote de la Mancha* of Miguel de Cervantes, whose hero resembles in many ways the Knight Zifar, I think it only fitting that this first Spanish novel should be more widely recognized. Although it cannot be proved that Cervantes ever read the *Book of the Knight Zifar*, it is entirely possible that he did, since the Seville edition of the *Knight Zifar* appeared only thirty-five years before the birth of Cervantes.

Two documents in the fourteenth century testify to the popularity of this book. The *Regimiento de los Príncipes*, which was written by Juan de Castrojeriz for the education of prince Don Pedro el Cruel and which dates from around 1345, placed the *Knight Zifar* on a par with *Tristan* and *Amadis de Gaula*. A letter from Pedro of Aragón dated October 27, 1361, and sent to Eximeno de Monreal, his chaplain and scribe, complains that the king has not yet received a copy of the *"librum militti Siffar,"* which he had ordered.

The noted scholar Charles P. Wagner, whose edition I am using, places the date of the original manuscript around the early years of the fourteenth century and suggests that the most convenient date to use would be 1300. Because it was not printed until 1512, when Jacob Cromberger published it in Seville, the *Libro del Cavallero Zifar* was assumed to be a novel of the early sixteenth century. This was proved an error when another manuscript was discovered in 1882 in the library of the Duke of Osuna which contained a prologue not included in the 1512 Seville edition. This prologue is included in the translation of this book. Since it contains many references to the year 1300 and to actual historical personages and events, we can logically assume the date of composition to be early fourteenth century.

Nothing certain is known about the author of the book. It has been suggested by many scholars of medieval Spanish, including Juan Hurtado and Angel González-Palencia, that he was Ferrand Martínez, archdeacon of Madrid in the church of Toledo. Much of the Prologue concerns the archdeacon's trip to Rome to obtain absolution and the details of his return to

Spain, escorting the remains of Don Gonzalo, bishop of Aluaña and cardinal in the Church. Because of the diversity of sources and styles of writing, the author may have been a cleric familiar with all the main elements of culture in his day. His notions of science and geography, the moralization and indoctrinations of the book, and the many references to the Bible, as well as his knowledge of military and chivalric tactics, would seem to support this. The author's attention to Christian morality throughout the book does indeed suggest ecclesiastical authorship. However, since it is a book of war, adventure, and chivalry, the author may have been a soldier as well as a cleric, for many clergymen were at the same time soldiers. Making the authorship even more speculative is the fact that one of its sources was the *Siete Partidas.* King Alfonso X's book of laws, so called from its seven divisions, was codified between 1256 and 1265, and furnished one of the most complete panoramas ever promulgated of medieval life among all strata of population. Anyone able to read it could have written all the accounts of knights, customs, and battle scenes, since the *Siete Partidas* discusses in great detail all aspects of chivalry and warfare: lineage, virtues, duties, and selection of knights; rules for the command of armies; division of booty; and every other conceivable detail. To state definitely that the author was a military man or a cleric would be risky, but that he was in love with things chivalric is certain. The unknown author seized upon the old and well-known story of Placidus (Saint Eustacius) for the vehicle to carry his long and rambling narrative. He also leaned heavily upon the thirteenth-century *Flores de filosofía,* the thirteenth-century *Siete Partidas* of Alfonso el Sabio, the Bible, and the fables of Aesop. The author's use of time as reckoned by the Roman Curia lends support to the theory that he was a clergyman, used to dealing with time not as a Spaniard but as a churchman. (The Roman Curia based its time on the calendar of Caesar, which began thirty-eight years before the Christian computation.)

Because of the similarity of the life of the Knight Zifar to the life of Placidus, a brief account of the legend may be helpful to te reader. This legend appeared in Greek in the eighth century and in Latin in the tenth. It was widespread through the West through the *Speculum Historiale* of Vincent de Beauvais, the *Legenda aurea,* and the *Gesta Romanorum.*

Placidus is the pagan commander of the Emperor Trajan's cavalry. One day while hunting, Placidus is separated from his companions. He pursues a stag, which speaks to him with the voice of the Lord, urging him to be converted. He and his family are baptized and he is renamed Eustacius. He is given the choice between present and later suffering and he chooses present. Like Job's, his suffering becomes almost unbearable as he loses his servants, his domestic animals, and his cattle. To escape the displeasure of the Emperor Trajan, Eustacius and his family embark for Egypt. The barbarian sea captain has Eustacius and his sons hurled into the sea but retains his wife for his own pleasure. She resists the barbarian but is carried away to his land. Eustacius and his sons arrive safely on shore, but later one of his sons is carried off by a lion and the other by a wolf. Unknown to Eustacius, his sons are rescued by peasants from the fierce beasts. Later the king of the barbarians declares war on the Emperor Trajan, who recalls Eustacius to his service. His two sons, unrecognized by him, serve Eustacius as military aides. The barbarian king is defeated and Eustacius recovers his wife and recognizes his sons. On their refusal to return to pagan worship, Trajan has them thrown to the lions. When the lions refuse to attack them, he has them encased in a heated metal idol. God allows them to die and preserves their bodies from the flames.

The *Book of the Knight Zifar* parallels the Placidus/Eustacius legend in a number of ways: Zifar is the commander of the king's cavalry; he is relieved of that command; he and his family fall upon hard times; they travel to another land to improve their fortunes; there a lion carries off one of his sons; the other son strays away and is lost; both sons are rescued by a rich townsman; the sons are raised in the military tradition; Zifar's wife is carried off by a sea captain; the Lord speaks to Zifar assuring him of eventual happiness; his wife travels to a strange land; later she and the two sons make themselves known to each other, and eventually Zifar is reunited with them.

The complete title of the book translates from Spanish as *The Book of the Knight of God Whose Name Was Zifar, Who because of His Exercise of Virtue and Heroic Deeds Became King of Mentón.* Wagner suggests that the book is divided into four separate and distinct parts. It is long and filled with knightly adventure, interpolated short stories, and the moralizing and didactic *exempla* of the medieval period.

The method of instructing by fables or apologues has its origins in antiquity, and the Bible attests to its longevity, popularity, and efficacy. Every Christian knows that Jesus used the short narrative or parable to simplify an understanding of the Word of God. Because of the great effectiveness of the *exempla,* the medieval preachers related these stories in their sermons to add some spice and to keep their largely illiterate congregations interested. Eventually these tales enhanced the reputation of the sermons to such an extent that the Church banned their use in a decree of the Council of Salzburg in 1386. The literature of the Middle Ages is replete with brief narratives, and the *Book of the Knight Zifar* is no exception. In fact, many of the stories are told here in much greater detail and in a more interesting style than in other collections.

Within the first ten chapters of Book I, "The Knight of God," and through the medium of the medieval *exempla,* the author sets the stage for the journey and adventures of the knight, his wife, and their two sons. Like most knights of medieval stories, the Knight Zifar sets out to search for better fortune on whatever road he finds, letting chance guide his steps. He and his family arrive at the besieged town of Galapia, where the Knight Zifar organizes the defense and breaks the siege. On the road to the town of Mella in the kingdom of Falac, he loses one son, the other is lost in the town of

Mella, and his wife is kidnapped by seamen on the beach near the town. The voice of God tells him he will overcome all adversity, he meets the knave who will become his squire, and he lifts the siege of Mentón. The king of Mentón has pledged to give his daughter in marriage to whoever lifts the siege of the town.

Integrated within these adventures of the Knight Zifar are eight brief narratives, among these a retelling of Pedro Alfonso's tales of the "half-friend" and the "whole friend," a story of a Roman emperor who was terrified of storms, the Aesopic story of "The Ass and the Lapdog," and the two tales involving the knave, squire to the Knight Zifar, one concerning the thief and the bag of gold, the other the often retold episode of the knave stealing from the turnip garden. Also, in the hagiographical tradition of the time, there is a tale of a queen miraculously resuscitated by the Virgin Mary, and the complicated story of the kidnapping and miraculous salvation of Zifar's wife.

Book II, entitled "The King of Mentón," begins with the marriage of the Knight Zifar to the daughter of the king of Mentón. The story then shifts to Grima, the first wife of the Knight Zifar, who has spent nine years in the kingdom of Orbín following her kidnapping at Mella. She decides to return to live and die in her native land. Eventually she makes a landfall in the kingdom of Mentón, where she is recognized by her husband, but she is doubtful of his identity. She is reunited with her sons, who have come to Mentón to serve the king. The sons are both involved in the fighting attendant upon the capture of the treacherous vassal of the king of Mentón. On the sentencing of the traitor to death, a strange tale is introduced concerning the supernatural, which is related to the Arthurian tradition. When the ashes of the cremated traitor are thrown into a lake, weird things begin to happen: the lake boils, strange voices are heard, and visions of men fighting are seen. The author then introduces a story of a land beneath the lake; a knight known only as the Bold Knight is induced by a beautiful lady to enter the lake with her. He marries the lady, who gives birth to a son in seven days, and the son grows to manhood in seven days. The knight and his son are forcibly ejected from the lake. This story of unknown origin is seemingly inserted by the author because of his own liking for the plot, but it is related to the main story by a slender thread, for the king of Mentón orders that in the future every traitor be cast into the mysterious lake. (There is another allusion to it in Book IV, "The Adventures of Roboán," Chapter 205, where Roboán, son of the Knight Zifar, visits the Islas Dotadas, the magic islands, and there experiences many of the same incidents as the Bold Knight. Tongue in cheek, the author tells us that all that supposedly happened to the Bold Knight "was a pretense and a lie and this was the real thing.") "The King of Mentón" concludes with the timely and fortunate death of the Knight Zifar's second wife so that he can recognize and be reconciled with his long-missing first wife, Grima, and his two sons.

Book III is entitled "The Instructions of the King of Mentón," a long and didactic discourse that interrupts the narrative of the Knight Zifar and his family. It is based mainly on the thirteenth-century *Flores de filosofía,* which is divided into thirty-nine chapters and claims to be wisdom of thirty-nine sages. This section of the book contains several *exempla,* as well as other interpolated tales to illustrate the king's instructions. For example, to emphasize the danger of listening to bad advice, the author relates the well-known tale of "The Hunter and the Calender Lark," in which the hunter, not heeding the advice of the lark, tries to fly from a high tower and is killed.

Book IV, "The Adventures of Roboán," tells of the deeds of the Knight Zifar's younger son, Roboán. Many of his adventures are repetitions of the events of the Knight Zifar and his sons from Books I and II. An unusual treatment of the brief narrative tale is revealed here. No longer is it simply interpolated to illustrate some didactic or moralistic point or as a lesson in statecraft; instead it is combined with the argument of the novel itself. This methods was used in Books I and II but to a lesser extent. In this part of the book, possibly written by someone other than the author of the first three books, Roboán becomes a participant in the brief narrative which occupies a great portion of Book IV.

The style of this book is quite readable; however, in many parts its syntax is confused and the grammar lacks uniformity. The lack of subject pronouns in many areas causes a confusion in which the reader has to determine for himself who said what and to whom. The author, however, does maintain a high standard as to agreement of nouns and adjectives, the action moves smoothly, and there is skillful and clever use of dialogue and humor.

The tone of the book is recreational as well as didactic. It was obviously intended to entertain and amuse the reader as well as to convey moral instruction, for the author states in his Prologue: "Every man who aspires to make a good work must interpose in it occasionally some things of pleasure and solace. And the wise man's proverb states: 'Some pleasurable things should at times be placed among afflictions and grief.' It is a very difficult thing to suffer continuous grief if a man is not given pleasure or solace at intervals." Most works of the medieval period were didactic in nature, and when the didacticism was not relieved by humor they were extremely tiresome. The inclusion of the *exempla,* then, is not unusual. A delightful comic element runs like a thread through the book and is obvious from the very beginning, where the author tells of a curse upon the family of Zifar which decrees that any animal that the knight rides will drop dead after ten days, certainly a most unusual curse. I have been unable to find any curse even faintly resembling it, unless we consider the biblical curse on Job which caused the death of his cattle. It would appear to be a device to impel the narrative and to pose challenges for the Knight Zifar. The curse is directly responsible for his fate, as is clearly stated in Chapter 2:

But this knight cost the king great expense, for he had to equip the knight with horses and other animals that he needed at the end of every ten-day period while the war lasted, until it seemed to the king that he could no longer tolerate it or allow him to serve out his time.

When one considers that the horse and the sword were the two most valuable of a knight's possessions, one can more easily understand and sympathize with the unhappy lot of the Knight Zifar because of the curse under which he lived. One can also understand the king's concern over the expense of replacing a horse every ten days as well. Envious courtiers advised the Knight Zifar's lord in India that he could obtain the services of five hundred knights for what the Knight Zifar was costing him in horses—or in other animals he might ride. The embarrassment to the knight and the expense to the lord were intolerable. In medieval times the fame of a knight's horse and sword were inseparable from the knight himself. Horses were the most coveted of all booty taken in battle, and surely must have been killed most reluctantly by the combatants. A horse capable of carrying a heavily armed and armored knight would be highly prized. If the horse was killed, capture or death for the rider was imminent.

The Knight Zifar is very careful with the horses he owns, and when he acquires a new one, he never rides it before the death of the old mount. The *Siete Partidas* reinforces the importance of the horse to the medieval knight. Under Law X, Part II, Title XXI, we find that:

Horses, armor, and weapons are things which it is highly proper for knights to have of good quality, each according to its kind. For, since they are obliged to perform deeds of arms with them, which is their profession, it is fitting that they be of such a description that they can get good service from them; *and of the things with which they should be thoroughly familiar, the knowledge of horses is of the greatest importance.* [Italics mine]

Under Law XXV, Part II, Title XXI we find that:

. . . *a knight can be deprived of knighthood* if he sells or disposes of his horse or his arms, or loses them while throwing dice, or gives them away while serving under his lord or while serving on the frontier. [Italics mine]

The significance of the curse upon the Knight Zifar, with the catastrophic effects that the loss of a horse every ten days has upon him and his family, cannot be overemphasized.

The Knight Zifar himself is a strange and confusing character in certain ways. He seems an admixture of brilliant militarist, loving father and husband, devout Christian, and warrior who must on occasion be saved from harm by his supposedly uneducated squire and guided by him in his actions.

We might take Chaucer's description of his knight in the Prologue to the *Canterbury Tales* as a picture of the Knight Zifar, but with some qualifications:

A knyght ther was, and that a worthy man,
That fro the tyme that he first bigan
To riden out, he lovede chivalrye,
Trouthe and honour, fredom and curteisye,
Ful worthy was he in his lordes werre,
And thereto hadde he ridden, no man ferre,
As wel in cristendom as in hethenesse,
And ever honoured for his worthinesse. [ll.43-50]

And though that he were worthy, he was wys,
And of his port as meeke as is a mayde.
He never yet no vileinye ne sayde
In al his lyf, unto no maner wight.
He was a verray, parfit, gentil knyght. [ll. 68-72]

Various glowing descriptions of the Knight Zifar occur in the text. He is "gifted with prudence, prowess, justice, wisdom, and truthfulness, no matter how fortune ran against him in reducing him to poverty. However, he never gave up his faith in God." "He was a great warrior who gave very wise counsel." "God always strengthened this knight in feats of arms, so with his good common sense and prowess, he always conquered and gained honor and victory for his lord, the king, and great esteem for himself." In speaking with his wife, the knight avers that "God endowed me, through His grace, with special traits of chivalry that He did not give to any other knight of this time." Statements of this kind are repeated throughout, so we must believe that the author intended to portray the Knight Zifar in such terms. Yet many times the protagonist in his adventures finds himself in situations in which his "good common sense and prowess" serve him little.

Although Zifar is a brave, courteous, and pious knight, he is no candidate for sainthood. He is ambitious to restore his family to its former glory, for one of his ancestors had been a king who had lost everything through his evil ways. In Book II, "The King of Mentón," he deceives his new bride, the princess of Mentón, by lying to her, for he is afraid that his lost wife still lives and he would be living in sin. There are also times when he cannot seem to fend for himself, and he casts himself wholly upon the wisdom and guidance of his squire.

The most outstanding character of the *Book of the Knight* is a character called El Ribaldo—the knave. He is a forerunner of the *pícaro* of the sixteenth century and surely the prototype of Cervantes' famous Sancho Panza, squire to Don Quixote. The knave is a rough and uneducated fisherman when he first meets the Knight Zifar. Attempting to better himself and acquire learning from a nobleman, he tries the knight's patience by asking him impertinent questions. From the knave, the Knight Zifar hears of the siege of Mentón and the king's offer to give his daughter in marriage to whoever lifts it. It is the knave who stiffens the knight's resolve to go to the aid of the king of Mentón when he appears to weaken. It is the knave who counsels the knight when he is downcast and in despair. The knave becomes squire to the knight after exacting a promise that the knight will raise him to high estate when he betters his own fortunes. He displays many of the traits later found in Sancho Panza. He, like, Sancho, speaks with wisdom from a rough and uncultured background, punctuates his conversation with proverbs, counts on making his fortune through his association with a knight-errant, is more than duly concerned with the welfare of his stomach, and displays a great sense of humor.

In the author's original descriptions, Grima, the wife of the Knight Zifar, and third of the three main characters, is a paragon of feminine virtues. However, her behavior sometimes belies these qualities: "She was an excellent and virtuous lady, uncommonly submissive to her husband and the keeper and protectress of his home." She is praised for her care of her children, she worries over her husband's despondency, she can keep secrets, she is compliant and obedient, she has faith in God, and she encourages her husband in every way. She is a strong-willed person and able to sustain great losses and privation. She has seen her husband lose all his wealth and position, suffered the loss of both her young children, endured kidnapping and perilous journeys, learned of her husband's second marriage, and undergone accusations of adultery. She also tells many lies as she undergoes her adventures. Possibly these are motivated through fear and the desire to keep her identity secret. Some of her lies are entirely groundless, since the Virgin Mary had spoken to her and had assured her of eventual happiness.

Grima is virtuous, charitable, hospitable, adventurous, clever, submissive, obedient, perceptive and like her husband, tells falsehoods when it seems convenient and to her advantage to do so. The Knight Zifar is a great fighter, steadfast, courageous, righteous, and with a confidence in his faith that endures through almost all his adventures. The knave is quick-witted, pragmatic, faithful to his lord, religious, obedient as a good vassal, courageous in war, perceptive, capable of leadership, and above all possessed of a sense of humor that never fails.

The present translation, which is the first into English, is based on the noted edition of Charles P. Wagner, published by the University of Michigan Press in 1929, and endeavors to stay as close as possible to the original Spanish, within the limitations of English style. The division of the original into four books has been retained.

The names of the characters and places that are easily translatable appear in English, but some of the names that have no English equivalent or would appear awkward or ill-sounding have been retained in Spanish. For example, the *ribaldo* is translated as the *knave,* but the name Amigo remains in Spanish since the English translation of Friend Knight or the Friendly Knight does not convey the real relationship of the Knight Amigo to the Knight Zifar and his sons, as the original Spanish does.

The style of the medieval period is retained as much as possible although at times it may seem stilted and awkward, but this awkwardness indicates an important characteristic of the author. One must remember that this is the beginning of the development of Spanish writing and does not represent style as it appears in the Golden Age. I have only very occasionally added a word or a phrase not in the original in order to make the meaning clear. The author had a sense of humor, and a number of puns abound. They are always a problem to a translator, but I have done the best I could.

To relieve the monotony of the use of *dixo,* "said," in conversations between the characters of the novel, I have taken the liberty of translating *dixo* as "responded," "stated," "declared," "answered," "inquired," "questioned," and so on. The original Spanish dialogues seldom supply the name of the character who is speaking, and the frequent use of "he said" and "she said" has been replaced by "the knight said," "the princess replied," and so forth. The repetitious "he" and "she," and often the use of the third-person singular verb, lead to a lack of clarity and the reader finds himself confused as to the antecedents. I do not believe my substitutions in any way detract from the author's intent or alter the meaning of the original.

When one tries to make the English rendering of any Spanish text convey exactly the sense of the original, the same difficulty arises as when two people view a rainbow and wonder if they are seeing exactly the same colors. As much as possible, I have tried to be faithful to the original. There is always the possibility that any translation may look like the reverse side of a tapestry, showing the same picture but not in the same clarity of detail. There are always passages in the writing of ages past in which the meanings are doubtful, and a span of almost seven hundred years between composition and translation tends to obscure some of the thoughts. I have chosen the interpretation I thought best by consulting variant forms in the other manuscripts of the *Cavallero Zifar.* On many occasions, I have broken long passages into short and concise sentences that help to clarify their meanings; otherwise, the original Spanish would have translated into lengthy English paragraphs that would have put Faulkner to shame.

Readers interested in further study and research into the sources of the *Book of the Knight of God* should consult Philip Wagner's article "The Sources of the *Cavallero Zifar," Revue hispanique* 10 (1903): 5-104. For a detailed and comprehensive bibliography, I suggest the monograph by James F. Burke, *History and Vision: the Figural Structure of the "Libro del Cavallero Zifar"* (London: Tamesis Books, 1972).

Without the help of others this translation could not have come into being. I have been encouraged and helped many times by my longtime friend, colleague, and mentor, Dr. John E. Keller of the University of Kentucky, and my friend and colleague Dr. Kathleen Kulp Hill of Eastern Kentucky University. I owe to both a debt of gratitude for the many long hours they spent reading the manuscript and for their suggestions for improvement. I hope that readers of English, lovers of the literature of the Middle Ages, and medievalists of all disciplines will find something of value herein.

Prologue

In the time of the honorable Pope Boniface VIII, the year of jubilee began on the birthday of Our Lord Jesus Christ in the year 1300.[1] It is called the centenary year because it comes every hundred years and the next year of jubilee would be celebrated during Christmas of the year 1400.[2] In the aforementioned year 1300, many full pardons were granted as far as the power of the pope could reach. The papal bull of our lord the pope proclaimed that all those who could go to the city of Rome for a period of fifteen days to seek out the churches of Saint Peter and Saint Paul would receive complete pardon. Our lord the pope understood the great faith and devotion that the Christian people had in the pardons of the year of jubilee. Aware of the trouble, the risks, the great hardships, the dangers on the highways, and the pilgrims' expenses, aware also that they would return happy to their companions, the pope decided that all the pilgrims from outside the city of Rome would be entitled to full pardons, although they might not spend fifteen days visiting the churches of Saint Peter and Saint Paul as the others had done. And thus pardons were also granted to all those who had left their homes to go on this pilgrimage and had died before reaching Rome and to those who had died after they had arrived and visited the churches of Saint Peter and Saint Paul. Moreover pardons were granted to those who set out on the pilgrimage with the intention of completing it but were prevented from doing so by sickness and other problems. They were grateful that they received pardons, just as those others who had arrived and completed their pilgrimages.

Truly a man was lucky who, knowing of this pilgrimage and that he could gain absolute forgiveness in this year, was able to travel without hindrance on this trip. On this pilgrimage those who had confessed, as well

1. The Christian jubilee was invented by Boniface VIII in order to obtain money needed for the Papacy and to exalt his own prestige. He issued a bull which determined that every one hundred years a universal jubilee would be celebrated, and this year of jubilee began on Christmas Day 1300.

2. Pope Clement VI could not wait until the next year of jubilee in 1400 and in 1342 he decreed a jubilee for every fifty years, with the second one to be held in 1350. Since the author of the *Book of the Knight Zifar* has clearly stated that the second jubilee year will be in 1400, it is clear that the book was written prior to 1342.

as those who had neglected to, were all equally absolved of sins and penance. The Holy Father's authority was extended to all those clergy who had fallen into sin or had profaned their office. It was also expended on clerics and laymen, on adulterers and those who failed to pray as they were supposed to, and on many things. The only exception to the pope's indulgence was on debts that each of the pilgrims owed and on anything they had borrowed, seized, or stolen, or in any way held against the will of the owner. It was considered proper to return these things, and because they might be unable at the time to return them, the pope set a time limit in which repayment could be made in order that they might also obtain the fullest pardons. This time limit was made in 1339 and expired at Easter.[3]

In the above-mentioned year, Ferrand Martínez, archdeacon of Madrid in the church of Toledo, traveled to Rome to obtain this absolution. He completed his pilgrimage and gained forgiveness as God considered proper. Don Gonzalo, bishop of Aluaña and cardinal in the church of Rome, a native of Toledo, was in Rome with the aforesaid archdeacon, whom he had educated and for whom he had done favors. When the archdeacon was preparing to take leave of him and set out for Toledo, of which he was a native, Don Gonzalo made him promise with his hands in his,[4] that if he should die while a cardinal in the Church of Rome, the archdeacon would go to Rome to request his body and would do all in his power to take his body to the church in Toledo where he had already selected his tomb. The archdeacon, grateful for his education and the favors he had received from the cardinal, resolved to carry out his wishes and fulfill the promise he had made in this matter, and he tried as best he could to obtain the body. And although the archdeacon had made many friends in the court of Rome, many citizens of the city as well as cardinals, the archdeacon did not meet anyone from whom he ventured to claim the body, except the pope. And no wonder, for no one was ever buried in the city of Rome and later disinterred to be taken elsewhere for burial. Thus it had been established by the Holy Fathers that any remains buried in Rome could not be taken from there. Don Gonzalo, arch-

3. The author has already stated that the year of jubilee began at Christmas of 1300 and that the next one will be celebrated in 1400. Now he says that the time limit will be set for 1339. Obviously, the jubilee year cannot extend from 1300 through 1339. Since he has used the dates of 1300 and 1400, which concur with those of the Roman Curia, it is probable that he intended to write 1301 and not 1339. Spain at that time was still using the Spanish Era Computation, based upon the calendar of Caesar, which began its reckoning thirty-eight years before the Christian calendar. By subtracting thirty-eight from 1339, a date of 1301 is reached, which would agree with the other dates. Thus the year of jubilee began in 1300 at Christmas, and the time limit on debts would have been Easter of 1301, rather than 1339. The mistake could have been a lapse of memory on the author's part if he was a clergyman accustomed to dealing with both time systems, or a scribal error.

4. In medieval times a vassal knelt before his lord and placed his hands in those of his lord to swear fealty.

bishop and nephew of the aforementioned cardinal, went to court and had already earnestly sought the body from the pope and had not succeeded. He was told that it would not be given to him under any circumstances.

When the archdeacon was preparing to go to claim it, he went to Alcalá to take leave of the archbishop. He told him he was preparing to go to claim the cardinal's body, for he had so promised before he had taken leave of him in Rome. The archbishop told him that he should not be so eager to go, as they would not give it to him, for they had refused to give it to himself when he had requested it from the pope, and he had had many cardinals helping him to claim it.

Taking all this into account, the archdeacon ventured to go to the king Don Ferrando and his mother the queen Doña María to request that letters be sent to the pope asking his consideration in this matter. Moreover Don Pedro, who was bishop of Burgos at the time and the legal agent of the pope, was a native of Asturias, from Oviedo. Having a real interest in the great friendship he had with the cardinal, the bishop was touched by his relationship with this archdeacon of Madrid. He resolved to show him the good will that he enjoyed among all the Spaniards for whom he had dispensed in this era many favors and honors from the pope, as occasion arose. He could see that the archdeacon had this matter close to his heart, for he desisted neither by day nor by night from zealously pursuing his goal. He felt sorry for him in his efforts and he resolved to go on demonstrating the true affection he had always shown to him. In addition he took into account the request that Doña María, queen of Castile and León, had sent him. She was an excellent lady who led a virtuous life, gave good counsel, had good common sense, and was well-educated and courteous in every way. She was a lover of justice and a godly lady. She was not arrogant in good fortune nor did she despair when ill fortune came to her. Moreover she was constant and enduring in all her actions, which were right and correct with God's consent as is related in the book of history. In addition, the bishop wanted to honor all Spain, where no other cardinal was interred.

None of the others had ever dared to make this request of the pope, but the bishop, because of his kindness, offered to make it. Although the pope was reluctant to grant his request, ultimately he ordered the body of the cardinal handed over to the supplicant. Then the archdeacon took it from the tomb where it was lying interred in the city of Rome in the church of Saint Mary Major near the chapel of the church of Christ where Saint Jerome lies interred. And there the tomb of the cardinal was constructed high on the wall and magnificently ornamented in his memory.

The archdeacon brought the body very secretly along the road, fearing that some who were not in accord with the church of Rome would impede him and that others would attempt to take it in order to inter it in their own cities. Once in Florence they attempted to seize it and inter it there, and they would have except that the archdeadon told them that it was the body of a knight who was a relative of his who had died on the pilgrimage and he was escorting it to his own land. After he reached Logroño, he made it publicly known and was welcomed there with great honor by Don Fernando, bishop of Calahorra, who came out to greet him dressed in his pontifical vestments and accompanied by his clergy in their silken capes and all the townsmen with candles and branches of devotion in their hands. On reaching Toledo, he was honored by all the clergy, all the religious orders, and the citizens of the town. Before they arrived with the body at the city of Burgos, the king, Don Fernando, son of the famous king Don Sancho, and of the queen, Doña María, which prince Don Enrique, his uncle, Don Diego, lord of Vizcaya, and Don Lope, his son, many other rich men, noblemen, and knights came to receive the body of the cardinal outside the city, where they accorded it much honor. And wherever they went, the townsmen came out to receive it as they would the body of a saint, with candles and branches of devotion in their hands. The clergy and all the orders had processions when they arrived at towns. They did not chant the responses for the dead, but the *Ecce Sacerdos Magnus* and other responses and chants, as if it were a celebration for a saint. The honor that this body of the cardinal received when they arrived at the illustrious city of Toledo was astonishing. No one, no matter how aged he might be, could remember or had ever heard of any king, emperor, or anyone else for whom so great honor had been done as for this cardinal's body; for all the clergy of the archbishopric were dressed in their capes of silk, as were the civic groups of the city, as well as all religious orders.

There was not a Christian, Moor, or Jew who did not come out to receive the body with their very largest candles and branches in their hands. Don Gonzalo, archbishop of Toledo, was there with his nephew, and Don Juan, son of prince Don Manuel. The archbishop came out to receive the cardinal's body at Peñafiel and did not leave it until it reached Toledo, where they did such great honor as you have already heard. The Archdeacon bore all the costs of the trip coming and going, and it cost him a very large sum—on the one hand because the road from Toledo to Rome was very long, and on the other hand because he had to bring along a large retinue at his own expense to render honor to the body of the cardinal. Another reason was that all along the route meals were very expensive because of the countless number of people from everywhere who were going on this pilgrimage to Rome. Fodder for the animals in many places each night cost four large "torneses."[5] It was a great miracle of God that on all the roads where the pilgrims were traveling, food was so abundant that none ever lacked anything he needed, for Our Lord God through His grace provided that none who traveled in His service should lack for anything. Although the archdeacon had gone to great expense on this trip, he had much to be grateful for because he put it to a good use.

5. A *tornés* was a coin minted in Tours, France. It was widely used and of variable value.

Aware of the favors and the education that he had received from the cardinal, he was grateful, as should be all men of good judgment and prudence who receive favors and kindness from another. Therefore the man is very fortunate who endeavors to have good and loyal servants, for such servants will not abandon him either in life or in death. Loyalty makes them remember the benefits that they received in life and in death.

Because man's memory spans a long time, men cannot remember the ancient things if they are not put into writing. Therefore the translator of the story you will hear from this point on, which was translated from Syriac into Latin and from Latin into Spanish, placed and established these two afore-mentioned things in this work in order that those people who will come after the people of this time will live when the year of jubilee is to be celebrated and that they may go to Rome to win the fullest pardons, which will be granted at that time to all who may go there, and that they may know that this was the first cardinal who was interred in Spain. This book is written so that others may emend it if they desire. And certainly those who know how and wish to emend it ought to do so, for the Scripture says: "The one who improves something is more to be praised than the one who first made it."

Furthermore, the one who originates a work should take more pleasure in it when others correct or improve it who have the knowledge and wish to do so; for the more a work is improved, the more it is to be valued. No one should encourage himself or believe in his own heart that he can remember everything, for to hold everything in one's memory without erring or making any mistakes is due rather to God than to man. Therefore we should believe that every man owes his complete knowledge to God alone and to no other source. Because of man's lack of memory, very good examples were placed in this work so that man might learn how to keep himself from error if he truly wishes to live and make use of them. There are also many other enter-taining accounts in which man can take pleasure. Every man who aspires to make a good work must interpose in it occasionally some things of pleasure and solace. And the wise man's proverb states: "Some pleasurable things should at times be placed among afflictions and grief." It is a very difficult thing to suffer continuous grief if a man is not given pleasure or solace at intervals. Because of the great trouble and vexation of work, man is often accustomed to abandon the good work that he has started; therefore, all men in this world ought to strive always to do good and to take heart and not be discouraged. Thus they can complete it easily with God's help. A work that has a reasonable and correct beginning is like a house that has a good founda-tion, and man should have hope that it will serve a good purpose. A good and decent work should commence in the service of God, as everything must do that ends well, for God is the beginning and end of all things and without Him nothing can be accomplished.

Therefore, any man who plans to begin some enterprise or good work ought first to make an acknowledgement to God in them, for He is the

Creator and Keeper of everything. In this way, man can complete successfully what he begins, especially if he has good common sense. For among all the good things God gave to man and amid all the knowledge that he acquires, good common sense is the candle that illuminates all. For knowledge that man may acquire cannot be properly used or put to a good purpose without good common sense. Although a man may memorize something and recite it, without common sense he cannot really comprehend it. And if he does understand it, lacking common sense, he cannot work with it or put any part of that knowledge to good use. Therefore, may whoever God endowed with common sense begin and complete good and decent works in the service of God and to the benefit of those who hear of them and with honor to himself. Even though the work may be long and cost much effort, one ought not to despair of being able to finish it no matter how many troubles happen to him; for that true God, Keeper of all things, whom a prudent man places first in his work, will allow him to carry out successfully what befits him. This happened to a knight from India, where Saint Bartholomew the Apostle had carried the gospel after the death of our Savior, Jesus Christ. This knight was baptized with the name of Zifar and afterwards was called the Knight of God because he was ever close to God and God was always with him in all his deeds, as you will hear from this point on. You will be able to see this and understand this by his deeds. Therefore, this book is entitled *The Knight of God*. The aforesaid knight was gifted with prudence, prowess, justice, wisdom, and truthfulness, no matter how fortune ran against him in reducing him to poverty. However, he never gave up his faith in God, considering that God would be able to change his misfortune into good fortune. Thus God did for him accordingly as you will now hear.

BOOK ONE

The Knight of God

1. Concerning the wife and sons of the Knight Zifar and how things in this book ought not to be judged until well studied

The story relates that this knight had as his wife a lady named Grima. She was a worthy and virtuous lady, uncommonly submissive to her husband and the keeper and guardian of his home. So adverse was her husband's fortune that he was never able to advance his estate to the extent that was proper. They had two small sons who encountered great dangers, as you will hear later, as did their parents. The older boy was named Garfín and the younger Roboán. But God, through His mercy, who is the director of all things—seeing the good intentions of the knight and the faith that he had, never despairing of His grace, and seeing the conduct of the good wife and how obedient she was to her husband, and what good upbringing she gave to her sons and how she taught them correctly—changed their bad fortune into the greatest and best fortune that a knight and his wife could have, first putting them through great hardships and great dangers.

Because up to now this book has never appeared in Spanish, nor have men seen it or heard of it, some will think that the things contained herein are not true, or that there is no benefit in them, because they will not pay attention to the knowledge of what is said here or will refuse to understand it. Even if they weren't true, they should not set such little value on them or doubt them until they hear them all completely and understand the knowledge that is in them. They should then take from the stories what can be of advantage to them. From each thing that is stated here, one can take good example and good advice in order to live his own life more surely and safely, if he so desires to use the knowledge herein. This book is like the walnut which has a dry shell on the outside and has the fruit hidden inside. The wise men of old, who made many books of great benefit, put in them many examples in the form of dumb beasts, birds, fish, and even stones and herbs, in which there is no knowledge, no reason, nor any sense. These little fables gave an understanding of good stories with good morals that made us believe true what we had not seen nor believed could possibly be true, just as the Holy Fathers made each one of the servants of Jesus Christ see clearly, and feel, and believe truly and completely the gospel of Jesus Christ, although they had not seen anything. Therefore no one ought to doubt the things or undervalue them until he sees what they mean and how they ought to be understood. Therefore, whoever wants to read, examine, and understand what is contained in this book will draw from it good lessons and good examples through the virtuous deeds of this knight, as can be understood and seen in this story.

2. Of the virtues of the Knight Zifar, of how the king he served was pleased with him although he cost the king great expenses, and because of this, envious knights induced the king not to summon him to duty in time of war

It is said that the Knight Zifar was a great warrior who gave very wise counsel to whoever asked him for it, and he was always willing to do whatever had to be done when it was asked of him. He was of great valor, never changing his character and taking pride in his successful feats of arms and never despairing over misfortunes when they occurred. He always told the truth and never lied when some request was made of him, and this he did with the good common sense that God had given him. Because of the fine qualities of the knight, the king of that country, whose vassal he was and from whom he received much pay and benefits each day, was fond of him. But he was so unlucky that a horse or any other animal that he rode never lasted him more than ten days, and even if he ceased to ride it or gave it away before the ten-day period, it still died. For this reason and his misfortune, he, his good wife, and his small sons were always in great poverty. However, the king, when there were wars in his country, outfitted him very well with horses, weapons, and everything that he needed and sent him to those places where need counted for more than horses. And thus God always strengthened this knight in feats of arms, so with his good native sense and prowess he always conquered and gained honor and victory for his lord the king, and great esteem for himself. But this knight cost the king great expense, for he had to equip the knight with horses and other animals that he needed at the end of every ten-day period while the war lasted, until it seemed to the king that he could no longer tolerate it or allow him to serve out his time. And on the other hand, those knights whom God had not aided as fully in feats of arms as He had the Knight Zifar were extremely envious. They informed the king that the Knight Zifar was a very costly knight to support and that for as much as he spent on the Knight Zifar in one year and his expenses in time of war, he could have five hundred other knights each year at his service. These wretches paid no heed to how God had endowed the Knight Zifar with great and noble qualities, especially prudence, truth, loyalty, prowess, fairness, and wise counsel, so that where he was surrounded by one hundred knights, he accomplished more and gained more honor for the king and more honor to them than any other thousand knights when the king sent them in his service to other places, for these knights lacked the qualities with which God had so endowed the Knight Zifar. Therefore, every great lord ought to honor, support, and retain a knight who has such qualities in him as this one has. If the lord has to engage in some battle, he ought to send for him and supply his needs, for great battles are won by a great knight, especially one in whom God has chosen to show such great traits of chivalry. They ought not to believe those who do not reveal prudence, truth, or wise counsel in themselves. Especially one ought not to believe in those who speak with deception and subtle lies. Many times some who are ingenious and clever will strive to change proper and wise advice into bad, and they interpret the laws, disguising what they say with deceitful words, thinking there is no one else as ingenious as themselves and who may see through it. Therefore one ought not to have confidence in such men as these, because it is a dangerous thing for a man to believe in those who are without virtue and full of deceits, for he will not doubt them and will be in danger.

The prudent lord, if he doubts his followers, should call them to council and listen to their advice carefully. He should examine and consider closely what each one advises, taking into account the deeds that he has accomplished in the past. If he examines them attentively, he can easily see who advises him well and who advises him badly. The lie will shine through the words of the liar as the candle gleams behind the glass of the lantern. Alas! Some of the greatest lords are most quickly inclined to believe the flattering words and adulation of liars under the pretext of some profit, which is not to their benefit or their honor. Although they may repent and want to return to the better counsel, they are unable to do so for they are ashamed to appear to have poor judgment inasmuch as they allowed themselves to be deceived. So they leave the truth behind and adhere to lies and flattery, as did this king who, realizing the honor and the benefit that had come to him through the good works of the Knight Zifar, scorned it all through fear of the expense. Believing those envious flatterers, he swore falsely, knowingly, and promised them that for two years he would not ask for the services of the Knight Zifar even though there should be war in his own country. He wanted to find out how much expense he could avoid that this knight was costing him, and so he refused to call the knight to service and discovered that he was receiving humiliations and great dangers in his own land. During those two years, there were great wars with his neighbors, and some of his own people rose in revolt against him. And when he sent two or three thousand knights to the frontier, when it should have been easy for them to defeat the enemy, they said that there was no way for them to win, and they allowed the cities of the king to be lost. Thus the king was dishonored, extremely disturbed, and greatly ashamed, but he dared not send for the Knight Zifar for he did not want others to say that he did not keep his promises. Surely it is a greater shame and disgrace to keep a damaging and dishonorable promise than it is to renounce it. If it was thought to be right and proper when it was made earlier, it should be emended when the primary reason for it is examined carefully. The correction should be made for other things that are to come, and it is right that if an error is made, the one who made it should be the one to correct it; for the proverb says that one ought not to be ashamed of revoking a mistake when it is his duty to emend the errors that others have recommended.

3. Of how the Knight Zifar complained aloud to God because the king did not send for him to go to war as he was accustomed

The king, being in this great war, was in a deal of trouble because his vassals were not serving him as effectively as they should. He did not dare to send for the Knight Zifar through shame at what he had promised those who had deceitfully advised him not to because of the expense. The good Knight Zifar, seeing this, wondered why the king, having great wars in his lands, had not sent for him as was his custom. He was greatly worried and saddened and he beseeched God, lamenting thus: "O Lord God! how much mercy Thou dost for me in so many ways although I do not deserve it, and misfortune plagues me, keeping me poor and debasing me with poverty and keeping me from serving my lord as I should. But I take comfort because I believe that whoever considers what he has as sufficient is called rich, and whoever possesses more is not rich, and the one who desires the least is truly rich. And I, Lord, consider that whatever Thou dost for me and whatever Thou thinkest well for me is abundance. Moreover, I wonder why the king avoids my service in such wars as these in which he is engaged, and I think that he has lost confidence in me. I am afraid that I may have erred in some service that I had to do for him or that I did not counsel him as well in some matter as I should have. And Lord God, since nothing is hidden from Thee, Thou knowest the truth, for I have never failed in anything that I owed to him, in my opinion, unless it was because I did not have the power to do so or through misunderstanding. Therefore, I ought not to be afraid or ashamed, for nothing can make a man's heart cowardly or shameful except his own conscience. If it is bad, he does not do what he ought to; and since my conscience is clear, the truth must save me and with the great trust that I have in it, I will not be afraid. I will go on to carry out what I have commenced, and I will not cease to do what I have started."

4. Of how Grima, wife of the Knight Zifar, heard the things that her husband was saying to himself, and how she asked him what was troubling him and what was his thought, and how he answered her

The words that the knight said were heard by his good wife, Grima. She entered the room where he was sorrowing and said to him: "My lord, what is the affliction and great trouble that you have? For the love of God, tell it to me; and since I share your pleasures with you, I would like to share also your worries and your problems. Surely I have never seen you disheartened over anything that bothered you, except now." The knight, when he saw his wife whom he loved more than his own life and understood that she had heard what he said, was deeply concerned and said: "For the Lord's sake, wife, it is better for one to suffer problems than that many should; because if I confide my worry to you, my worry would not be decreased—instead it would grow because I would worry more if you were worried."

"Dear husband," she said, "if the problem cannot be solved, then forget it; because if evil things cannot be avoided, there is no other remedy except to forget it and not think about it. Perhaps it will pass away. But if it is a matter in which good thinking can be of advantage, a man ought to share his worry with his friends, for many can think and set their wits to work more than one can, and can more easily ascertain the best answer. A man ought not to trust in his own thinking alone although God has given him good sense, for where one man has good sense, there is always another who has more. Therefore, every man who wants to undertake some enterprise ought to do it with the advice of those whom he is sure will counsel him well. And, dear," she said, "I heard you say when you were lamenting that you wanted to go ahead with your plan and not to discard something that you had already begun, and because I know that you are a man of great courage and bravery, I consider that your intention is some noble and mighty deed and, in my opinion, you ought to follow your own counsel."

"Surely," replied her husband, the knight, "you have sustained me and have given me comfort before when I suffered adversity. Therefore, I am compelled to share with you my problem that I have kept secret for a very long time. I have never revealed it to any person in this world, for just as a sheltered fire lasts longer than an open fire, and is brighter, a secret known to oneself lasts longer and is better kept than if many know it. However the one who keeps a secret to himself worries much, for he has to contain himself and suffer great afflictions in order to keep it. Very fortunate is that man who has a whole friend to whom he can reveal his heart and can let his friend share completely all his secrets and other things that he ought to do. When the problem is shared by both, they can more quickly and easily find out what they have to do. However, many times men are deceived by some that they believe to be their friends and are not friends, only pretended ones. Surely, men cannot know whether they are friends until they test them; just as gold is tested by fire, so is a friend known only when he is tested. Thus did it happen when the son of a good man in the land of Sarapia tested his friends, as you will now hear."

5. Of the parables that the Knight Zifar told his wife in order to persuade her to keep his secret; the first parable is that of the half-friend

"It is said that a good man was very rich and he had a son whom he loved very much. He gave him everything that he wanted and he wasted it. He taught him that he should value friendship above all things and that he should strive to gain friends, for this would be the most gainful thing he could do. He should acquire whole friends or at least those who were half-friends. There are three kinds of friends: the false friends who are friends only as long as it is advantageous to them; the next are the half-friends who stand ready to help if danger appears, but it is doubtful if they will; and the whole friends who see death or great danger facing their friend and take his place so that their friend does not die or receive harm. The son told his father that he would follow his wish and endeavor to acquire as many friends as he could.

"With the wealth his father gave him, he treated others, spent much money, and gave generously of his wealth, so that there was no one in the city with a greater following than he. At the end of ten years his father asked him how many friends he had acquired, and he answered him more than one hundred. 'Surely you spent well all I gave you if it is as you say,' said his father. 'In all the days of my life, I could only acquire a half-friend, and if you have gained one hundred friends, you are fortunate indeed.' 'Well, father,' replied the son, 'there's not a one of them who wouldn't place himself between me and any danger that might happen to me.' His father listened to him, became silent, and said no more to him. After this conversation with his father, it happened that the son got into an argument and had some ugly words with a youth of the city who was of higher station than he, and the latter went searching for the son of the good man in order to do him harm. The father, when he found this out, was deeply worried and ordered his son to go to a safe house outside the city limits and that he should remain there until the argument had died down. The son complied, and afterward the father got an assurance from the other party and made peace with him. The next day, he had a pig slaughtered and the hair cleaned from the body, and then cut off the head and the feet, which he kept. He put the body of the pig in a sack, tied it firmly, and placed it under his bed. He then sent for his son to come that evening. When it was evening, the son arrived. His father welcomed him warmly and told him how his antagonist had reassured him, and they had supper. Later the father, seeing that the people of the city were calmed down, said: 'Son, what I told you when you arrived—that your enemy had promised not to make trouble—I tell you now was a lie. This morning, when I was returning from mass, I found him here inside the house, behind the door, his sword drawn, believing that you were in the city and that when you entered the house he would kill you. By good fortune, I killed him and cut off his head, his feet, his arms, and his legs. I threw all that in the well and placed his body in a sack and put it beneath my bed. I do not dare to bury it for fear they would find us out. It seems to me that it would be better for you to carry it to the house of one of your friends, if you have one, and bury it in some secret place.'

"'Certainly, sir,' said the son, 'I'm very glad to do so, and now you will see the friends I have acquired.' And he took the sack on his shoulders and went to the house of his most trusted friend. When he arrived, his friend wondered why he had come so late at night and he asked what he was carrying in the sack. The son told him everything and asked if he could bury it in his backyard; and his friend answered him that since he and his father had done this folly and had gotten themselves into trouble, he should leave his house, for he did not wish to be endangered by them. And all his friends responded in the same way, and he returned to his father's house with his sack and told him how his friends had refused to be endangered through them.

"'Son,' said the good man, 'I was greatly surprised when you told me that you had acquired a hundred friends, and it seems to me that among all that hundred you did not find even a half-friend. Go to my half-friend and tell him for me what happened to us and that I am asking him to hide it for us.' The son went away and carried the sack and knocked at the door of his father's half-friend. Servants came out and asked him what he wanted; he told them that he wished to speak to his father's friend. They all went to tell him and he asked the son to enter. When he saw him enter with the sack on his back, he ordered the others to leave the room, and they remained alone. The good man asked him what he wanted and what he was carrying in the sack. He told him what had happened to his father and to himself, and he requested him, on his father's behalf, to hide it for them. He answered that he would do that and more for his father. He took a shovel and they both dug a grave under his bed and put in it the sack with the pig and covered it completely with earth. Then the youth returned to his father's house and told him how his half-friend had welcomed him, that he had recounted the deed, that he had answered that he would do that and more also, and that he had dug a grave under his bed and buried the body there. Then his father said, 'Now what do you think of my half-friend?'"

"'Surely,' the son replied, 'it seems to me that this half-friend is worth more than my hundred friends.' 'Son,' said the good man, 'in times of trouble friends are tested; and therefore you ought not to trust every man who acts as a friend, until you test him in things that are vital to you. Since you found my half-friend to be good, I want you to go to him before the dawn and tell him to slice up that body that he has buried and roast it, and that tomorrow you and I will be his guests.'

"'You mean we are going to eat the man?' asked the son.

"'Certainly,' said the father, 'a dead enemy is better than a live one, and he is better cooked or roasted than raw. The greatest vengeance that a man can have is this—to consume him completely so that not a trace remains. Where some part of the enemy remains, so does ill will.'

"Early the next morning, the son of the good man went to see his father's half-friend. He told him how his father had sent him to request him to slice up the body in the sack and prepare it all, cooked and roasted, because he and his father would be coming to dine with him. The good man when he heard him began to laugh, for he understood that his friend wanted to test his son, so he told him that he would be glad to do so. He told him that they should come early to dine for they would find the body already well prepared, for man's flesh was very tender and cooked very quickly. The boy returned to his father and told him the response of his half-friend. His father was very pleased that his friend had answered so well. When they realized that it was time to dine, the son and his father went to the good man's house where they found the table already set with plenty of bread and wine. The good men began to eat very vigorously, as those who know what they have before them. The youth was fearful of eating it, although it appeared good to him. His father, when he saw his hesitancy in eating, told him that he could eat safely, for the flesh of an enemy had the same flavor as that of pork. He began to eat and found it good, so he started to eat even more vigorously than the others, and he said: 'Father, you and your friend have had me eat the flesh of an enemy; and surely you may believe that since the flesh of the enemy tastes good, the other enemy of mine who was with this one when he insulted me cannot escape my killing him and eating him with great pleasure; because never have I eaten meat that tasted so good as this.'

"The two friends began to think about the words that the youth had spoken, and they started to talk to each other. They considered that if the youth persisted in this notion he would be very cruel and they would be unable to change his ways. A man can hardly ever be separated from the things he fancies while he is a youth, and especially those things in which he takes great delight. On this account, the father, trying to disillusion him, began to speak to him:

"'Son, because you told me that you had acquired more than a hundred friends, I wanted to test if it were so. Yesterday, I killed this pig that we are now eating. I cut off his head and his feet, and I placed the body in that sack you brought here. I wanted you to test your friends as you did. You did not find them to be as you thought, but you did find this half-friend good and loyal, as he ought to be. However, you ought to pay attention to which friends you can trust; it would be a very ugly and vile thing and against nature for man to want to eat the flesh of man, even if he were starving.'

"'Father,' said the youth, 'I am very grateful to God because you have so quickly cured me of this folly. If through my sins, the other enemy had died and I had eaten him, and he had tasted as good as this meat we are eating now, I would never be satisfied except to covet man's flesh. Through what you have just said to me, I will abhor even more the flesh of man.'

"'Of course,' said his father, 'I am very pleased and I want you to know that your enemy and the others who were with him have forgiven you, and I forgave them on your behalf. From now on, stay out of arguments and do not allow false friends to mock you, for when they see you in trouble, they will abandon you, as you have seen in these whom you tested.'

"'Father,' said the son, 'now I have tested which is the pretend friend, as were all those that I had acquired, who never aided me except while I shared all that I possessed with them. When I needed them, they failed me. I have tested which is the half-friend. Tell me if I will be able to know and to test who is a whole friend.'"

6. Of the parable that the Knight Zifar told his wife of how the other friend was tested

"'May God protect you, son,' said the father, 'for this would be a very strong test of faith of friends on this occasion; for this test cannot be made except when a man is in certain danger of receiving death, or harm, or great dishonor. And there are few who can be certain of such friends who are willing to risk death knowingly for a friend in great danger. However, son, I heard that in the land of Canaan, two youths grew up in a city who loved each other so much that what one wanted, the other also desired. However the wise man says that between friends one ought to be the advocate of good and pure things and the other ought not. However, one of these two friends wanted to search for knowledge and to sample worldly things. He searched through foreign lands for a long time until he happened upon a land where he fared well, and he became rich and very powerful. The other remained in the town with his father and mother, who were rich and had things in abundance. And when they had news of each other or when some arrived who were from those places, they were very pleased. Thus it happened that the one who remained in town after the death of his parents became poverty-stricken and knew no one to ask for help, so he went to see his friend. And when the other one saw his friend so poor and so downcast, he was deeply concerned and asked him why he was in this state. He told him of his great poverty. 'I swear to God, friend,' said the other, 'that while I live and have all that I need, you will never be poor. Praise be to God that I own great wealth and am powerful in this land. You will lack for nothing of which you may have need.' He took him into his home and treated him lavishly. His friend was master of his house and of all he possessed, for a very long time. He lost all he owned later for the sake of this friend, as you are now going to hear.

"The story is told that this friend of his was married in that foreign land and his wife died leaving no children. A good man, who was his neighbor and was of high station and very wealthy, sent him his young daughter to be reared in his house and when she came of age, he was to marry her. As the young girl was around the house so much, his guest met her unexpectedly and fell in love with her. However, she did not speak to him, nor did he say anything to the girl or to his friend, for he considered that he would not be a true and loyal friend as he ought to be if he did so or proposed any such thing. Although he endeavored to forget his love for her, he was unable to, and his worry grew more and more so that he began to sicken and his strength failed him because of the great love he held for the girl. His suffering and weakness worried his friend very much, and he sent everywhere for good physicians, and he gave them great wealth to cure him. No matter how much medical knowledge they possessed, they were unable to diagnose that illness. He became so weak that he had to send for a priest to give him confession.

"And they sent for a chaplain who gave him confession, and he told him of his sin, from which came the malady of which he believed he was dying. The chaplain went to the lord of the house and told him that he wished to speak with him privately and that he should hold it in secret. And he promised him that what he had said to him he would keep secret. 'I say to you,' said the chaplain, 'that this friend of yours may die of love for your ward whom you are to marry; although he forbade me to speak of it to anyone and that he should be left to die.' After he heard this, the master of the house acted as though he did not give credence to it. As soon as the chaplain left, he went to his friend and told him to be of good cheer and that he had so much gold and silver that he would give as much as he should wish, and he should not want thus to let himself die through great despair. 'Surely, friend,' said the other, 'alas! there is no gold or silver that holds any use for me. Let life run its course, for I consider myself fortunate to die in your company.'

"'Surely you are not going to die,' said his friend. 'Since I know what your illness is, I will cure you of it. I know that your illness is caused by your love for this girl here that I am supposed to marry. And since she is of age and fate wants you to have her, I wish for you to marry her and I will give you great wealth. Take her with you to your country and I will take responsibility for this with her kinsmen as God sees proper.'

"His friend when he heard this, fainted away over the great grief that he felt, because he cared so much for his friend. His friend believed him to be dead and went out weeping and shouting to his people, 'Go to the room where my friend is, alack and alas! He is dead, and I am unable to help him.' The people went to the room and they found him unconscious. There was lamenting all around him and when he heard the young girl crying, who was among all the others, he opened his eyes. At this, all became silent and went to see their master, whom they found very grief-stricken and crying. They told him of how his friend had revived. The master then went there and ordered the young girl and her duenna to care for him and for no other. In a very short time, his friend recovered his health. However, when his friend came, he was unable to look him straight in the eye because of the great embarrassment that he felt. Then the master of the house called the young girl, his ward, and told her that his friend loved her deeply, and she without thinking answered that she also loved him dearly, but that she had not dared to say so because of her great love for him.

"'Well, thus it will be,' he said. 'I want you to marry him, for although he is from the same country as I, he is of higher station than I. I will give you great wealth to take with you so that you will want for nothing.'

"'Whatever may be your wish,' she replied.

"Early the next morning, he sent for the chaplain who had confessed his friend. He had them married and gave them great wealth and then sent them to their country. As soon as the relatives of the girl learned of this, they considered themselves dishonored, and sent a challenge to him. They pursued him for a long time, so that no matter how rich and powerful he was, with continuous warfare every day, he became so poverty-stricken that he was unable to support even himself.

"He thought to himself about what he should do, and there was no other help except to go see that friend of his whom he had aided. He set out on his journey with the small amount of wealth that remained, but it lasted him only a short while, for the way was very long, and he was left afoot and reduced to poverty. And it happened that he arrived at night at the house of a good man of a town, which this day may be seen by the grace of God, near that place where Abraham intended to sacrifice his son. He asked for the sake of charity that they give him something to eat. They told their master how that good man was asking for something to eat. The master of the house was very stingy and said that he ought to buy it. They told him that the good man had nothing with which to purchase anything. What little the master gave him, he gave slowly and grudgingly so that he might feel shame and humiliation over it. He was very weak and wretched, so that there was not a man in the household who did not feel great pity for him.

"Therefore the Scripture says that there are three kinds of men for whom one ought to feel pity, and these are: (1) the poor man who has to beg from the miserly rich, (2) the wise man who has to be guided by the stupid, and (3) the just man who has to live in a land without justice. These are sad and afflicted, because they do not receive their just dues accordingly as God endowed them.

"When he arrived at that city where his friend lived, it was already night, and the gates were locked so that he could not enter. As he was very tired and suffered from hunger, he lodged himself in a hermitage without doors that he chanced upon near the city. He threw himself down behind the altar and fell asleep until the next morning, for he was tired and afflicted. During that night two men of the city were carousing and had an argument and cursed each other. Some others separated them and made them go away. One of them that night planned to kill the other one in the morning, because he knew that he usually attended matins, and he went to ambush him behind his door. As the other was leaving his house, he drew his sword and gave him a blow on the head which killed him. Then he left for his own lodging, for no one had seen him when he killed the other.

"Later in the morning, the dead man was found at his door, and there was a great uproar throughout the city, so that the police, together with a great number of people, went searching for the murderer. They went to the gates of the town, and all were locked except that open doorway in the front of the hermitage where that afflicted and suffering man was sleeping. All the gates were opened before the dawn by some messengers who hurriedly sent word to the emperor. They believed that the killer had come out through that door, and in searching they found no trace of him. In preparing to return, they entered the hermitage and discovered that wretched man sleeping, his sword girded on, and they began to shout and to say, 'Behold here the traitor who killed the good man.' And they arrested him and took him before the judges. The judges asked him if he had killed that good man, and he in his despair, desiring death more than to endure that life he was leading, said that he was guilty. They asked him why he had killed him, and he answered that he had murdered him just for the pleasure of it. The judges came to agreement and ordered him to be executed, since he had confessed. At this moment, his friend to whom he had given his ward in marriage and who was among the crowd, recognized him. He considered that since his friend had saved him from death and had done so much for him, he would die in his stead, and he said to the judges: 'Lords, this man you ordered to die is not to blame in the death of that man, for I myself killed him.'

"They ordered him arrested and because both had confessed they had killed the man, they ordered both executed. And the one who had killed the good man was among the others at their door paying close attention to what the others were saying and doing. When he saw that those two innocent men were ordered to be executed for what he had done, he thought to himself, saying: 'Miserable sinner! how will I appear in the eyes of my Lord on Judgment Day, and how will I be able to face Him? Surely with shame and great fear, and in the end, my soul will receive punishment in hell on account of these people whom I let perish, and they innocent of the death of that good man whom I in my madness murdered. Therefore I consider that it would be better to confess my sin and to repent, and allow myself to die to make amends for what I did and not let these men be executed.'

"He went then to the judges and said: 'Lords, these men whom you ordered executed have no blame in the death of that good man, because I through my own bad luck am the one who killed him. If you do not believe it is so, then ask some of these good men, and they will tell you how late last night he and I had our argument, and they separated us. But the devil, who always is working to do evil, inspired me that night to go kill him and I did so. Send someone to my house and you will find a piece of my sword from the blow that I gave him. I believe that it stuck in the head of the dead man.' Then the judges sent to his house, and they found the broken sword as he had stated. They examined the dead man, and they found the broken piece of the sword in the wound. They discussed these findings and considered that these things had happened through a miracle of God, so that they should know the truth. They agreed to hold the prisoners until the emperor should come, as he was to be there in two weeks. Thus they did.

"When the emperor arrived, they related all that had happened, and he ordered them to bring in the first prisoner. When the prisoner arrived before him, he said, 'Oh you wretched man, what motive impelled you to confess to the death of that good man, since you were not at fault?' 'Sire,' said the prisoner, 'I will tell you. I am a native of this land, and I went to seek my fortune in foreign lands, and I became very rich and powerful. Afterwards I became so poor that I knew no one who could help me, so I came to my friend to ask him for charity. He confessed to the death of the good man after I had already confessed, for he had supported me on his charity. When I arrived at this town I found the gates locked, and I was forced to sleep behind the altar in the hermitage near the town. While I was sleeping, I was awakened by a lot of noise in the morning and people saying, "This is the traitor who killed the good man." As I was in despair and tired of life in this world, I desired death more than life, so I said that I had killed him.' The emperor ordered him taken away and the second prisoner brought in. When he arrived before him, the emperor said: 'Tell me, you simple fellow, what was the reason you confessed to the death of that citizen, since you were not involved in it?'

"'Sire,' said he, 'I will tell you. The prisoner who was just before Your Majesty, is my friend. We grew up together.' He told him all that had happened to him and how he had escaped death, and the favors his friend had done for him when he gave him his own betrothed for his wife. 'And, sire, now seeing that they were preparing to execute him, I wanted to take his place and venture death so that he should not die.' Then the emperor sent him away and ordered the other prisoner brought in and he said to him: 'Tell me, you sinful and unfortunate fellow, since the others had taken the blame for you, why did you place yourself in jeopardy, since you were able to avoid it?'

"'Sire,' replied the prisoner, 'the one who allows himself to lose much for the gain of little, and who excuses himself through a pretext, has little sense and shows a lack of prudence. In trying to avoid martyrdom of my flesh through fear of death, I would lose my soul and it would be taken by the devil and not by God.' And he related to him all that he had done and the worry he had that these innocent men would be executed, and he would then lose his own soul. When the emperor heard him, he was pleased to his heart and ordered that none of them should be executed, although the last prisoner deserved death.

"God had performed His miracle in making known the truth about this deed. The murderer had confessed to it, although he could have avoided blame for it. The emperor pardoned him and ordered him to make compensation to the relatives. Thus he made reparations as requested. And these three men became very rich, very good, and very powerful in the domain of the emperor. Every one loved them and esteemed them highly for what they had done and they became good friends.

"'And my son,' said the father, 'now you understand what the test is for the whole friend and how much good the murderer did by confessing to the slaying and not valuing his own soul more than the souls of the others. You can understand that there are three kinds of friends: (1) the one who loves his body and not his soul, (2) the one who loves his soul and not his body, and (3) the one who loves his body and his soul, just like the last prisoner who loved his soul and his body. He gave a good example of this by being willing to sacrifice himself rather than risk his soul to avoid harm to his body.'"

7. Of how the Knight of God told his wife that he wanted to tell her his secret

The Knight of God related to his good wife all these things in these stories about the friends, in order that she should understand how to protect her beloved and his secrets, and he said to her: "Dear wife, however it may be that some say that women cannot keep a secret well, I consider that there are exceptions to the rule; because God did not make all men equal or of the same judgment, or the same understanding, but different—the same for men as for women. Because I know how prudent you are and how careful you are in all matters from the time we were married until today itself, and how compliant and obedient you have been to me, I want to tell you my secret. I have never told any person in the world, but have always kept it in my heart as a thing that men would consider a great madness if I should tell it or think of telling it. However, I cannot resolve it although it seems to me that God is willing to aid me to pursue it, for He endowed me, through His grace, with special traits of chivalry that He did not give to any other knight of this time. I believe that He, who showed me this grace, has inspired me to embark on this quest that I now will tell you in confidence. If I should not pursue this course, I would consider myself to be lacking in those good traits with which God endowed me."

8. Of how the Knight of God told his good wife all that his grandfather had told him

"Dear wife," said the Knight Zifar, "when I was a small boy in my grandfather's house, I heard that his father had said that he came from royal ancestry. I audaciously asked how that royal lineage had been lost, and he told me that it had been lost through the wickedness and wongdoings of a king in his family line. He was deposed and they made a simple knight king. However, he was a very good man, of good common sense, a lover of justice, and a complete gentleman in all ways. I asked him, 'Can a king be made or deposed so easily?' He replied: 'So, my friend, you think it is such an easy matter to make or to unmake a king? Of course, because of great evil he can be deposed and by the great strength of goodness and fine qualities he can become a king. This evil or virtue lives within the one who is king or who is to be a king as well as within those who depose or make him.'

"'And if we came from such high position,' I said, 'why are we poor?'

"My grandfather answered: 'It was through the evil of the king from whom we are descended that we have come to such humble station as you now see. And I in truth have no hope that I will regain your rightful inheritance and ours until another member of our family comes who is the opposite of that deposed king—one who does good deeds and is virtuous. If the king who reigns at that time is wicked, they will depose him for wickedness and make the latter king on account of his virtues. And this can be true with the grace of God.'

"'And if I were so exemplary,' I said, 'would I be able to reach such high estate?'

"He answered me with a smile, 'My very young and wise friend, I say that you can, with the grace of God, if you strive hard and do not tire of doing good. By doing good, a man can surely rise to high position.'

"Having said this, and deeply satisfied, he made the sign of the cross over himself and me and relinquished his hold on life, smiling in the presence of all who were there. Everyone marveled at the manner of the death of my grandfather. These words that my grandfather said to me touched my heart in such a way that I proposed then to reach for that goal from that day forward. No matter how much I want to abandon that goal, I am unable to, for it always comes into my mind whether I am sleeping or awake. If God favors me in some feat of arms, I believe that I can do it because the words of my grandfather come to my mind. Moreover, lady, I see that we are living here in degradation and in great poverty, and if you consider it proper, I think it would be better for us to go to another kingdom where we are unknown and perhaps our fortune will change. The old proverb says that God helps those who help themselves. This is said by those who are unfortunate just as we are in our own misfortune. The person who is well off has no reason to move, for by moving away he often loses what he possesses. Therefore it is said that a rolling stone gathers no moss. Since we are not well off, alas! either concerning our honor or our estate, the proverb about the one who is well off not moving does not apply to us. I think it would be better for us to move away than to remain here."

9. Of how the knight's wife was very grateful to her husband for the secret that he told her

"Dear husband," said his wife, "you have spoken sense. May God be grateful to you for the great favor that you have done me in choosing to tell me your great secret. Certainly I want you to know that as quickly as you related these words that your grandfather told you, so quickly did my heart tell me if they were wisdom or madness. I believe that they have to be true. Everything is in God's power. He can make the rich poor and the poor rich. In the name of God, you can move when you wish, and what you have to do, do it quickly; for at times, delay in a good intention can be disadvantageous."

The knight said, "And how did you know so quickly that what my grandfather told me was true?"

"Just this fast," she replied. "Whoever would look into my heart now would find it already deeply touched on this matter, and it brought out my agreement."

"Surely it happened thus when I heard my grandfather tell it. Therefore it is not fitting for us to remain in this land, even though men would understand our folly."

10. Here the story speaks of the Knight Zifar's lineage

This Knight Zifar, according to ancient history, was descended from King Tared, who was ruined because of his evil traits. However, other kings of his lineage before him were good and enlightened. But the foundations of kings and royalty are uprooted and humbled on account of two things: one is evil character and the other is extreme poverty. Thus King Tared, although the king, his father, left him very rich and powerful, became poor and was overthrown through his evil ways just as the grandfather of the Knight Zifar has already related, as you heard; so that his descendants never were able to regain that high position that King Tared lost. This kingdom is in what was formerly called India and was populated by the gentiles, as you will now hear.

Ancient history says that there are three Indias: one which borders on the land of the negroes, the second borders on the land of Cadia, and the third borders on the region of darkness. India Primera, which the gentiles inhabited, is the one that borders on the land of the negroes. The Knight Zifar was from this India where Tared was king. It is found in the ancient histories that Ninbros the brave, called Nimrod by the Christians, great-grandson of Noah, was the first king in the world. With great effort he built the city of Babylon in the desert and began to construct a tower against the will of God and against the orders of Noah. It rose up to the clouds and they named the tower Magdar.

God, seeing that they were building it against His will, did not want it to be completed, nor did He want them to speak one language, for they would be able to understand each other and would be able to finish it. He divided them into seventy languages: thirty-six in the lineage of Shem, sixteen in the line of Canaan,[1] son of Noah, and eighteen in the lineage of Japheth. And this lineage of Canaan, son of Noah, had the greatest share of these languages through the curse that his father put on him at that time; for he had sinned in two ways—the first one when he lay down with his mother in the ark where she had a son named Cush, whose son was this King Nimrod—and then he was cursed in all worldly things.

Furthermore, the Jews say that Canaan was cursed because he lay with the wife of the leader in the ark. And the curse was this: as many times as he lay with the wife of the leader, that many times would they tear one another apart. We Christians say this is not true, because it has been the nature of dogs since God created the world and everything here.

The other sin that Canaan committed when he discovered his father drunk was to reveal his nakedness.[2] Therefore this King Nimrod who was his grandson sinned against God by following the example of his grandfather Canaan, from whom he descended. Asshur, the second son of Shem, seeing that King Nimrod was committing deeds to the disservice of God, did not choose to dwell there, and with all his family he went to live in Nineveh, a great city which was three days' journey away. God chose to destroy this city on account of the wickedness of the people there.

Nebuchadnezzar destroyed it. And a company of gentiles who loved knowledge and the sciences arrived there to study. They segregated themselves on the bank of a river that is beyond Babylon. They decided to cross that river and to settle beyond it and live all for each other. The ancient wise men say that when Noah named the seas and the rivers, he called that river the Indus, and because of that name those who remained to dwell there were called Indians, and they called the province where the people are, India, on account of the name of the population. After they were rested, they concentrated on study, and learning, and observing; wherefore Abu Ybeyt, a wise man, said: "The first wise men who observed the sun and the planets after the deluge were from ancient India."

To live in peace and to have someone to lead them, they elected and raised to be king over themselves a wise man whom they called Albarheme the elder, because there was also there another sage by the same name. He was the first king of India who formulated the law and the signs of the Zodiac and the planets. The gentiles of India were a great people, and all the kings in

1. Canaan was the grandson of Noah. The text mistakes Canaan for Ham.
2. It was Ham who revealed his father's nakedness, not Canaan.

the world and all the sages recognized them to be superior in intelligence, nobility, and knowledge.

The kings of Sind say there are five kings in the world and that the others follow in their footsteps: these are the kings of Sind, the kings of India, the kings of the Turks, the Persian kings, and the Christian kings. They say that the king of Sind is king of men, because the men of Sind are more obedient and more submissive than other men are to their kings and masters. They say that the king of India is the king of knowledge, for the Indians have always studied and striven for knowledge. They call the king of the Turks, the king of the lions, because they are very strong men of great prowess and daring in war. The king of the Persians is called the king of kings because they were always very great, of lordly demeanor, and had great power. With their power, their knowledge, and their great intelligence they populated half the world, and none could oppose them, although they did not share their heritage or faith. The king of the Christians is called the king of courtiers because they are more courtly than all the others, of great prowess, more genteel, and more elegant on horseback than other men.

Of course, from time immemorial, India has been the source and way of knowledge. The Indians were men of great moderation and great intelligence. Although they are dark-skinned and resemble negroes in color, for they share common borders with them, God protected them from the negroes' way and their stupidity. He gave them good deportment and goodness in manners, and intelligence more than to many whites. Some of the astrologers say that the Indians had these good traits because the province of India falls naturally under Saturn and Mercury. They acquired their dark complexion from Saturn; they are wise, discreet, and clever, having obtained these traits from Mercury, mixed with Saturn. Their kings were always well born and believers in God and for this reason are men of good faith and sagacious, and all believe in God deeply. Therefore, there are few of them who have any belief in Sabaa and worship the planets and the stars. All this about India was studied and was placed in this story because it is not found in any other writing that there was any other king more reprehensible than King Tared from whom the Knight Zifar descended. However, this knight was exemplary in everything; and he gained great renown and great honor through virtue and through chivalry, as you will hear henceforth in this story.

11. The story tells of how the Knight Zifar and his wife went away with their sons to live in a foreign land

The story relates that the Knight Zifar and the good lady, his wife, sold what little property they owned and bought two palfreys on which to leave. They made a hospital of their home and left all their linen on which the poor could lie, and they went away. He took one of his small sons on his horse behind himself and his wife took the other. They traveled so far that in ten days they had left behind the kingdom where they were natives and had traveled two days' journey into another land. At the completion of the ten days, about the eleventh hour of the morning, having been ridden the whole journey, the knight's palfrey suddenly died. This grieved the wife of the knight exceedingly. She let herself drop to the ground weeping and said to him:

"Dear husband, do not worry so much, because God will aid you. Mount this horse and take the two boys with you, for I can easily walk the rest of today's journey, with the help of God."

"For Heaven's sake, wife," said the knight, "I cannot do that, because it would be a fine state of affairs and unreasonable for me to ride and you to go on foot. According to nature and reason, it is better for a respectable man to suffer the fatigue of the road than his wife. Therefore, I think it better for you to ride your horse and take your children, one in front of you and the other behind you." She did as he said and so they completed the rest of the day's travel.

The next day they went to worship at the church and to hear mass as they were accustomed to do every day before their departure. After hearing mass, they set out on the road that led to a town named Galapia. A widow named Grima was the mistress of the town. She was at war with a great man, her neighbor, who was more powerful than she. He was the lord of the land of Ephesus, a very great and very rich country. He was named Rodan. When they reached that town, they found the gates locked and well guarded for fear of their enemy. They asked for admittance, and the gatekeeper asked them who they were. The knight told him that they were from a foreign land and had happened to go where fortune had guided them. The gatekeeper told them that he would go to ask permission of the mistress of the town and that they should wait for him, as he would return with her reply. He then departed to see the mistress of the town.

While the knight and his wife were at the gate awaiting the reply of the mistress of the town, behold there came an armed knight riding on a warhorse toward the town. He approached them and said: "Lady, what are you doing here, you and this man who is with you? Leave here and proceed on your way. Do not enter the town. My master does not wish anyone to enter there, especially those mounted, for he is at war with the mistress of the town"

The Knight Zifar answered him: "Sir, we are from a foreign land and we happened by chance upon this place. We are very tired and it is very late—the hour of vespers—and we could not find another town where we could find lodging. May it please you for us to remain here tonight if they will accept us. Then early tomorrow we shall go wherever God leads us."

"Of course," replied the other knight, "you shall not stay here, for I have nothing to do with your weariness. Leave here. If not, I will kill you and carry away your wife and do with her as I wish."

When the Knight Zifar heard these harsh words, he was deeply concerned and replied, "Surely if you are a knight, you ought not to do harm to another nobleman without challenging him, especially as he has done you no wrong."

"Being a serving boy for this lady," exclaimed the other knight, "how can you pretend to be a knight? If you are a knight, mount that lady's horse and defend her."

When the Knight Zifar heard this, he was quite pleased, for so much walking had given him the desire to ride again. He mounted the palfrey from which his wife had dismounted. A sentinel in the tower over the gate, feeling sorry for the knight and his wife, threw him a lance he owned and called to him, "Friend, take this lance and may God help you."

12. Of how the Knight Zifar killed the nephew of the count who was the enemy of the mistress of the besieged town

The Knight Zifar took the lance, for he was only wearing his trusty sword. He said to the other knight, who was irate, "I beg you for the love of God to leave us in peace and let us rest here tonight. I make you a solemn pledge that we will leave tomorrow, God willing."

"Certainly, it is agreed for you to go away later. Defend yourself!" replied the knight.

The Knight Zifar answered, "May God, who is able, defend us."

"Is this God so idle," answered the other, "that he has nothing to do except come to your defense?"

"Of course," replied the Knight Zifar, "to God nothing is too difficult and He always has the time to do good. Whomever He wishes to help or defend, to that person He gives help or protection."

The other knight then responded, "Are you trying to stop me with words?" He sank his spurs into his horse and charged. The Knight Zifar charged against the other knight. And such was the fortune of the mailed knight that he misjudged the lance of the Knight Zifar. He was wounded so badly that he fell to the earth dead. The Knight Zifar took the dead man's horse by the reins and led it to his wife, who was very worried but was praying to God to guard her husband from harm.

13. Of how the Knight Zifar killed the nephew of the count who had the town surrounded[1]

At this moment, the gatekeeper and a knight were on their way. The mistress of the town had sent him to take a pledge from the Knight Zifar that no harm

---

1. The manuscript is in error—Zifar kills no one in this chapter.

should come to the town from them if they were given asylum. The gate-keeper opened the gate and the knight accompanying him said to the Knight Zifar, "Friend, do you wish to enter here?"

The Knight Zifar replied, "We would like to if it pleases you."

The knight queried, "Friend, are you a nobleman?"

"Certainly I am," replied the Knight Zifar.

"And are you a knight?"

"Yes," he replied.

"And those two small boys? And this lady, who is she?"

"My wife," he responded, "and those two boys are our young sons."

"Then will you make me a pledge," said the other, "as you are a noble-man, that through you or your actions, no harm shall come to this town or to anyone who dwells here?"

"Yes, I will make that pledge for as long as I may dwell here."

"No," replied the knight, "but for all time."

The Knight Zifar told him that he would not do it, because he did not know what might happen with someone in the future in the town.

"Certainly then, you shall not enter here," answered the other knight, "if you do not make this promise."

While they were disputing, the sentinel who was on the tower—the one who had given his lance to the Knight Zifar—said, "Enter right away because a hundred knights are leaving that forest and are coming here as fast as they can."

Considering this the knight from the town said: "Friend, are you going to make the pledge that I'm asking of you? If not, I will enter and close the gate." Then the Knight Zifar said that he would make a promise to defend the town and those who were there as long as they did not give him a reason not to do so.

"Friend," replied the knight, "here they will do nothing to you against your will."

"And I make you the pledge," replied the Knight Zifar, "as you request, since thus it must be." And so he, his wife, and his sons received asylum, and the gates of the town were closed.

14. Of how the knights outside found the nephew of the count dead, and carried the dead man away

While Zifar and the others were riding in and on their way to the inn, the hundred knights arrived and questioned the sentry.

"Tell us, friend, did an armed knight enter here?"

"Who are you," said the sentry, "to be asking?"

"Surely," said one of them, "you ought to recognize us, for you have spent many long and wakeful nights and days in this town because of us."

"That's true," answered the sentry, "but I am certain that you are going to leave here this time unhappy."

"You stupid peasant," snarled the knight, "how could that be? Is the knight who came here that we ask about a prisoner?"

"He certainly is not," said the sentry, "he is dead. Look for him where he lies in that ravine and you will find him dead."

"And who killed him?" asked the knight.

"His arrogance," answered the sentry.

"But who?" asked the knight.

"Well then," replied the sentry, "a wandering knight who just arrived here with his wife."

The knights went to the ravine and found him dead. The dead knight was the nephew of that nobleman who was at war with the mistress of the town. They began to lament greatly for the dead knight, more than could possibly be done for any other man. And they took the dead knight and went away in deep sorrow.

15. Of how the mistress of Galapia learned of the death of her enemy

When the mistress of the town heard this outcry and such loud bewailing, she wondered what it could be, and she asked them to tell her what it was. At this moment the knight entered whom she had sent to receive the pledge. He related to her all that happened as one who had witnessed it all. As soon as he heard the noise, he climbed up to the ramparts with the other people who were there to defend themselves. He told her how this knight who had entered the town had killed the nephew of her enemy. The nephew was the most daring and arrogant of the enemy's knights. He had caused the most damage to her town. War had erupted between his uncle and the mistress of the town because she had not wanted to marry that great lord's nephew.

When the mistress of the town heard of his death, she was greatly pleased, and she considered that God had led that strange knight to her town to put an end to their war. She ordered her knight to give him the finest lodging and to treat him with great honor, and so the knight did. The next morning after mass, when the Knight Zifar and his wife were preparing to mount and leave, a message arrived from the mistress of the town for them to come to her for she wished to talk with them. It worried the Knight Zifar because they would be detained and would lose a day's journey. However, they went there to see the mistress of the town, and she asked them in what manner they had arrived there. The knight told her that they had left their land not through any evil they had done, but through the great poverty in which they had fallen. They were ashamed to live among their relatives;

therefore, they had left their country to search for life in another place where no one knew them.

16. Of how the mistress of the town was very pleased with the great wisdom and composure of the knight and his wife

The mistress of the town was pleased with the wisdom, intelligence, and composure of the knight and his wife and said:

"Sir, if you wish to dwell here with your wife, I will give you my small son to rear and I will grant you anything in my power, and you will raise your sons with mine."

"Lady," replied the knight, "it doesn't seem to me that I could do so, for I would not want to begin something and not carry it through."

The mistress of the town answered him, "Wait here today and tomorrow think more about it; and then give me your answer."

This worried the Knight Zifar but he had to grant her request. During these two days they received great honors and many favors from the mistress of the town. All the knights and nobles came to see and to converse with the Knight Zifar, and all the ladies visited his wife and gave them gifts openheartedly. They took so much happiness and comfort from the knight that it seemed to them they had been freed from all the war and the pressure they had been under by the good fortune that God had granted the knight in killing the nephew of that great lord, their enemy.

17. Of how the wife of the Knight Zifar asked her husband to remain there a month, for they were tired, and he so granted it

At this time, the mistress of the town sent for the wife of the Knight Zifar and beseeched her to request her husband to remain there with her and she would share willingly with them whatever her people possessed. And so great was her insistance that she had to consent to intercede with her husband. Then the wife of the knight went to their lodging and spoke to her husband. She asked him his opinion of the request that the mistress of the town had made of them.

"Of course," he said, "I don't know how to choose best, for I see that we need the benefits from the nobility because we are poor, but on the other hand to remain here I realize is very dangerous and fraught with great difficulty. The war that exists up to now between the lady and that great nobleman will be intensified between them from now on because of the death of that knight, his nephew, whom I killed through his misfortune."

"Dear husband," she replied, "we arrived here very tired from the long road and our little boys are very weak. If it is agreeable to you, I think it would be well for us to rest here a while."

"Of course," said the Knight Zifar, "If it pleases you, it pleases me too, and through God's grace, this stay here may redound to our advantage."

"So be it," said his wife.

At this moment, a knight from the town entered through the door, and spoke to them, "Sir, the mistress of the town sent me to tell you and your good wife that she would be pleased to have you come to see her." And so they did as requested. When they reached the lady of the town, they found all the knights and the citizens with their wives there. The mistress of the town arose to greet them warmly and stated, "Sir, tell me that you and your wife have agreed to the request I made of you."

"Truly, my lady," replied the Knight Zifar, "I would not want to be involved in anything that is unworthy of a knight; however, since you requested it, I am ready to serve you in everything you order and to be at your command."

The mistress of the town and all the knights who were there were grateful to him because he had promised to remain with them for one month.

18. Of how one of the most powerful knights of the town requested the Knight Zifar to remain there, saying that he would give him his two daughters to marry his sons

One of the most powerful of the knights of the town arose from among the group and said to him: "Stranger, I do not know who you are, but from what I know about you, I believe that you are a great and wise nobleman. However, I am sure that you are God's agent for good, and it would please me very much for you to remain here with our mistress. I have two daughters that I will give you as wives for your sons. I will also give you and your wife a third of all that I own for your maintenance."

"Thank you very much," said the Knight Zifar, "for your good will."

The mistress of the town said: "Good sir, doesn't it seem well to do what this knight is telling you, not counting the great favors and benefits that I will gladly do for you? You may believe me that this knight who made you that promise is one of the most powerful, noblest, and richest men in this land."

"Lady," said the Knight Zifar, "I am grateful to you and the knight for all you say; however, it was not my intent to come to this town to enter into kinship with anyone."

"Lady," said the wife of the Knight Zifar, "ask him to stay here with you one month and in the meantime we will talk over what you think is the correct thing to do."

"By Heaven, lady," replied the mistress of the town, "you speak sense. And sir knight, I ask you to do so."

"Well then," responded the knight, "I will do it since it pleases my wife; however, it would suit me better to spend less time in this idleness."

19. Of how the mistress of the town begged the Knight Zifar to help her in any way that he could

All those who were at the palace were greatly pleased with the knight's decision to stay. The mistress of the town said then, "Good sir, since you have done this favor for me and the people of this town, I beg you to guide and direct our deeds in those matters that you understand best."

The Knight Zifar answered that he would very willingly do what he could do. Then the mistress of the town ordered that he be provided for and given all those things that he might need.

20. Of how the mistress of Galapia was then besieged by her enemies

On the third day after these events, in the early hours before daybreak, the town was surrounded by the enemies of the mistress of the town—three thousand well-armed knights with a great number of infantrymen and crossbowmen. They began to pitch their tents in a great hurry, encircling the town. When the sentinels heard them, they began to cry out, "To arms, to arms!" At the same time, the uproar was so great in the town that everyone went on the run to the parapets, thinking that the enemy was trying to enter. If they had not reached them, the town would have been lost, so quickly had the enemy reached the gates. As soon as it was day, they could see them better, and they were well prepared for their task for they had numerous grappling hooks, huge catapults, and portable shields for the assault, and the crossbowmen forced them to retreat from the town. The Knight Zifar, who was still abed, asked his host what the tumult was about. Then his host told him of how their enemies had surrounded the town. He asked his host how many troops were there, and he told him more than three thousand knights and a huge number of infantry. Zifar questioned him as to how many knights were in the town. He replied about one hundred good ones.

"Certainly," said the Knight Zifar, "With the help of God, I wouldn't hesitate committing one hundred good knights against one thousand not so good."

"And if you have the courage to do such a feat, you have here enough good knights with whom to do it. I wonder, if you are as good a knight as they say you are, how can you allow yourself to remain in bed during such an emergency as this?"

"What!" replied the knight, "you mean these knights here want to go outside to fight the others?"

The host replied, "Would it not seem a great folly for one hundred to fight one thousand?"

"And will they always be beseiged thus and unable to do anything about it?" asked the knight.

"I don't know," replied the host, "but I believe that you would be prudent and wise to attend the council that the knights are now holding."

"Surely," said the knight, "I will not do so, because it would be foolish to attend a council before one is called; for the wise man says: 'never attend a council until summoned.'"

"For Heaven's sake, sir!" replied the host, "It seems to me that you are quick to make excuses not to fight; and I believe you are a better talker than a fighter."

"Really," said the Knight Zifar, "the truth is that it is easier to say things than to do them."

When the host heard this, he lowered his head and left the room saying, "We are defending ourselves, all the others are in great danger, and he lies here unconcerned." He then went to see the mistress of the town, with whom the knights and the others were in council. When the mistress of the town saw him, she questioned him, "How is your guest?"

He replied, "My lady, he lies in his bed unconcerned about the peril you are in."

"Surely," replied the mistress and the others who were there with her, "we wonder much about what kind of knight he is and how intelligent he is to stay away thus. And what did he say to you of the predicament in which we are?"

"My lady, I asked him why he did not come to this meeting that we are holding and he answered me that it would be folly to come to anyone's council before being summoned."

"By Heaven!" all said at once, "He spoke wisely."

"And did he say more to you?" asked the mistress of the town.

"Certainly, my lady. I told him that he appeared more a preacher than a warrior, and he replied that I was speaking the truth because it is easier to say things than to do them. He even asked me more—how many knights were there in the town. And I told him one hundred good ones. He told me that with one hundred good knights a man could attack more than one thousand not as good." These words pleased some and troubled the others; because they understood that if they were to be led by this knight he would place them in positions where danger was greatest.

21. Of how the Knight Zifar advised the townsmen to sally forth and strike the enemy army

"Surely," said the mistress of the town, "it is no longer necessary to delay sending for him." She ordered two of her most worthy knights to fetch him then and to escort him back. When they reached him, they found the knight and his wife attending mass with deep devotion. After mass was over, the two knights informed him that the mistress of the town had requested him to come to her.

"Very gladly will I go," said the knight, and returned with them. As they were traveling together one of the townsmen asked, "Sir, how does this situation with our enemies seem to you?"

"Well," he replied, "friend, it seems to me that they have you in a dangerous fix if God does not help you and your efforts—all is needed here."

When they reached the main reception room the mistress of the town and all attendant arose to greet him and she addressed him, "Good sir, can you not see how our enemy has us in a predicament?"

"Certainly, my lady," he answered, "I was told that they came to attack right up to the gates of the town."

The mistress of the town replied, "Well, good sir, what do you think will be the outcome?"

"My lady, whatever you command," said the knight.

"Will you use your strength," responded the mistress of the town, "to take action against these enemies of ours?"

"My lady," he replied, "with the strength of God and these good citizens."

"Well, I command that all the people of the town be led by you and place themselves under your orders. And this I order with the agreement and approval of everyone," said the mistress of the town. Then the mistress of the town asked all her subjects, "Is it agreed as I say?"

They all answered her, "Yes, my lady."

"My lady," the knight said, "order all your knights of the nobility to assemble and all the others who are equipped with horses and weapons."

The mistress of the town ordered it to be done thus, and the messengers withdrew.

Afterward he had them swear that they would follow him and not abandon him in any place where he needed their help. And they did so swear.

"Now, my lady," said the knight, "order a review of the troops tomorrow morning, everyone at his best, the knights as well as the squires, crossbowmen, and infantry; and if you have some armament for a knight, order it lent to me."

"Certainly," she replied, "I'd be most happy to. I will give you my husband's equipment, which is excellent."

"My lady," replied the knight, "I would rather have it lent and not given, because it belongs to your son by inheritance. Therefore you ought not to give it to anyone."

22. Of how the Knight Zifar and the townsmen were observing the disposition of the enemy from the walls

The next morning they came out for the review well equipped. There were one hundred ten knights of the nobility and fifty noblemen's sons as squires; however, they did not have breastplates for their horses. There were another sixty townsmen also battle-ready. All together there were two hundred twenty troops.

"Surely," thought the Knight Zifar, "there are enough people here to defend their land with God's aid."

The mistress of the town gave the knight the beautiful and ornate armor that she had promised him. In front of the troops he tested it and adjusted it where needed. He also ordered the others to test their equipment. It was obvious that he was experienced in warfare, for he knew so well how to handle all the equipment of war. He stood out among the others splendidly armed, handsome and valiant. The mistress of the town, on the ramparts of her fortress, observed what each soldier was doing. She saw how the Knight Zifar was supervising and instructing the troops, and she was well pleased.

Afterwards, the Knight Zifar ordered each to go to his lodgings and eat and for all to gather at the town square at the hour of nine. And so they did. Zifar found that the horse he had acquired from the knight he had slain at the gate to the town was a fine horse, broken to the bridle, high spirited, and he was very pleased with him. At the hour of nine all the soldiers gathered in the square as he had ordered, and he spoke to them:

"Friends, those who are oppressed and in danger ought not lend themselves to idleness, but ought to do whatever they can to escape that oppression and danger. It is a natural thing for one who is in danger to want to escape that danger just as a servant wants to escape servitude. Therefore, it is necessary for us to make a surprise attack during the morning before our enemy is prepared and strengthens himself."

The troops replied that as he ordered so would they do. "Well, prepare yourselves," replied the Knight Zifar, "in such a way that before the break of dawn, we will fall upon them."

They all responded that they would do so willingly. The Knight Zifar then replied, "Let us walk along the ramparts and we shall see how the enemy forces are disposed." They climbed to the platforms of the ramparts and saw how the enemy was disposed, and the Knight Zifar saw two large breaks in the lines at which there were no troops and he asked:

"What is that space which is vacant yonder?"

"No doubt," they replied, "the walls of the town are long and they cannot surround it all."

He saw a place where there were two tents set up and not many people near them, and asked, "Who dwells in those tents?"

A knight from the town replied, "The commander of the enemy army."

"And where did you learn it?" asked the knight. "How else," he replied, "than from one of our spies who came from there?"

He sent for that spy and the Knight Zifar questioned him: "Tell me, friend, does the commander of the enemy forces live in those tents?"

"Yes," the spy replied.

"And how many troops does he have with him, if you know for sure?"

The spy replied, "I saw him ride out the other day, and it seemed to me that it could be as high as thirty-five hundred knights, counting the good and the bad."

"And are there many noblemen?" asked the knight.

"Well," he answered, "I believe there could be a little over two hundred."

"And all these royal knights are with the commander of the army in his camp?"

"Certainly not," he replied, "because he disperses the noble knights throughout the army, for he does not trust the others, who are scoundrels and did not willingly join the army."

"I am really pleased," said the Knight Zifar, "because it appears God favors us." He then spoke to another knight: "If we are to succeed there, we have to strike at the enemy chief first."

"By Heaven," said the other knight, "You speak sense and thus we shall do. If we overcome the stronger force, the weaker will be unable to defend itself against us."

"And through there we will force our way, and they will not realize we are coming forth to strike their rear," said the Knight Zifar.

"I know it well," replied the other knight.

"Well," said the Knight Zifar, "in the name of God let us get under way early tomorrow. You guide us through the best opening you know." And the knight replied that he would gladly lead.

23. Of how the enemy army attacked the troops of the town, and how the townsmen defended themselves handily

At this moment, six hundred knights and a large number of infantrymen were approaching. The troops of the town asked the Knight Zifar if they should go out to meet them. He told them they should not go out but should defend the town, for it would be better if the enemy outside did not discover how many soldiers were in the town. This way the enemy would be unaware of their number and would believe that the townsmen were few in number and thus would not attack them. The enemy approached close to the town walls, hurling stones from slings, firing arrows, and making a great clamor; but whoever reached the gates or the wall did not go away unhurt because of the hail of stones and arrows from the town. In this way many were killed and wounded that night. Among them walked a tall knight in a magnificent suit of armor decorated with two lions of blue on a field of gold.

"Friends," asked the Knight Zifar, "who is that knight wearing that armor?"

"The commander of the enemy," replied the others.

The Knight Zifar became silent and asked no more questions; however, he continued observing the armor of the enemy commander and could see it well. He said to the others: "Friends, good night to you. Rest until early tomorrow morning when you hear the horn. It is necessary that you be alert and well armed. Come to the plaza so that we may go where God may lead us."

They all dispersed and headed for their homes and other lodgings, and the Knight Zifar left for the church. He asked the priest to go to the plaza the next morning before matins and prepare an altar for mass. The priest replied that he would gladly do so.

24. Of how the townsmen set out to strike the enemy before the dawn

Then the Knight Zifar went to his lodgings, and well before dawn he arose and had the horn sounded. Then all the knights, crossbowmen, and foot-soldiers armed themselves and went to the plaza. When he arrived there, the Knight Zifar found the priest dressed in his robes. He dismounted and asked the priest to say mass. The priest said a fine mass, and very quickly, so that all the troops were aware of the presence of God and commended themselves to Him. Afterwards the Knight Zifar mounted his horse and addressed them: "Friends, you hundred cavaliers and you fifty mounted squires form with the noble squires on foot. With these troops I will make the main assult. You ten noble knights, the other townsmen, the crossbowmen, and the infantry will remain and station yourselves at that little bridge on the road. If you are needed, I want you to be close to come to our aid." All replied that they would willingly obey. Then the Knight Zifar with the one hundred knights, fifty mounted squires, and two hundred squires on foot, went stealthily and as secretly as they could through a small ravine where the enemy had retreated earlier. And the knight who had said night before last that he would guide them, did lead them. When they were inside the enemy lines, the knight who was leading them stopped and said to the Knight Zifar, "We are now distant about two bow shots from the enemy."

"Well, which way do we go," asked the Knight Zifar, "to reach the enemy commander's tents?"

"I will guide you," the knight answered.

"Lead on," said the Knight Zifar, "for it seems to me to be almost daybreak. Go as close as you can to the headquarters, and when you are near, sound this horn and we shall advance then and fall upon them. And let's all keep close watch for the enemy commander, for if God is merciful we shall defeat him."

He gave a horn that he was carrying around his neck to the knight so that he could give the signal. They advanced very quietly toward the enemy commander's tents. And such was God's grace to them that not a horse neighed. The horses remained very calm until they approached quite close to the enemy. The knight who was guiding them sounded the horn, for he believed that the night sentries had spied them. Then the Knight Zifar and his troops advanced against the enemy and fell upon them suddenly, crying, "Galapia, for the mistress of the town!"

The troops of the enemy army were thrown into confusion by this sudden onslaught and were unable to run to their horses or to get their weapons. The attackers slaughtered the horses as well as all the soldiers they met. They paid no heed to taking prisoners but concentrated on killing. Those who escaped them headed for their commander's encampment. When the Knight Zifar reached there with his company, so many troops had reached the commander's camp and barred the way all around with shields and anything they could lay their hands on that they could not penetrate through the barrier of the tents. They were defending themselves so stubbornly that the troops of the Knight Zifar were suffering great losses. He turned to his men and said, "Friends, it is already day, and I see great dust being raised by the enemy behind us, and it appears they are preparing to attack us. Let us go, for we have done enough for the first time." And so they departed, returning the same way to the town.

25. Of how the commander of the enemy army attacked the town and was badly wounded, and how one of his sons was taken as a prisoner to the mistress of the town

The enemy commander armed himself very quickly in his tent and left on horseback, accompanied by one of his sons and six knights who were able to run for their weapons. They advanced toward the town. The Knight Zifar, when he saw them, ordered his men to go faster before the enemy overtook them, for it is not a disgrace for a man to save himself when he sees a great strength in the enemy, especially under a leader of such great stature. The Knight Zifar was in the rearguard, urging them to hurry since the enemy was coming very close, although advancing in loose formation.

The enemy commander saw the armor and weapons that belonged to the commander of Galapia and said: "Is the lord of Galapia alive? Surely if he is alive, I believe him capable of such a feat as this, for he was always a valiant knight. But it cannot be, because I verified his death and his burial, and he left only a very small son. Rather I believe that his armor was given to someone who could lead the others."

The enemy had now approached so close to the troops of the town that each army could understand what the other was saying. The Knight Zifar turned his head and saw them approaching very close to himself, and he recognized the armorial insignia of the enemy leader he had seen the night before last. He was coming in advance of the others, accompanied only by his son and another knight. They were very close to the little bridge where the Knight Zifar had stationed his reserve troops. He gave a great shout to his company: "Wait for me!" He turned to face the enemy leader, positioned his lance under his arm, and warned, "Knight, defend yourself."

"And who are you," asked the enemy commander, "to be so daring?"

"Certainly," replied the Knight Zifar, "you will find out now." He plunged his spurs into his horse and rode full tilt against him. He gave him a thrust of the lance, which penetrated his armor and sank into his side at least two hand spans, so that he fell to the earth. His troops advanced to his aid, attacking all around while trying anxiously to place him on his horse. Meanwhile the Knight Zifar rejoined his troops and passed safely through the ravine. And God did an even greater favor for the Knight Zifar and his soldiers; for the son of the enemy commander, when he saw his father felled, plunged his spurs into his horse and attacked one of the knights of the town. Although he was not hurt, he was caught up in the mass of troops and taken prisoner. Thus they took him captive to the town.

There was great grief in the camp of the enemy, for they believed their commander was dead. After they carried him to the royal quarters and undressed him, they found that he had a serious wound in his side. When they inquired about his son and did not find him, they considered themselves even more unfortunate, for they believed him to be a prisoner or dead. When the commander regained consciousness, the doctors came to examine him and said they would soon heal him with the help of God. He felt strengthened and asked for his son. They told him that he was passing among the troops to reassure them. He was very pleased and said his son was doing well. The leaders of the army then sent one of their knights to the town to learn whether the commander's son was dead or a prisoner.

26. Of how a knight from the enemy army went to ask the town whether their commander's son was a prisoner or dead

When the knight approached the gate of the town, he rested his lance on the ground and asked the crossbowmen not to fire, for he was coming only to find the answer to a question. The sentinel on the gate said to him, "Sir knight, what do you request?"

"Friend," replied the knight, "tell me what you know of the commander's son, is he a prisoner or dead?"

"All right," answered the sentinel, "he is not dead but a prisoner."

"And is he wounded?" asked the knight.

"No," replied the sentinel.

"Surely," said the knight, "we fared badly in this attack." And with that, he returned to his own lines and told them how the commander's son was a prisoner but had not been wounded at all.

27. Of how the commander of the enemy army found the war going adversely and told his vassals so

When it was near vespers, the commander summoned those leaders whom he was accustomed to summon to give counsel, and he asked them what they thought of this matter. Some told him to ignore it, for God would quickly grant him vengeance. Others told him that such things as these always happen in battle, while others advised him to think about the justness of the demands that he had made against the mistress of the town. If these demands were unjust, he should cease to make them, because of what had happened to him and to his son on this day.

"Is my son dead?" exclaimed the commander of the army.

"No," replied the others, "he is a prisoner but is not hurt."

"And how was he taken prisoner?" asked the commander.

"In truth," they replied, "when you were wounded he sank the spurs to his horse and attacked the enemy and was surrounded in a crowd and overpowered."

"Blessed be God!" exclaimed the father, "for my son is alive and unhurt. Friends and relatives, I want to tell you one thing: since they killed my nephew in this place and they hold my son prisoner and wounded me, I believe that God wishes to help them and hurt us. I have done the lady a great wrong. I have committed a great wickedness in this place and she has not deserved it. Therefore it is necessary to recognize our error and repent of it. Let us make amends to God and the lady. If we do not, I truly believe God will condemn us even more harshly."

A knight, vassal of the commander, a Christian and very wise, stood up and went to kiss his hands, and said: "Sir, I am very grateful to God for the mercy he has shown you and us this day for making you realize in your own heart that you have wronged this lady. You never recognized this until now, although it was obvious to all the people that it was so. Therefore, sir, recover your son and ask forgiveness of the lady for the evil that you have done her. Assure her that she will receive no injury from us henceforth. I will guarantee, at the risk of my own head, that God will help you in every good thing that you do, for just as this lady is your enemy now, everything will turn out as you desire."

"As a matter of fact, my good and loyal vassal," replied the commander of the army, "I am pleased with what you say, for you have advised me properly with honor and benefit to my body and soul. You and these fine men strive to carry on in the way you believe best. However, I would like to know who that person was that wounded me."

"Why," asked the knight, "do you wish to punish him?"

"No," replied the commander, "but I would like to know him in order to honor him whenever I meet him. Mark my words that I have never seen a knight who rode so handsomely, was so powerful, or could use weapons as that one did."

"Now, sir," said the knight, "rest tonight and tomorrow we will go on this mission."

"In the name of God," answered the army commander.

28.   Here the story ceases to tell of the commander of the enemy army, and tells of the mistress of Galapia

When the mistress of the town, before matins, heard the horn sound in the town to summon her troops against the enemy, she arose and sent for the wife of the Knight Zifar. They were continuously at prayer, imploring God to protect ther troops from harm. She believed that her troops would be defeated because of her sins, the town would then be lost, and she and her son made captive and deprived of their rights forever. But almighty God, the protector and defender of widows and orphans, seeing the great wrong and harm she had received up to that day, did not choose for her to receive any greater injury but wanted her to gain honor and happiness from this battle. When her knights were battling the troops in the enemy encampment, she sent one of her handmaidens to the observation platforms where she could see what they were doing. The maiden returned and said: "My lady, in the camp of the enemy commander there is so much dust that it towers to the sky, so that we could not see what was causing that dust. The rising sun made the dust so brilliant a red that it seemed blood; however, we could see that all the others who were besieging the town armed themselves hastily, and rushed to the enemy commander's tents where all that dust was."

On hearing these words, the mistress of the town believed that her troops were being defeated in their battle and would be unable to resist the foe who outnumbered them. Holding her small son in her arms, she began to worry about it and gave a shout like a wild woman, "Saint Mary protect us!" She fell overcome with grief to the ground, so that her son would have been badly injured if the wife of the Knight Zifar had not caught him in her arms. All the ladies who were present thought she was dead. Even though they poured water on her face and tried other remedies, they were unable to bring her to consciousness. There was great lamentation and wailing, for all the maids and ladies of the town were present with her. Some had husbands in the army; some had brothers in the army, and others their relatives and their fathers and sons, and all believed their relatives were in danger of death, and that they themselves would be taken prisoner and the town lost.

29. Of the grief of the troops of the town who had fought with the enemy, because they believed their mistress dead

Those who were on the observation platforms saw a disorderly mass of knights leaving the dense dust cloud and heading toward the town. Then they came to the mistress of the town and spoke to her to comfort her: "Our lady, behold your knights are returning unhurt and happy. Praise be to God, and may you be consoled." But they were unable to get any response from her. It seemed to all that she was dead. After the knights had passed through the little ravine and entered the town, they were told the news that the mistress of the town was dead. It grieved them deeply, and the great happiness they felt for the grace God had shown them turned to great sorrow, and as they heard the news, all the knights dropped from their horses to the ground, lamenting loudly and weeping copiously.

30. Of how the mistress of the town regained life through a miracle that the Virgin Mary performed, who intervened with Our Lord, her Son

The Knight Zifar was greatly worried and he called all of them together and said: "God has never been inconstant in His actions. Because of this I do not believe that He would willingly give us such heartbreak. It would appear contrary to His own nature to want something he started to have a bad ending. He is always accustomed to have a good start and a better ending, and to increase the wealth and bounty of those who believe in Him. Let us go find out if she died, for I cannot believe that it is true. Perchance they lied to us."

The ladies were gathered around their mistress, lamenting and crying exceedingly, when they heard a voice in the chapel where their mistress lay: "Friend of God, arise, for your people are disconsolate and they believe that the taste of victory which God, my Son, the Saviour of the world, granted them on this day, has been turned to wormwood by your death. I believe that it is the will of my Son to redress this deed for your happiness and delight." All the ladies there were terrified, and wondered where this voice came from which they could hear so clear and sweet. So brilliant was the light then in the chapel that they were blinded and unable to see one another. After a short while, they saw their mistress open her eyes and raise her hands together toward Heaven, saying: "My Lady, Saint Mary, advocate for sinners and consoler of the sad, guide to those who stray, defender of helpless widows and orphans! Blessed be the son of God who through the Holy Spirit was incarnate in Thee and praise be the fruit that was born and blossomed from Thee! Thou hast returned me through Thy holy mercy from death to life, and Thou hast freed me from great sorrow and brought me unto great happiness." All there heard clearly what she was saying, and they sent word to the knights that their mistress was alive. All were overjoyed and went there, except the Knight Zifar, who had gone to his lodging. When they arrived, they found her sitting on her dais and weeping with the great pleasure she felt because she was seeing all her soldiers alive and well.

She questioned them: "Where is the good Knight Zifar who went with you?"

They replied, "Our lady, he went to his lodging."

"And what did you think of him?" she asked.

"My lady," responded an old knight, "I swear to God and to you that I do not believe there is a bolder knight nor a more gallant one than this knight in all the world."

"And did he aid you worthily?" she asked.

"By Heaven, my lady," replied the knight, "he attacked the royal camp of the enemy commander very strongly and fearlessly, comforting us and inspiring us to do better. And, my lady, there could not be another man so virtuous in all the world whose words could comfort and inspire his troops as this knight's did. And in truth you may believe that he is a man of high station and of heroic achievements."

The mistress of the town raised her hands to God and thanked Him for the grace He had shown her on this day, and then ordered them to return to their homes. Then they disbanded and went to eat and to rest. The wife of the Knight Zifar wanted to go to her husband, but she would not allow her. She insisted that the knight's wife dine with her, and she had to do so. The mistress of the town honored her by seating her at the table and said in the presence of all: "Noble and virtuous lady, servant of God, when will I be able to reward your husband and you for the mercy that God has done for me this day through him and you? Truly I could never show you enough gratitude; but God has the power to reward all deeds and He will give you the reward you deserve. If it had not been for you, my small son would have died had you not caught him in your arms when I fell senseless with him from the observation platform. In truth, I do not know where I fell, for it seemed to me that I was straightway going to fall from the platform with grief and fear in my heart that those knights who were struggling for me against the enemy would be defeated, and I and my little son made captive. However, God through His mercy caused your husband with his native sense, his gallantry, and his good fortune to rescue us from the evil and danger in which we found ourselves." Afterward they began to eat and drink, and to be entertained. The mistress of the town sent all the provision she received to the Knight Zifar, to show her gratitude for the mercy that God had shown her.

31. Of how the mistress of the town sent for the count's son whom she held prisoner, and of the things they discussed before all the assembly

When it was the ninth hour, she sent for all the knights of the town and the Knight Zifar to appear before her. And weeping she said: "Friends, relatives, and good and loyal vassals, I beg you to help me to show our gratitude to this knight for what he has done for us. I would not know how to begin to show my gratitude to him, because it seems to me that God through His mercy saw fit to guide him to this land to put an end to this war. However, I am very much afraid that the war may expand, because the enemy commander is wounded and we hold his son a prisoner here. The commander is related by marriage to many great and powerful nobles, and as soon as they receive this information they will come to him with all their power to seek vengeance."

"My lady," said the Knight Zifar, "be of good spirit and take consolation in God, for He who has protected you unto this day looks with favor on you and will free you of your great fear, and with honor to you."

"Good sir," she replied, "it could come to pass with your great strength and your wisdom."

"Certainly, my lady," he replied, "I shall do here what I can, with the help of God."

The mistress of the town asked them if it would be wise to send for the son of the enemy commander in order to talk with him. All responded affirmatively, because by some chance, he might hit upon a course that would put an end to the war. Then they sent for him, and he came very humbly and knelt before her.

"Friend," she said, "God knows I am very pleased with you."

"Certainly, my lady," he replied, "I well believe it, for the more you are pleased, the more I am worried."

"Aren't you pleased to be here alive with me rather than dead?" she asked.

"Certainly I am," he replied. "If my father is alive, I am sure he will do everything possible to get me out of this prison; and if he is dead, I would not want to live."

"And was your father wounded?" she asked.

"Certainly, my lady," he replied.

"And who wounded him?" she asked.

"A knight wounded him who vigorously pressed on in the battle. I don't believe I ever saw a knight who wielded his weapons as that one did," he answered.

"And did you recognize him?" she asked.

"I did not," he replied, "but he was wearing your husband's armor and weapons."

Smiling slightly she said to him: "My friend, you know that I have not wronged your father but he has done me great harm and evil for unknown reasons. However, friend, tell me if there is some way that this war and this evil that exists between us could end."

"Surely, my lady, I know only one," he replied.

"And what is it?" she asked.

"That you marry me," he stated. She rested her eyes on him and began to study him. However, the knight was a very handsome and sensible youth of high nobility. Furthermore, his father had no other son but him. The mistress of the town ordered him to be taken away and for all the others to leave except the Knight Zifar and those who were her counselors, and she said to them, "Friends, what do you think of this proposal?"

32. Of how the mistress of the town asked the Knight Zifar if she should marry, and he and the others advised her to do so

They were all silent for there was no one there who felt he should answer. And the Knight Zifar, when he saw that no one was responding, said, "My lady, one who has little wisdom is quick to use it, and what little I have, I want to tell you in these words, subject to the agreement of these good men who are here."

"My lady," the Knight Zifar said, "I see that God wants to guide you in the path of honor with no harm or discredit to your son. I believe it is to your honor and of great advantage to your son for you to marry this knight, son of the enemy commander. This town and the other castles that belonged to your husband will all belong to your son, and you will be esteemed and prosperous with this knight." The knights and the citizens who were with her agreed with what the Knight Zifar had said. They told her that he had analyzed the problem wisely.

"Friends," replied the mistress of the town, "since you consider it right, I shall not fail to follow your counsel. Weigh your counsel and order it in such a way as you believe will be most in the service of God and of advantage and honor to me and my son." The Knight Zifar said that he would hold her request in abeyance until the morrow, when they would speak with the enemy commander's son. Then each of them went to his own quarters to rest.

33. Of how the commander of the enemy army sent his messengers to speak with the mistress of the town and her advisers

Early the next day, six of the enemy commander's knights arrived at the gate of the town on their palfreys. They were elegantly dressed and completely unarmed. The guards on the towers told them they would open fire unless they withdrew. "Friend," said one of the six knights, "do not do so, for we come bearing good news."

"Well, what do you want?" asked the man on the tower.

"We want to speak to the mistress of the town," replied the knight.

"And would you like for me to inform her?" replied the man on the tower.

"Yes," answered the knight.

The man who was on the tower went then to the mistress of the town and gave her the message—of how six honorable knights of the enemy army were at the gate and wanted to talk to her and that they had told him that they came bearing good news.

"May God through His mercy wish it," she said. And then she sent for the Knight Zifar and the other men of the town. She told them those knights had been at the gates since early morning. She asked them if they considered it proper for them to enter and if some citizens of the town should go there and escort them. They chose from among themselves twenty of the oldest and most distinguished knights and sent them there. They opened the gates of the town and went to meet the six knights. They asked them if they wished to enter. The knights responded that they did, in order to speak with the mistress of the town.

"Well, make us a pledge," said the Knight Zifar, "that through you or your actions no harm will come to the town or to any who dwell here."

"Of course," replied the knights, "we do so pledge."

"And you assure us," said the knights of the enemy army, "that we will not receive harm or treachery on entering here?" "We assure you," replied the knights of the town, "that you will receive nothing but honor and pleasure." Thus they entered the town and went to the mistress of the town who was awaiting them. When she saw them enter, she arose to greet them.

All the others who were present arose and greeted them warmly. The envoys requested all to be seated and they would deliver their message. Then all sat down and remained very quiet.

"My lady," said one of the knights of the mission, "our commander, the count, sends you greeting."

"May God grant him as much health as he wishes for me," replied the mistress of the town.

"So be it!" replied the knights of the enemy army, "because we are certain that he wishes you honor and good health; and do not doubt it, for he wishes you all there is in the world."

"May God so wish it," she replied.

"My lady," responded the knight, "our commander sends us to tell you that God has burdened him with many cares and problems in this world, and they place him in great danger and He does it to him for the distress he has caused you and because he is the greatest sinner in the world. You did not deserve this, nor did you give him any reason for doing anything to you, and neither did your husband who was master of this town. He says that prior to this he had been his lifelong friend, and that he has made war against you and done great harm to you and caused great evil in your land. And therefore he considers that should God burden him with more afflictions and greater dishonors than those he has suffered up to this day, they would be justly deserved. Therefore he sends us to ask you to forgive him and that he will be your friend and support you against all those who might wish to do you harm. He promises this without any deception or reservations whatsoever. Besides this, he sends you word that if it should please you, he would be extremely happy to have his son marry you. You know that he has no other son as an heir except the one you hold prisoner. Then he will give you in your lifetime two great cities that are near here and eight of the strongest castles in the surrounding area."

"Sir," replied the mistress of the town, "I will not be able to give you my answer until I speak with my privy counselors. You may withdraw over there and I will speak with them."

"Certainly," they replied, "with great pleasure." And so they did.

34. Of how the emissaries delivered the message from their lord, the count, to the mistress of the town

The mistress of the town was somewhat shy and hesitant with her privy counselors and said nothing. The counselors were discussing the matter among themselves and considering that to delay an answer was bad. This was not a matter demanding total agreement for this was a God-sent opportunity. While they were pondering, an aged knight, uncle of the mistress of the town, arose, and said: "My lady, delay is good at times and bad at others. Delay is good when a man is thinking of doing some evil deed from which some danger can spring. By delaying what he could do quickly, something could happen so that harm or a greater part of it could be avoided. That same thing applies to the one who wishes to do something recklessly which afterwards he will regret. He ought to delay; because he ought first to consider in what way it would be better to act, and after he has considered it and understood it, he could more directly accomplish the matter. He should also delay when the time has become less propitious, so that the deeds are not carried out as would have been seen fitting. For in such a time as this, men should be patient and allow events to determine matters. It is better to detour from a bad and dangerous road and take another, although the other might be longer and off the beaten track, than to travel along the rough and fearsome one. When one is making progress, it does not matter if it grows late. Rather, whenever the right moment arrives for accomplishing things, and those things are good, and having foreseen their completion, one ought not to delay in any manner, just as we should not in this matter which is similar, for a delay of one hour or one day may perhaps be fatal. One should address himself to the task and do it then without delay, for there are times when one must strike at the opportune moment or the moment is lost forever."

"Of course I am at your disposal," replied the mistress of the town. "Order what I should do as you think fit." Then they summoned those six knights, vassals of the enemy commander, and asked them under what authority they were acting. They replied that they had power of attorney, which their lord would honor. Furthermore they were carrying his seal to verify the things they might do there.

35. Of how the marriage contract of the mistress of Galapia and the son of the count was signed by those knights

The uncle of the mistress of the town told them, "Friends, all the things that you are asking, speaking for and in the name of the count, your lord, all are granted to you and are done in the name of God." A knight of the group of the commander of the enemy army spoke: "My lady, do you forgive the commander of the army of whatever harm, damage, and trouble he has caused you up to today itself and will you give up your complaint against him before all these good men who are present?

"Yes, I forgive him," she replied, "and I yield my complaint against him, if you keep your word you have given here to me."

"And I make you my promise and pledge," responded the knight, "with these knights who are here with me, and I promise with them for the commander of the army that he will be your friend for all time and he will fulfill to you all we have here stated and he will stand with you against all those who might be against you. We request a public notary to make out a legal document to this effect for greater security, and I will sign it with the seal of our lord. In addition, my lady, what is your answer relative to marriage with the son of our commander?"

She was silent and did not answer. He asked her again and she remained silent. The others saw that she did not wish to respond to this question, so the uncle of the mistress of the town spoke: "Sir, I assure you that in the matter of the request for marriage, when the commander of the army is here with my niece, all will absolutely be done. She will fulfill her part of the bargain if you keep your promise on behalf of his son." "Do you pledge to me?" asked the knight. "I so promise," replied the uncle of the mistress of the town.

"I accept your pledge," answered the other knight. And on this agreement they had a legal document drawn.

36. Of how the messengers went to their lord, the count, with the reply of the mistress of the town

Then the knights, very happy and very pleased, took their farewell of the mistress of the town and those others present, mounted their palfreys, and departed for home. As they were traveling, they were chanting this psalm in a loud voice: *beati inmaculati in via qui ambulant in lege domini.* Surely they spoke the truth, for very fortunate are those, and surely they are, who travel doing good work in the service of God. The rest of the army were awaiting them and wondered greatly why they were so long delayed. They had been gone since early morning and did not return until the hour of nine so long had the bargaining lasted. And when they reached their lord and he saw them, he said to them, "Friends, are you coming to me with peace?"

"Certainly, my lord," they replied, "be of good spirit, for God has done what you wished."

"Am I forgiven by the mistress of the town?"

"Certainly you are," they answered.

"Now," he said, "I am cured in body and soul, blessed be God for it."

"We bring even more news," they said. "We know what will please you most, for we bring assurance from the uncle of the mistress of the town that when you visit her, the marriage between your son and her will be fulfilled, according to your instructions to us."

"Truly," he replied, "I am greatly pleased. Send word to the mistress of the town that early Sunday morning, at the first hour, I will be with her, if God is willing, not as a soldier, but as a good friend at her service." Then he ordered all his people the next morning to abandon their siege of the town and to go to their homes. He retained for himself two knights of his finest cavalry and ordered them to send their armor and weapons away and to keep their best vestments, for on Sunday he was planning his son's wedding, by the grace of God, to the mistress of the town. All these troops were very happy and grateful to God for it, for they believed he had escaped from crime and sin. When it was early Sunday morning, the commander of the army arose and heard mass, and so did the mistress of the town. They were all ready and knew that the commander of the army was to be there that morning, and all were very happy, especially when they saw the enemy army disperse and decamp.

37. Of how the marriage of the mistress of the town and the son of the army commander took place

When the commander of the army reached the gates of the town, the gates were opened and he was told to enter when he wished. All the town plazas and streets were strewn with flowers. All the knights came out to welcome him, and the ladies and the maids of the town were dancing and celebrating the great favor that God had done for them in freeing them from the great affliction which had beset them. The commander of the army approached the mistress of the town and greeted her. She arose to welcome him and said, "May God's blessing be on you." They both sat down on her dais in the presence of all the knights, and he began to speak words of solace and pleasure to her: "My dear lady, do you truly forgive me?"

"Certainly," she replied, "Yes, if you really keep your promises that you sent to me."

"Certainly I will," he said, "because of the wrong that I did to you, I have had many troubles. I was never able to complete anything successfully that I started; rather harm and great dishonor befell me. And I well believe that this happened to me through your prayers to God."

"Well may you believe that I always prayed to God to afflict you so that no harm would come to me through you, but from here on, I will pray to God to guide your actions rightfully and in honor," she replied.

"May God show his gratitude to you for that," he answered. "And dear lady, what is your answer to the matter I sent my knights on concerning the marriage of my son?" She became silent and did not respond at all. The commander of the army was embarrassed and thought that he should not have asked the question. He summoned one of his knights who had been a messenger and said to him, "Who is the knight who assured you of the marriage?"

"Sir," he replied, "it is that one over there."

Then the army commander went to him, took him by the hand, and drew him aside: "Sir, what about this marriage? Can it take place?"

"Yes," said the knight, "of course."

"And can it take place right away?"

"Yes," he replied, "if you wish it to."

"Well, arrange it," said the army commander, "And may God guide all your deeds."

"It's my pleasure," replied the knight. He went to the mistress of the town and told her that consultations on the marriage would be held right away. She told him that she would do as he wished, for she had placed all responsibility on him.

The knight then went to fetch the son of the army commander, who was being held prisoner. When they arrived before the mistress of the town, the knight said to the army commander, "Ask what you wish of me and I will answer you."

The army commander stated, "I request this mistress of the town as wife for my son."

"I so grant your wish," replied the knight.

"And I give you my son for the lady, although it is not in my power, for the marriage can not be unless he and she agree."

They agreed to be man and wife; however, the commander spoke up: "If such a measure is valid, on such words as these, my son ought to be set free, since we have made peace."

"Of course," replied the mistress of the town, "this was not stated in the treaty. He is my prisoner and I will free him whenever I wish; I would not want him to escape from my hands through some trickery."

"Certainly," replied the army commander in a burst of laughter, "I am pleased that you will always have him in your power." They sent for the chaplain and he asked the commander's son if he would receive the mistress of the town as his wife, as the Holy Church commanded. He replied that he would do so. And the chaplain asked her if she took him to be her husband and she said that she did. When the wedding was over, she asked for the key to the shackles that held him. The shackles consisted of a belt of iron with a chain. She opened the lock and the shackles fell to the ground, and the chaplain said, "Sir, you are free and under no coercion."

"Yes," he said.

"Well, do you take this lady as your wife, as the Holy Church commands?"

He replied, "Yes, I do." They then joined hands and went to hear mass in the chapel and afterward to dine. Later, the knights were jousting, challenging, making their horses prance, fighting bulls, and celebrating wildly. Many articles of clothing and many jewels were given to the minstrels, the knights, and to the poor.

The commander of the enemy army was high on a tower watching how each of the knights was performing, and he saw a youthful knight outdoing all the others who were there. He asked the uncles of the mistress of the town, "Who is that knight yonder who wins over all the others in jousting, horsemanship, all the other crafts of war, and all the other things of renown?"

"A knight who is a stranger," replied the uncle of the mistress of the town.

"He certainly appears to be much like the one who wounded me. Please send for him."

"Why," answered the uncle of the lady, "do you wish him evil?"

"Surely not," he said, "for he wounded me in a fair fight."

The uncle of the mistress of the town sent for the Knight Zifar. When the Knight Zifar learned that the enemy commander had sent for him, he feared a confrontation with him. But considering all that, he went there very quickly and with a good demeanor.

The commander of the army questioned him: "Sir, where are you from?"

"From right here," replied the Knight Zifar.

"You are a native of here?" the enemy commander queried.

"Of course not," replied the Knight Zifar, "I am from the kingdom of Tarta, which is very far from here."

"Well, why did you come to this land?" asked the commander.

"Just as chance would have it," replied the Knight Zifar.

"Sir," said the commander, "You are the one who was dressed in the armor of the lord of this town on the day I was wounded?"

Then the Knight Zifar answered, "That knight who is next to you knows that answer."

"Do not be suspicious," replied the commander, "for I esteem you much more for being such a valiant knight. And if you are the one who wounded me, I forgive you. If you wish to remain in this country, I will give you much property and I will share all that I have with you."

"Thank you very much," replied the Knight Zifar, "for all you have said to me here. But the road that I have started on lies ahead of me and I will be unable to stay any longer than the time I promised the mistress of the town."

"Well, let's go for a ride," said the army commander.

"It would be a pleasure," replied the Knight Zifar. They mounted up and passed beyond the town where others were frolicking and having fun. As they rode along, the army commander talked with the Knight Zifar, asking him where he was from and how his trip had been and many other things that pleased him. Nightfall was drawing near and the ten days were about completed since he had obtained the horse when he killed the commander's nephew. While they were conversing, the horse dropped to the ground dead. The Knight Zifar leaped free of the dead horse and stood a short distance to one side.

"What in the world is this?" exclaimed the commander.

"This is what always happens to me," replied the Knight Zifar, "for such is the fortune that God grants me that no horse or beast of mine ever lives more than ten days; and therefore I am always obliged to be poor."

The commander of the army then replied, "That is certainly bad luck for a knight to have, but if you approve, I will do much for you—I will supply you with horses, weapons, and all the other things you may need if you wish to remain here."

"Thank you very much," said the Knight Zifar, "but you would not like it, for it would be a great expense to you and my stay would not be convenient for you; for praise be to God, war no longer exists in your land."

"You mean that a knight has no other use except in war?" asked the commander.

"Yes," replied the Knight Zifar. "He should be well born and should give good advice in matters of arms and other related things when the occasion arises; for weapons are of no benefit to a man, if he has not earlier received good advice on how they should be employed."

And the commander of the army sent for a beautiful horse that he owned and gave it to the Knight Zifar. He ordered him to climb into the saddle and said to him:

"Take this horse and treat him as your own."

"Thank you very much," replied the Knight Zifar, "for I certainly need one." Afterward they went to the palace and took their leave of the mistress of the town and went to their lodgings.

The next morning, the commander of the army came with all his retinue to the mistress of the town and handed over to his son the deeds to the towns and castles that he had promised him. Each of the two towns was larger and more prosperous than Galapia. He commended his son and the mistress of the town into the care of God and departed for his own land.

38. Now the story ceases to speak of the aforementioned things and relates how the Knight Zifar departed from that land with his wife and sons

The Knight Zifar dwelt there for the month that he had promised the mistress of the town. The horse that was given to him by the army commander died at the end of the ten days, and he did not have a horse on which to leave. When the mistress of the town heard that he was preparing to leave, she was distressed and sent for him.

"Good sir, do you really wish to go?"

"My lady," he replied, "I have completed the month that I promised you."

"And is there anything one could say to you to make you stay?" she asked.

"No indeed," he replied, "I am ready to move on."

"It grieves me," she said, "for such a gallant knight as you, through whom God granted us so much grace, to leave my country, but I know I can do nothing since your decision is firm. Take that palfrey of mine, which is a fine horse, and you will be given anything you need for the trip, and may God guide you." He said goodbye to the mistress of the town and so did his wife. The mistress of the town wept profusely because she could do nothing to convince him to remain. The uncle of the mistress ordered the palfrey given to him, along with a great amount of wealth. All the knights in the town set out with him, pleading and begging him to remain with them and telling him that all would serve him and labor for him as their own lord. However, their words were insufficient to persuade him to stay, for he had earlier told them that his intention was to go away no matter what. And when they had gone a long distance from the town, the Knight Zifar drew aside and said to them, "Friends, I commend you to God's care, for now is the time for you all to turn back."

"May God guide your way," the others replied, and with heavy hearts they turned back weeping.

39. Of how a lioness carried away Garfin, the older son of the Knight Zifar

The Knight Zifar traveled so far that he reached a kingdom that was called Falac, which had very noble and handsome people. When the ten days were completed since their departure from Galapia, the horse that the mistress of the town had given him dropped dead, so that he had to travel afoot for three days. They arrived one day at the third hour near a small wooded area where they found a beautiful and clear spring with a meadow all around. The lady, feeling great sympathy for her husband, who was walking, said to him, "Dear husband, let's go down to the spring and eat this cold meat that we brought." "I'd like to," replied the knight, and they remained near the spring and ate at their leisure, for there remained only a day's journey to a city named Mella, which was near the sea. After they had eaten, the knight lay down a short while with his head in his wife's lap and while she was picking lice from his hair, he fell asleep. Their children were playing merrily around the meadow and as they were getting closer and closer to the woods, a lioness came out of the woods and seized the older boy in her jaws. At the sound of screaming from the other boy, who came running, his mother turned her head and saw the lioness carrying her son away, and she began to scream. The knight awoke and said, "What is the matter?"

"A wild beast is carrying off your older son, and I don't know whether it is a lion or a lioness, and it has entered that forest." The knight mounted his wife's palfrey and rode into the forest. However, he found not a trace of it. He returned grief-stricken and sad and said to his wife, "Let us head for that city which is near here; because we can do nothing more here except show our gratitude to God for what he has done for us and be grateful."

40. Of how the Knight Zifar and his wife lost their other son in the city of Falac

They arrived at the city of Falac at the hour of vespers and took lodgings in the first rooms of the inn they found. The knight said to his wife, "I will go to look for food for us and fodder for this palfrey." And while she was wandering through the apartment chatting with the innkeeper's wife, the palfrey left the house, and she had to go out after it, telling those she met to return the horse to her. When her son saw that his mother was not at home, he followed, calling to her. He took the wrong street, lost his way, and wandered through the city. When his mother returned to their lodging she did not find her son, and said to the innkeeper's wife: "Friend, what became of my little boy whom I left here?"

"He followed you, calling for you," she answered. When the Knight Zifar arrived, he found his wife sad and grief-stricken. He asked her what was the matter, and she replied that God had brought great evil upon her, because now He had caused their other son to be lost. He asked her how he had gotten lost and she told him. "Surely," replied the knight, "our Lord God wants us scattered, and therefore may His name be blessed." However they paid some men to search through the city for him, and they walked the streets throughout the city, searching all night and the next day until the third hour. They never found a trace of him except a good lady who told them: "In truth last night after vespers, he passed by here crying and calling to his mother; and I felt pity for him and asked what was wrong. He refused to answer me, turned away, and disappeared down the street." When they reached the knight and his wife with this message, they were extremely grieved, especially the mother. She lamented so loudly that she attracted all the neighborhood. When they heard that on that very day the elder son had been carried away by a lioness near the spring and how the other son had been lost the same day, everyone felt great sorrow and great pity for the lady and the knight because of the great losses they had suffered in one day. And thus the lady, becoming hysterical, wandered like a crazy woman among all the others, uttering very strange words because of the great grief that she felt for her sons. However, the other ladies comforted her as best they could.

41. Of how the sailors carried away the wife of the Knight Zifar in a ship, leaving him all alone

The next morning, the Knight Zifar went to the seaside, and walking along there, he saw a ship that was preparing to go to the kingdom of Orbín where it was said there was a just and good king. The Knight Zifar asked those on the ship if they would take him and his wife there. They replied that they would if he paid them. He bargained with them and returned to the inn and told his wife how he had bargained with the sailors to take them to that kingdom where that good king reigned. His wife was very pleased and asked him when they would go. "Surely," he replied then, "early tomorrow if God is willing."

His wife said, "Let us go immediately. Let us leave this land where God has so ill-treated us."

The Knight Zifar replied, "By going from one kingdom to another do you think you can flee from the power of God? Surely it cannot be so, because He is Lord of the heavens, the earth, the seas, and the deserts. Nothing can escape His power, any more than a Roman emperor who thought he could flee the power of God, as you will now hear."

"The story relates how there was an emperor in Rome who was very afraid of thunder and lightning and fearful of the storms which struck in those times. And with his fear of the lightning, he ordered a palace constructed underground of great stones and many vaults. When it was cloudy, he would never go outside. One day a group of knights, his vassals, came to him in the morning and told him it was a very clear and beautiful day and they should go out of town to hunt and take their pleasure. The emperor mounted his horse and went with his knights outside the town. When they were about a mile away, he saw a little cloud in the sky, a very small one, and he rode his horse as fast as he could to get back to that fortress he had built underground. Shortly before he reached there, a bolt of lightning flashed from the cloud, which had grown very large and threatening, and he fell dead to the ground. He is buried in a tower of his fortress, for he could not flee from the power of God. And no one should say, "I don't want to remain in this place where God treats me so ill," for God is in one place the same as another, and no one can escape His power. Therefore we ought to be grateful to Him for whatever happens for good or ill, for He is the one who can give happiness after sadness, and pleasure after sorrow. And let us strive in His grace, for I am sure that He will grant us great consolation from this unhappiness we suffer."

"Thus God commands it!" she said.

The next morning after they had heard mass, they went down to the seaside to embark. The seamen were waiting only for the wind to rise. They saw the lady with the knight on shore. The devil, who never hesitates to put evil thoughts in the hearts of men in order to make things as bad as possible, inspired the ship's seamen to take the lady aboard the ship and leave the knight on the shore. So they did.

"Friend," they said to the knight, "wait for us with your horse here on the shore, for we do not have room for all on this small vessel. We shall return later for you and for the other things that we have to load aboard the ship."

"It's all right with me," replied the knight, "and I commend this lady into your care to guard her from evil."

"Certainly we shall do so," the others said. After they took the lady aboard the ship, a light breeze arose, and they raised the sail and started on their way.

42. Of how the knight departed the seashore and went away very sad and disconsolate

The knight was strolling along the shore, meditating and paying no attention to them, nor did he see the ship as it sailed away. In a short while he saw the ship in the distance, and he asked others who were walking along the shore: "Friends, that ship yonder, is it the one that goes to the kingdom of Orbín?"

"Certainly it is," they replied.

"And are they going to return for me?" he asked.

"Not this time," the others answered.

"You see, friends, what a deceitful thing they have done to me! They said they would return for me. They lied to me and kidnapped my wife," said the knight. When the others heard this, they were surprised at the great wrong committed by those seamen. If they could have helped him, they would have done so willingly, but the ship had gone so far and there was such a good wind, that they did not dare to go in pursuit of it. When the good Knight Zifar saw himself thus forsaken of the things of this world that he loved, he said thus in great sorrow:

"Lord God, blessed be Thy name for whatever mercy Thou has granted me. But Lord, if Thou art angry with me in this world, take me from it; because now I am tired of life and I cannot endure with patience as I was accustomed. And Lord God, most powerful, full of mercy and pity, Thou who hast power over all things, who aid and give comfort to Thy servants in their tribulations and aid those who are separated through the misfortunes of this world; thus as Thou didst aid Thy more fortunate servants Eustacius and Theospita, his wife, and their sons Agapito and Theospito, indulge Thy mercy to join me and my wife and my sons who are similarly separated. Do not examine my sins but see the great faith that I have always had in Thy grace and in Thy mercy; but if it still please Thee that I should suffer greater trials in this world, do unto me at Thy will; for so prepared, I can endure anything that may happen to me."

But our Lord God, seeing the patience and excellence of this good knight, sent a voice from heaven to him. All those present were comforting him the best they could and heard the voice. "Good sir," said the heavenly voice, "do not be discomforted for you will see from now on, for the many misfortunes that have happened to you, there will come to you as many pleasures, joys, and honors. And do not fear that you have lost your wife and sons, for all will eventually happen as you wish."

"Lord," replied the knight, "all is in Thy power and do as Thou thinkest best."

Moreover, the knight was comforted by these words, and the others who were present on the shore and heard this, were greatly astonished and said, "Surely this is a man of God, and the one who put him into such a predicament sinned." They tried to persuade him to remain in the town, saying they would give him everything he needed. "Certainly with all the grief I have suffered, I could not stay here; and I commend you to God's care," the knight said. He mounted his horse and rode away along a path beside the sea. All the people marveled at the misfortune that had happened to the knight in the city. Relative to this misfortune, some told of how he lamented for his sons, relating how the lioness had carried away one of them near the spring—which they now call the Spring of the Lioness—and how he lost the other one in the town; and others spoke of how those treacherous sailors carried off his wife through fraud and deceitfulness.

43. Of how the townsman told those people on the seashore he had found the sons of the knight, and of how he and his wife had adopted them

And while they were talking of this matter, one of the greatest, richest, and most powerful of the townsmen arrived unexpectedly. He asked them what they were talking about and they related everything to him.

"Of course," said the townsman, "his sons are not lost."

"And why not?" asked the others.

"I will tell you," replied the townsman. "I was out hunting the other day with my dogs and my servants, and I heard the dogs in great excitement. I went after them, and I found them running and barking in pursuit of a lioness which was carrying a very handsome little boy in her mouth. They took the little creature from her, and I took him in my arms and to my home. And because my wife and I have no children, I asked if she wanted to adopt him, since he had lost his mother and father. She approved of the idea, and we adopted him. In the evening my wife was holding the boy in her arms at the window and saw another very handsome boy the size of the first one, or a little younger, crying along the street; and she said to him: 'Friend, what's the matter?' He did not answer her. The little boy in her arms saw the other one crying, and he gave a shout and the other one raised his eyes and saw him and headed for the door, making a signal to let him in, because he did not know how to talk well. My wife sent a maid for him, and she took him to her room. When the boys saw each other, they began to embrace and to kiss, celebrating happily as those who were born of the same mother, reared together, and knew each other. And when either one was questioned: 'What has become of your father and mother?' they answered, 'I don't know.' When I reached my lodging, I found my wife very happy with that little boy that God had sent her; and she said to me: 'Dear husband, see what a beautiful child God has brought to my arms! I think God has granted me a greater boon in sending me this boy than he did in giving you the other one. I believe surely they are brothers, because they resemble each other, and I ask you as a favor to adopt this child as we did the other.' And I answered her that I would be delighted, and we adopted him."

"Praise the Lord!" said another townsman, "What great news for the knight, if he had someone who could take the news to him."

"Certainly," replied another, "I intend to go on this quest for a week, and if I find him, I will tell him the good news." And he took affidavits from the good men of the city in order that Zifar would believe him. He mounted and departed on his quest for the knight; but such was his luck that he never could find any news of him, whether he was dead or alive. He returned to the city and told the good men how he was unable to find any trace of the knight. They were all deeply grieved. All of them strove to help and to make those children happy, and the father and mother who adopted them tried even more. They were very pleasant, very graceful, very clean and well-mannered, although only small boys; for the good lady, whom those scoundrelly seamen on the ship had kidnapped, had taught them and reared them well. The story will now tell you of how that deed occurred.

44. Now the story ceases to relate of the Knight Zifar and tells of his wife, who was carried away in the ship over the sea

The story tells that when the lady saw that the seamen were getting under way and were not going for her husband, she knew she had fallen into evil hands and that they intended her no good. Overcome with grief and worry, she tried to throw herself into the sea. Such was her luck, that in falling, her sash became entangled in some of the ship's ropes. When the sailors saw her fall, they ran to her and found her suspended in midair. They caught her and pulled her aboard the ship.

"Sweetheart," said one of the seamen, "why do you want to kill yourself? Don't do it, for your husband will be here soon. On account of his horse, which we could not easily place aboard ship, we asked other seamen who were anchored near the shore to take him aboard. He will be with you very soon. Do not doubt it. And furthermore, all of us present wish you only well, and I more than all the others." When she heard these words, she knew they were false and deceitful, and she cried out: "Holy Virgin Mary, Thou who comest to those afflicted and in danger, come to my aid if Thou believest I am in need." And then they took her and placed her in the hold of the ship, so that she could not again throw herself in the sea.

They sat down to eat, for it was now near noon. As they were eating and drinking at their pleasure and conversing about the beauty of the lady, the Holy Virgin Mary, who willingly listens to the afflicted, heard this good lady and did not agree that she should suffer, as you will understand, as a reward from the devil to those deceitful seamen for the evil thoughts they had. So as they were eating and drinking more than they should and more than they were accustomed to, the devil inspired each of them to desire the lady for himself. One of them said, "Friends, I want that lady more than anything in this world, and I want her for myself. I beg you all not to attempt her love, for I am the one who will defend her until death takes me."

"Certainly I will do the same for myself," replied another, "for I desire her more than you do." Then all the other crewmen from the youngest to the oldest quarreled violently, drew their swords, and attacked each other so that none remained alive.

45. Of how the wife of the Knight Zifar found dead all those who had carried her away on the ship, and how she cast their bodies into the depths of the sea

The lady was below in the hold of the ship and heard the uproar they were causing. She heard screams and blows and because she did not know what the noise meant, she was so frightened that she dared not go on deck. And thus she remained all day and all night saying her prayers and praying that God would be merciful. When the dawn came, just before the sun rose, she heard a voice which said: "Good lady, arise and come on deck and cast the evil things you find there into the sea. Take for yourself all the other things that you find; because God wants you to have them and to spend them on good works." When she heard this, she was extremely grateful to God, but she was suspicious that it might be a trick those treacherous seamen were playing in order to violate her. She did not dare to leave until she heard the voice again, and it said to her, "Come up and do not be afraid, for God is with you." She considered that these words sounded so good and so holy they could not belong to those deceitful seamen; and furthermore, if they had wanted to enter the ship's hold, they could easily have done so.

She came up on deck and saw all those treacherous men dead and their bodies swollen. And as the voice had told her, she seized them by the legs and heaved them into the sea. They seemed as light to her as if they were made of straw. She was not frightened of them, because God gave her strength and comforted, and aided her to do it. She clearly understood that all this strength came to her from God, and she gave thanks to Him in profusion, blessing His name and His power.

When she had the ship free of all those evil bodies, and having swept and cleaned the blood from the deck, she lifted her eyes and saw the sail filled in the wind. The ship was sailing with the most favorable wind possible. There was no one on the ship to guide it, except a very fair and beautiful child that she saw above the sail. She was amazed that such a small child could be there. This was Jesus Christ, who had come to guide the ship at the request of his mother, Saint Mary; for thus had the lady seen him in a vision that night. And this child did not leave the lady either by day or night until he delivered her to the port where she was supposed to arrive, as you will hear from now on.

The lady wandered through the ship examining everything in it, and she found there many magnificent things of great value—gold, silver, pearls in abundance, many precious gems, expensive cloth, and varied kinds of merchandise, so that even a king of a large kingdom would consider that wealth quite plentiful. Among these things she found many dresses styled and ornamented in many ways, and a bountiful supply of ladies' bonnets according to the styles of those lands. It seemed to her that she had clothing and accessories for two hundred ladies and she marveled at how this could be. For this good fortune she raised her hands to our Lord God and thanked Him for the mercy He had shown her. She took this material that was on the ship and decorated the room in which she stayed. She dressed herself in clothing of the most appropriate that she found and sat down in her room. There she prayed to God night and day to have mercy on her and to grant a good ending to what He had started. And the story relates that this lady was surprised to see the things on the ship and to realize what they were and to take possession of them. It was a miracle how she traveled alone on the sea for two months from the day she had boarded it until she arrived in port.

And this port where she arrived was the city of Galán, which is in the kingdom of Orbín.

46. Of how a man boarded the ship in order to learn who came on it, and of how he found the lady and went to tell his lord, the king

In that city, the king and the queen were celebrating the festival of Saint Mary, about the middle of August, and the people on the seashore saw the ship at rest in the port, with its sail billowing. With a strong wind blowing, the ship was not moving in any direction. They wondered greatly at this and climbed into their boats and went there to find out the answer. They approached the ship and seeing that it had no anchor, believed it was a miracle of God—as indeed it was—and no one dared to climb aboard the ship. One of them said that he was going to risk going aboard, with God's grace, to find out what was going on. He climbed to the ship's deck and as soon as he saw the ship as it was, and the lady seated on a dais so elegant it was a marvel to behold, he became very frightened and said to her, "My lady, who are you and tell me who guides this ship?"

"And are you a knight?" she asked.

"Indeed I am not one," he replied. As a consequence she declined to stand up.

"And why don't you answer my question?" he asked.

She replied, "Because it is not fitting for you to know who I am."

"My lady," he said, "will you tell the king, if he can come here?" "Certainly," she replied, "it is proper, for it is because of him that I came from my land."

"And this ship of yours," said the man, "how can it be thus without an anchor?"

"It is, as you can see," she replied, "in the power of that One who sustains and guides it."

"And who is guiding it?" he asked.

"He who sustains and guides all things," she answered. "Well, my lady, I will go to the king with this message and with the news," he replied.

"May God guide you," said the lady. He climbed down to his boat and headed for those on shore. They were wondering about his delay and asked him why he had taken so long and what he had seen there.

"I was delayed," he replied, "because of a lady I found there who is one of the most beautiful and most prudent women in the world. However, she refused to tell me anything about her business." Then he went to the king, who was on the shore accompanied by the queen and a large crowd. The king had come to learn what was going on.

47. Of how the king of Orbín went aboard the ship and learned of the lady's affairs and of how she had arrived at his kingdom

The man who had climbed aboard the ship said to the king, "I will tell you what I saw on that ship." And he related to the king what had occurred between him and the lady and the adroit answers she had given him, so that the king understood by the lady's replies that she was very wise and in God's care. He went aboard a galley accompanied by many others, while some went in additional boats. They proceeded toward the ship. When they reached it, they wondered how it could remain there, for it had no anchor, and those people were apprehensive and said to the king, "Sire, don't endanger yourself in something you don't understand."

The king, a very good Christian, replied to them: "Friends, this is not a deed of the devil, for the devil does not have the power to stay the winds and things that are subject to them. This can be done only through the power of God, Maker of all things, and Who has them at His command. And therefore I will risk this for the sake of God and in His name, and I will place myself at His mercy." And a few of the people whom he had selected, climbed aboard the ship. When the lady saw that he was wearing a crown of gold on his head and carrying a golden scepter in his hand, she realized he was the king and rose to greet him and went to kiss his hands. The king refused to let her kiss his hands and sat beside her on her dais and asked her who she was. She told him that she was a lady from a land in India who had been abandoned by her husband and she did not know whether he was dead or alive. In times past the king of her land had been very cruel and unjust and she had been afraid that he would seize all their wealth. Because she had heard that king of Orbín was a good and very righteous king, she had wanted to live under his protection. She had the ship loaded with all the wealth she possessed and had come to him. The king said, "How does this ship travel without a crew or a captain? Didn't people accompany you?"

"Certainly," she replied, "Sire, they did leave with me."

"And what became of the people?" he asked.

"Sire, they committed a treacherous and deceitful trick against me," she replied. "Because the devil had inspired the thought in their hearts, they tried to dishonor me, and for their sins, they killed each other."

"Well then, who was guiding the ship?" asked the king.

"Sire," she answered, "I do not know unless it was the power of God and a small child above the sail who guided it. That is my opinion."

The king looked up and saw a beautiful child above the sail. He crossed himself for he realized it was the Son of God. He knelt and worshiped him and at that moment the child disappeared. The king sent word to the queen that she should come to the shore with all the other ladies and maids of the city in celebration. And after he took the wife of the Knight Zifar and alighted with her into the galley, he ordered the anchor dropped and the ship's sail lowered. He left good men aboard the ship to guard it and everything aboard it. They made their way to the shore while those at sea were rejoicing and celebrating. When they reached the shore, the queen was there and many ladies dancing with joy. As soon as the king debarked, he took the lady by the hand and said: "My queen, receive this lady that God has sent you, for I trust through His grace that much benefit will accrue to us, our land, and our kingdom through her."

"And I welcome her on these terms," said the queen, and she took her by the hand and she and all her retinue proceeded to the palace. As they were going their way, the queen asked her all about her affairs. She answered her properly in the manner of a fine lady and with great wisdom, so that the queen was very pleased with her and said: "My lady, if you would like, you may dwell in my house with me, so that we can see you every day and talk together."

"My lady," she answered, "as you command." And so she remained with the queen more than a year in her house and never left her. And the queen believed that God worked many benefits for her, the king, and all their land through this lady. Especially did the farmers believe that the great harvest they had that year, in addition to many other benefits, had come through the prayers of this good lady, and therefore they loved her and honored her greatly.

48. Of how the lady, wife of the Knight Zifar, built a convent in the kingdom of Orbín where she was living

And this good lady, as soon as she had arrived, had all her property taken from the ship, and she asked the king and queen to give her a tract of land as a boon where she might build a convent. They gave it to her freely. The lady was so persistent in the building of the convent that it was completed at the end of a year. Then she asked the king and queen as a favor to found an order, not because she wanted to enter the order, for she had faith that she would, in God's mercy, again see her husband, but rather that she might fill the convent with nuns and appoint an abbess. She asked them to give her permission to accept all the ladies and all the maidens who wanted to enter the convent. They could bring whatever belonged to them without restriction. The king and queen thought this to be good, and they ordered it proclaimed throughout the land that any lady or maiden who wanted to enter the convent could come safely in the service of God and they would be grateful to them for doing so. And many ladies and maidens—more than four hundred—came and she chose two hundred from among them whom she believed would be suitable for the convent and who could endure and support the strict regimen of the order. She selected a lady who was of the nobility and a very good Christian to be abbess. She endowed the convent richly, bestowing on it many towns and castles that she bought, much arable land, many cattle, and all those things necessary to a convent, so that it should never lack for anything. It belongs to the Order of Saint Benedict and to this day is called the Convent of the Blessed Lady. She gave in marriage the other ladies and maidens who were unable to enter the convent. She gave them dowries and dressed them in those expensive and elegant dresses that were in the ship. The queen and the other ladies who saw them were astonished at the precious materials of which the dresses were made.

When the lady saw that the queen was pleased with those materials, she sent her a great gift of them and had them made into gowns adorned with pearls, many ornaments, and other precious jewels. The queen wondered why she had brought so many materials and dresses and asked her: "My lady," she said, "Tell me why you bring so many beautiful materials?"

"Mistress," she replied, "I will tell you. I planned to build this convent for nuns in my country, and my plan was to fill it with the same number of married ladies as are in the convent, and I ordered these clothes made. I was afraid that the greedy king wanted to take all I had, and so I had to come here to this foreign land."

"Blessed be God," said the queen, "and the day on which you originated that plan, and blessed be the name of God Who guided you here, and blessed be the days in which you are to live, and may you be as successful as you desire."

"Amen," said the lady.

From the day she had arrived in the city and begun construction of the convent she had lived nine years there and was honored, loved, and visited frequently by all the good people of the land. When the nine years were completed, she asked the king and queen as a favor to permit her to go to her own country to see her relatives and friends, and to die among them.

49. Of how the wife of the Knight Zifar departed the kingdom of Orbín and went to live in another foreign land

When the king and the queen heard this, they were surprised and deeply worried because she wanted to go, and the king said: "O good lady, beloved of God, for God's sake do not leave us. We sincerely believe that if you depart, things will not go as well in this land as they have since you came here."

She replied: "Sire, I cannot stay, for you would gain no advantage through my remaining, and it would result in great harm to me. You have here these ladies in this convent, who are very good Christians and will pray to God for you and for the queen and for guidance for your kingdom. And you, sire, keep and defend the convent and everything concerning it. And God will therefore keep you in honor, for God will do much for you through the prayers of these good ladies."

"Certainly," replied the king, "we will for the sake of God and for your love."

"Sire," she said, "let me buy a ship from among these in the port, because mine is old and unsound."

"My lady," answered the king, "I will order one of the best of mine given to you, and everything you need."

"Thank you very much," replied the lady, "however, sire, order the ship given to me along with some dependable men to accompany me. I have sufficient of everything else already, praise be unto God!" The king ordered the ship given to her and good men to accompany her. She ordered her vast property including many precious jewels placed aboard, and she bade farewell to the king, the queen, and all the townspeople. She went aboard the ship to remain there overnight in readiness to depart the next day when the wind should arise. Oh Lord! How the king, the queen, and all their subjects were grieved when they saw her go aboard the ship! The great happiness with which they had welcomed her when she arrived was equaled by the great sorrow and grief they felt as she departed.

50. Of how the lady beheld the child who had appeared before over the mast to guide the ship

Early the next day, the good lady raised her eyes to see if the wind was blowing, and saw above the mast that same child who had guided the ship on her arrival. She raised her hands to God and said: "Lord, blessed be Thy name for the grace Thou hast done for me. Fortunate is that one whom Thou desirest to aid, to guide, and to show the way, just as Thou dost to me Thy servant, through Thy holy mercy and Thy holy compassion!" And as she was praying, the good man who had been recommended by the king to be captain of the ship came to her and said: "My lady, what are you doing? What guide are you asking for the ship? Is there another captain besides myself?"

"There certainly is," she replied. "Raise the sail, set the course, and let the ship proceed in the name of God." The worthy man did so and then came to take the helm. He found it so strong and unyielding that he was unable to turn it any direction. He was greatly surprised and said, "My lady, what is wrong? I cannot turn the helm."

She replied, "Leave it alone; for another stronger than you holds it. Go rest from your work with the crew and let it sail as it will." And the ship began to move with a good wind that had arisen and sailed briskly on course. All the crew members marveled over this and said among themselves, "This is the power of God Who chooses to guide this good lady, and for love of her, let us pay her as much honor as we can and serve her properly." And she wondered if she would find her husband alive, but she did not worry, for she knew that through God's grace she would be able to do it.

51. The story ceases to tell of the lady and relates what happened to her husband, the Knight Zifar, and the hermit

Whereupon the story relates how her husband, when he parted from her on the shore where they had seized her, went up the shore, as you have already heard above, and into the mountain near the seashore where he found the hermitage of a worthy man, a servant of God, who dwelt in it.

And he said to him, "Friend, may I lodge here tonight?"

"Yes," replied the hermit, "but I have no barley for your horse."

"It doesn't matter," replied the knight, "because tonight he is going to die."

"How do you know that?" asked the hermit. "That's easy," said the knight, "because I have had him for ten days, and nothing can prevent his dying."

"And how do you know all this?" asked the hermit.

"Because it is my luck that animals never last me more than ten days." And while they were thus conversing, the horse dropped dead on the ground. The hermit was greatly astonished at this and spoke to him:

"What will become of you from now on? How will you be able to travel afoot since you have been so accustomed to riding? It would please me if you want to rest here for some time and not set yourself to so much hardship so quickly."

The knight replied: "Truly, I am very grateful to you, though I have little money to share with you. I come very deeply grieved with great sorrows that have happened to me, more even than I had before I arrived in the city of Mella." And afterward, he remained with the recluse in his hermitage praying to God that He might have mercy on him. And on the seashore below the hermitage, there was a fisherman's shack where the hermit was accustomed to go whenever he needed fish.

52. Of how the knave told the hermit that he wanted to go and amuse himself a little with the knight

In the fisherman's hut lived a knave and whenever his master went away, the knave would come to the hermitage to spend a little leisure time with the hermit. And on the day that the knight arrived there, the knave came and asked the hermit who was his guest. He told him that he was a wandering knight who had just happened to arrive there and that as soon as he had arrived, he had told him that his horse was going to die, that no animal of his ever lasted more than ten days, that the ten days were completed yesterday, and that the horse would not live any longer—and the horse had then dropped to the ground dead.

"Well," replied the knave, "I think he is an unlucky knight and of little intelligence. I wish to go to him and tell him some ugly and serious things and see if he will become angry, or how he will answer me."

"Get on your way, you crazy scoundrel," said the hermit. "Do you think you will find in all other men what you find in me, for I suffer patiently whatever you want to say? Of course if you say foolish things to some that you say to me, you'll find yourself in trouble, and perhaps that could happen to you with this knight if you don't keep a civil tongue in your head."

"There's truth in what you say," replied the knave, "if this knight is short-tempered. If he is sensible and wise, he will not give me trouble. The way in this world to test a man to see if he is irrational is this: when something harsh and against his nature is said to him, an irrational man is quickly moved to anger and to respond in an ugly manner, and a rational man is not; for when something unjust is said to him, he knows how to tolerate it with patience and to give a wise man's answer. By chance," continued the knave, "this knight may be more patient than what you believe."

"May God so order that your daring does not bring harm upon you," replied the hermit.

"Amen," said the knave; "however, it suits me to test him, because no harm should come to a man in testing things unless he goes about it the wrong way."

"I am afraid," said the hermit, "that your test may not be good. If you think you are doing something to please a man, you may be doing something to plague him and therefore it is not welcomed by sensible men. And may God guard you from what happened to an ass with his master."

"And how was that?" asked the knave.

"I will tell you," replied the hermit.

53. Of the parable that the hermit gave the knave about what he said that he would say to the Knight Zifar

"A good man had a small dog that he kept in his room. He liked the dog and took great pleasure in him. He had an ass which hauled wood and other things for him that were needed in his house. One day the ass was resting very tranquilly in his stable—for there were days in which he did no work— and he saw his master frolicking and playing with the dog and fondling him. The dog was placing his paws on his master's chest, jumping on him, and racing around in front of him. Musing on this, it seemed to the ass that he served his master more than the dog, who did nothing except eat and rest. The ass decided it would be a good idea for him to go play with his master. He broke away and went to his master, running in front of him and kicking up his heels. He put his forefeet on his master's head so that his master was badly hurt. His master screamed, and his servants came hurriedly and battered the ass with big sticks until they left him for dead. And certainly this was just, for no one should try to do anything against what nature intended. For the proverb says that one ought not to try to act contrary to nature's laws. And you know that nature has not intended for you to test this knight, for you were not reared among noblemen, nor do you know how to debate. This knight seems of high station and intelligent, and by chance you may believe you are saying one thing to him and you will be saying something else."

"Come now, good man," said the knave, "you would always hold me to be stupid if I didn't test things. And don't you know that fortune aids those who dare? By chance I can learn good manners from this knight and improve my fortune through him."

"May God so order!" said the hermit. "Go and be courteous in your speech, and may God help you!"

"Thus it will be," replied the knave, and he went to the knight, and instead of saying to him, "God's greeting to you!" he said to him these words that you will now hear.

54. Of the questions that the knave asked the Knight Zifar and how he responded to all of them

"Unlucky knight, you lost your horse and you don't show any concern?"

"I did not lose him," said the knight, "because he was not mine. I only held him in trust for ten days and no more."

"Well, do you believe that you ought to pay the person who entrusted him to you, since the horse died in your possession and possibly through ill treatment?"

"I will not pay," replied the knight, "because that one who owned him, killed him and it was in his power to do so."

"Well, since that's the way it is," replied the knave, "I excuse you from answering."

"Thank you very much," said the knight, "because you gave such a fine ruling, and it really seems to me that you are a man of intelligence, for without wisdom one would not have given such a good decision."

And the knave replied, "Don't answer me with flattery or with trickery, thinking that way to escape me, because I am smarter than what you think."

"Certainly, God gave knowledge to every one. I honestly believe that since He created you a man, He gave you intelligence. I consider that what you say, you say with intelligence," the knight responded.

The knave departed very pleased with himself and went to his hut. The next day he came again to the knight and said to him: "You wretched knight, men speak ill of you."

"That certainly could be," said the knight, "because they always speak ill of those whom they don't know well. Therefore a man should bear with a calm mind insults from ignorant people."

And the knave said to him: "You ill-fated knight, you are poor, and poverty is a very serious thing for a man such as you."

"Surely I'm more a problem to poverty than it is to me," replied the knight, "for there is no sin in poverty if a man bears it patiently. But the one who does not consider what God gives him as sufficient thereby sins. And I believe that one is poor who believes himself poor, and the one who possesses much is not rich; instead, the one who is not greedy is rich."

The knave said to him, "Unlucky knight, you are going to receive many wrongs."

"I am pleased because I cannot, nor do I wish to, do them to anyone else," replied the knight.

The knave said to him, "You hopeless knight, you will never achieve power."

"Surely while I have patience and happiness, I will be powerful," stated the knight. "I believe that one who has no control of himself is not powerful."

The knave said, "Unlucky knight, you will never be as rich as the lord of yonder castle."

"Are you speaking to me about the lord of that castle?" asked the knight. "May you know that a coffer of riches is a dangerous thing, for everyone is eager to destroy him."

The knave answered, "Unlucky knight, I tell you that he possesses great wealth."

"He does not possess it," replied the knight. "If he is miserly, he does not know how to enjoy it, and if he is extravagant, he will not have it for long, for he does not know how to regulate his own life."

"Unlucky knight, that rich man has many friends," said the knave.

"What wonder is that?" said the knight. "Flies follow honey, wolves follow meat, and ants follow wheat; but you can be sure that company you see was not serving, nor do they serve, that rich man. They follow for profit and what they believe they can obtain."

The knave said to him, "Wretched knight, you were rich and you lost all your wealth."

The knight replied, "Surely that person is very fortunate who lost his greed with his wealth."

"But you lost your wealth," reiterated the knave.

"It is the nature of wealth to go from hand to hand," replied the knight, "and therefore you must believe that wealth is never lost. May you know that when one loses it, another gains it; and may you also know that when I had it, another had lost it."

"But," persisted the knave, "you did lose your wealth."

"And why do you keep hounding me?" asked the knight. "It was better that I lost it, than for it to ruin me."

"Misfortunate knight," said the knave, "you lost your sons and your wife, and you do not grieve?"

"What man is there who grieves over the death of mortals?" said the knight. "What advantage does grief have? How can one bring back the dead by lamenting? Surely if the lives of the dead could be restored through tears, all the people in the world would go around crying in order to recover their relatives or friends; moreover what passes once through this world can not return except through a miracle of God, as with Lazarus, whom Our Lord Jesus Christ raised from the dead. Therefore a person is very fortunate who knows how to endure his losses in this world with patience. And, friend, what marvel is involved in the loss of my sons and my wife? What was lost was destined to be lost, and perhaps God has received them unto Himself. What wrong does God do a man if He takes from him what He entrusted to him, wanting only for Himself what is His? Surely whatever we have in this world, we only hold in trust; and let no one dare to say, 'This is mine,' because in this world, no one possesses anything except the good that he does, and this he carries with him to the next world and nothing else."

The knave said to him, "You pitiful knight, a great affliction will now come to you."

"If it is a small one," replied the knight, "let us bear it; for with patience it is a light burden; and if it is a great affliction, let us hold up without flinching; for great is a man's glory in understanding how to suffer and endure the sorrows of this world."

"Notice well," said the knave, "that grief is a strong and terrible thing, and there are few who can bear it well."

"And what concern is it of yours if I should be one of those who can endure it?" replied the knight.

"Take care," said the knave, "for a terrible thing is the pain of suffering, and therefore, avoid it if you can."

"Easy," answered the knight. "You who cannot endure it say that we should flee from grief, and this cannot be. Grief follows the one who flees, and surely he who flees does so with the grief he feels and already has within himself, and he flees from a greater one that follows him."

The knave said to him, "You ill-starred knight, you will fall sick with fever."

"I will be sick," replied the knight, "but you may believe that I will get rid of the fever or the fever of me."

"The truth is that a man cannot flee from natural grief, such as comes through the death of relatives or friends, but he can avoid unforeseen grief if he is careful," replied the knave.

"It is surely as you say," said the knight, "but there are few in this world who are careful in everything."

The knave said to him, "You unfortunate knight, you will die in exile." The Knight Zifar answered, "A nightmare is no more painful at home than away from home, and that is what death is; for at the hour of death, a man is laid to rest in whatever house he may be."

The knave replied, "Unlucky knight, you will die young."

The knight answered: "It is much better for a man to die unexpectedly, because a man does not want to die unless he is tired of a life beset by the many misfortunes of this world. Those who live to an old age suffer, for they will see many afflictions in their long lives, and being always beset with grief and trouble, long for death. Such as these old ones cannot live without seeing the deaths of friends and relatives, from which they receive great heartbreak, worry, deprivations, and suffering, so that they long for death. And therefore it is a good thing for a man to die when he does not yearn for death and when he can better endure it through his strength and his understanding. For if I am to die young, by chance, death may come so quickly to me that it may take me from some evil that would come to me if I should live. Therefore I shall not count how many years I am to have, but how many years I have had, if I cannot have more; I have lived my life to the fullest. Therefore no matter when death comes, it is the last days of one's life, and it is one's destiny to die old and not young; because old age is the last stage of life. And therefore you say falsely that I am to die young; rather I am to die old, and shall not be a youth when my days are fulfilled."

The knave said to him, "You luckless knight, you are going to die beheaded."

"And what difference is there between being beheaded or dying by another injury?" asked the knight. "Surely, however many wounds one has in this world, one will be fatal, and no more."

"You unfortunate knight," said the knave, "you will lose your eyesight."

"When I lose it," replied the knight, "I will lose the greed in my heart; for what the eye sees, the heart desires."

"Unlucky knight," replied the knave, "why are you so obstinate? You must believe that you will die finally."

"Friend," said the knight, "what a small wonder there is in dying! This is the nature of man and no trouble to him. Every man must die and I came into this world under such conditions and I shall leave it the same way. And therefore, according to reason, to die is not a problem but an obligation that I have to fulfill. Do not wonder about the life of a man, for it is like a pilgrimage. When the pilgrim has arrived at the place where he proposed to go, his journey is complete. Thus is the life of a man when he fulfills his course in this world; for from then on, he has no more to do. Certainly the law is established among men that a man return what he owes to him from whom he receives it. And since we receive it from God, we must return it to Him; and that which we receive from the earth, we ought to return to the earth; because man receives his soul from God and his flesh from the earth, and therefore it is insanity for a man to fear what he cannot avoid, such as death, which he can not escape; for it is the very last affliction in this world, if it can be said to be an affliction, and a man returns naturally to the earth from whence he came. Therefore man should not fear death, for although he postpone it, he cannot escape it. And I do not wonder because I am to die, for I am neither the first nor the last, and already all those who lived before me have gone before me, and those who exist now and will come after my death, all will follow me; for all things are created with the condition that they have a beginning and an end. However much zest a man has for living in this world, it is certain that he is to die and he must be forewarned in this way, for death will find him as it must. For what advantage or honor is there to a man who resists leaving when he is told, 'Leave although it is against your will'? And therefore it is better and less shameful for a man to leave willingly than to be thrown out by force. So, the man is fortunate who does not fear death and is well prepared, so that when death comes, he does not worry and can say: 'I am ready; come whenever you wish.'"

The knave said to him, "Unlucky knight, after you die they will not bury you."

"And why not?" asked the knight, "the easiest thing in this world is to place a body in a tomb, expecially since the earth is the home of everyone in this world and it receives them willingly. And you may believe that a tomb is made only for the honor of the living, and so that those who see it may say: 'May whoever lies in the tomb go to heaven, and may those who ordered it constructed so nobly have a good life.' And therefore all ought to strive to prepare the best tomb they can."

"You pitiful knight," said the knave, "how can you waste your time? There is a way in which you could use your knighthood."

"And in what way could I make use of my knighthood?" asked the knight.

"In truth," said the knave, "you know that yesterday they proclaimed in that town yonder how the king of Ester has besieged a city of the king of Mentón. It is called Grades, and they call it thus because it is in a high place and they climb there by steps. This king of Mentón sent word and has proclaimed throughout the land that he will give his daughter to whoever lifts the siege. He will make him heir to his kingdom when he passes on, for he has no heir."

The knight began to laugh scornfully and the knave was upset, for it seemed to him that the knight believed little of what he had said to him.

"Luckless knight, you consider my words so lightly?"

"I tell you that I consider them lightly," replied the knight, "because I am not the man for such a great feat as the one you speak of."

"Without a doubt, I now do not consider you as intelligent as I thought you to be. Don't you know that each person makes his own luck in this world, some to win and others to lose? And some to be lost and some to be found? And don't you know that God can turn a man of little consequence into one of high station? And were not you the one who told me that you were able to endure great pain and adversity as though it were a trifle?"

"Yes," answered the knight.

"Well," said the knave, "how will you be able to suffer great grief when it happens to you, since you do not want your body to endure the stress through which you will gain renown and honor? For you well know that misfortune always brings grief, and on this account you are avoiding the strain and stress through which you might gain your fortune."

"And if now, while you are young, you do not accomplish it, I have no faith that you will do it when you are old. And doesn't it seem that you would be better off in the field with those knights using your knowledge of how to raise the siege of the king of Mentón?" said the knave.

"Certainly," answered the knight, "there is no good on that field that I can see."

"And how can that be?" asked the knave.

"I will tell you," replied the knight. "On the battlefield there is no sin, but there is much deceit and much trickery in the people. Each one of them labors to deceive the others in order to gain honor by seizing the kingdom. When people are striving to conquer and dominate others, then justice and truth are the first to suffer."

"Well," questioned the knave, "don't you wish to rule and be in a position of power?"

"Yes, I would like to," answered the knight, "if it meant not doing harm to another."

"This cannot be," stated the knave, "for you cannot be king or a lord of high station except by overthrowing another from his position."

"Yes, I can," replied the knight.

"And how?" asked the knave.

"If this king of Mentón were to have the siege lifted by me, and if he should give me his daughter in marriage and his kingdom after his death, as he has proclaimed throughout his land, I would thus have it without doing harm," explained the knight. "But I feel the task is too great for a person such as I am. The magnitude of the task requires another king of greater power to carry out such a great undertaking."

"Unlucky knight," replied the knave, "how little attention you pay to the words a man speaks to you! You are already making me lose the good opinion that I had of you. I beg of you, sir, for the love of God, please heed me, for God can do much for you. If not, may you know that you will not lose the name of "unlucky." Now help yourself and God will help you; because God is not inclined to aid or help to advance the fortune of anyone who does not strive to do his best or demonstrate it through his work. And therefore they say that God does not give bread unless the earth is sown, so if you help yourself, I am certain that He will help you and your affairs will prosper from here on. Do not think that the aid of God counts for little. For if man's intentions are good, He considers them His and carries them out. If men have the desire to follow Him, and do follow Him, they successfully fulfill whatever they wish."

55. Of how the knave went with the Knight Zifar and how they came to an agreement

"Oh, friend!" exclaimed the knight, "for God's sake, please be quiet! I cannot answer so many questions as you ask; but you may believe me, I would go to those places in the kingdom that you speak of if I but had some one to guide me."

The knave replied: "I will guide you, for I know where the king is besieged. From here to there is only ten days' walking distance. I will serve you gladly under the condition that when God raises you to high estate you will do me a like favor. I am sure that God will guide you if you want Him as your companion, because God willingly accompanies and guides whoever welcomes Him as his companion."

"I willingly agree to do as you advise me," replied the knight. "Now, go on your way and return here early in the morning."

The knave departed, and the knight paced back and forth through the hermitage a long time until the hermit came. The knight asked him from whence he came.

"From the town," replied the hermit, "from searching for something to eat."

"Did you find anything?" asked the knight.

"As a matter of fact, I found a fine bird for you," replied the hermit.

"Let us eat it then," replied the knight. "According to my plans, tomorrow I will be ready to depart, for I have inconvenienced you enough in this hermitage."

"God knows," answered the hermit, "that I am not inconvenienced by you; for I am greatly pleased with your company. However, I do believe that you have been annoyed with the things that knave said who came to see you."

"I did not take offense," said the knight. "Rather his words were a comfort to me. He wants to go away with me to serve me."

"How can you want to take that evil scoundrel with you!" exclaimed the hermit. "Be careful that he doesn't bring harm to you."

"May God protect me!" exclaimed the knight.

56. Of the vision that the hermit saw concerning his guest the Knight Zifar

After supper was prepared, they dined and rested, and in conversing, the hermit said, "Sir, you have never heard such an outcry as echoes through the town. A king has another one under siege and the beleaguered king will give his daughter in marriage and his kingdom after his death to whoever lifts the siege. Many counts, dukes, and other noblemen are gathering there." The knight was silent and did not respond to what he was saying, and the hermit fell asleep. While the hermit was sleeping, he could see in a vision that came to him the knight his guest in a very high tower, with a golden crown on his head and a gold scepter in his hand. At this moment he awoke and marveled at what this could mean, and he arose and went to his oratory to pray. He prayed to our Lord God to reveal to him what it signified. After he had completed his prayer he went to sleep again. And while he was sleeping, a voice from heaven came to him, "Arise and tell your guest that it is time to depart; for it is certain he is to lift the siege of that king, he is to marry his daughter, and he is to inherit the kingdom after his death."

The hermit arose and went to the knight and asked, "Are you asleep or keeping awake?"

"As a matter of fact," replied the knight, "I am neither sleeping nor keeping awake; I am waiting until day is near so that I may be on my way."

"Arise," said the hermit, "and go in this auspicious time, for you are to be the most fortunate of all those knights who have ever been here."

"And how can that be?" asked the knight.

"I will tell you about it," said the hermit. "Tonight while sleeping, I saw you in a vision in a very high tower. You were wearing a golden crown on your head and holding a scepter in your hand. At this moment, I awoke greatly startled and I went to pray. I begged God to be kind enough to show me the meaning of what I had seen in the vision. I returned to my bed to sleep. While I was sleeping, a voice came to me and said: 'Tell your guest it is the hour to depart; and he is certain to raise the siege of that king and marry his daughter, and to inherit the kingdom after the king's death."

"And do you believe that this can come true?" asked the knight.

The hermit replied: "I believe that it will be true with the grace of God, because He is powerful enough to create or to destroy whatever He considers proper, and to make the very poor become rich. And I beg you, when God leads you and lifts you to high estate, remember this place."

"I will with pleasure," said the knight, "and I promise you that when God bestows upon me this honor, the first thing that He places on my head of nobility and honor I will donate to this place. Let us go, for the time is right," stated the knight. "Where can we attend mass?"

"In the town," replied the hermit.

57. Of how the knave quarreled with his master the fisherman, and took his leave of him

And they both went to the town and while they were hearing mass, the knave was haggling with his master to give him some of his wages. And he had to give him a tunic that he owned, a dagger, and a little money that he had in his purse, and he said that he had no more. The knave said to him, "Don't you want to pay me all my wages? A time will come when you will repent!"

"Be on your way, you stupid knave," retorted the fisherman. "What will you be able to do in the future that you cannot do now?"

"Nevertheless there will come a time when I will have greater power than you," replied the knave.

"You'll surely never see the day! There's nothing about you to indicate that that can ever be!" retorted the fisherman.

"Why do you think that God cannot accomplish what He wishes to?" asked the knave. "Don't you know that a good year comes to every bad field? Although I may not be as clever now as I should be, God will give me the sense and intelligence when I most need it."

"Yes," said the fisherman, "but right now He has not shown any indication that He has His eye on you."

"You will remember the words you are saying to me now," replied the knave, "for I saw a good man who possessed little, who answered the questions I asked him in a very proper manner, and you do not know how to respond fittingly. I commend you for your lack of good sense, and now I am leaving."

58. Of how the knave rescued the Knight Zifar one night from some thieves who tried to rob him, and how he killed both of them[1]

The knave went to the hermitage and did not find the knight or the hermit there. He went to the town and found them hearing mass. When the knight saw him, he was pleased and said, "The time is right for us to leave."

"You don't mean that we are leaving without first having lunch?" asked the knave. "I bring a fish out of the sea from my master's hut."

"You eat it then," replied the knight, "and we shall do as you think best, for it suits me to follow your lead while you are my guide, but for a while it has not been my habit to eat in the morning."

"That may be right while you are traveling on horseback, but when you go on foot you will be unable to walk without eating and drinking, especially having to make a long journey," replied the knave.

Then they went with the hermit to the house of a citizen, and they ate the fish, which was large and tasty, took their leave of the hermit, and started on their way. It happened one night that they took lodging at an inn where two evil thieves, dressed in the manner of pilgrims, were lying down. Because they could see that the knight was well dressed, they thought that he was very wealthy although he was traveling on foot. When midnight came, these two evil men arose in order to slit the knight's throat and to take whatever he carried. One of them threw himself astride the knight and the other went for his throat so that the knight was unable to twist away from them. At this moment, the knave awoke. When he saw them in this struggle by the light of a lamp in the middle of the room, he started for them, yelling, "Do not kill the knight!" The innkeeper awoke and came running at the shouts. When

---

1. Note that the chapter title is mistaken—the knave only kills one.

he arrived, the knave had killed one of them and was attacking the other, so that the knight was able to get up while the innkeeper and the knave captured the second thief. They asked the thief what it was all about. He told them that he and his companion believed the knight was carrying something of value, and therefore they had arisen to cut his throat and to rob him.

"You certainly labored in vain," said the knight, "because if you were poor, you could never escape poverty from whatever you found on me."

Afterward, the innkeeper took the thief before his neighbors who had responded to their cries and tied him securely until the next morning, when they turned him over to the law and he was sentenced to death.

59. Of how the Knight Zifar freed the knave who was about to be hanged, and how he cut his rope

As they were going along the road, the knave said, "I served you well tonight."

"That's certainly the truth," replied the knight, "and I am very pleased that you have started out so well."

"You will be able to test me more on this road," said the knave.

"May God grant that no harm come to us through the tests," answered the knight. "Everything in its own season," said the knave, "for all apples are not sweet; therefore it is suitable that we prepare ourselves for whatever happens."

"I am pleased with your words, and let us do thus," said the knight, "and may you be blessed because you are doing so well."

At the end of six days after they had left the hermit, they arrived at a well-fortified and lofty castle named Herin. There was a walled town at the base of the castle. When they reached there at the hour of vespers, the knight was very tired, for he had walked a long day's journey. He ordered his companion to go search for something to eat, which the knave did very willingly. While he was purchasing a pheasant, a thief who had stolen a purse full of gold coins approached him and said, "Friend, I beg you to keep this purse for me while I put a bridle on my horse." He was lying, for he had no horse at all, but was fleeing for fear of the lawmen of the town who were pursuing him to arrest him. As soon as he had given the purse to the knave he mingled with the crowd and disappeared.

The lawmen, searching for the thief, found the knave holding the pheasant he had bought in one hand and the purse that the thief had given him in the other. They arrested him and took him to the castle, where he would be tried by the judges the next day.

The knight was awaiting his companion, and after night fell he realized he was not coming. He wondered why he was not returning. The next morning he went in search of him and could find no trace of him. He thought that perhaps he had fled out of greed for the small amount of money he had entrusted to him for marketing, and he was greatly saddened. However, he still had a little expense money left, and he was more worried over the companion he had lost than the money, for the knave had served him well, and he had been happy with him, for he had said many things that pleased him. And deprived of all his wisdom, resourcefulness, and strength, he realized that he missed him very much.

The next day they brought the knave down from the castle to have him appear before the judges. When they asked him who had given him the purse, he answered that a man had given it to him to hold while he was buying a pheasant and that he did not know the man, but if he should see him again he believed he would recognize him. They showed him many men, to see if he could recognize him. He could not identify him, for the person who had given the money to him was hidden, through fear of his crime. On this note, the judges ordered him taken away to be hanged, for in that country the law was maintained stringently. For the theft of five sueldos[1] or more, the punishment was execution. They tied a rope around his neck, tied his hands behind him, and mounted him on an ass. A large crowd followed to see justice done. A town crier preceded him saying in a loud voice, "As ye sow, so shall ye reap." And it is a true statement that who believes in the devil and serves him will come to no good end. However, the knave was innocent of the theft, but he was guilty of taking in his charge something from a man whom he did not know, and he did not see what was entrusted to him. Surely whoever receives something in trust from another ought to ask himself three things: the first, who is the person who entrusts it to him; the second, what is being entrusted to him; and the third, will he know how, or be able, to guard it properly. It could be that some evil man could entrust something to him, and that the thing entrusted to him could be given deceitfully, and by chance he would receive . . .[2] that he would not be in a position to understand how to keep it, just as happened to the knave, for the one who gave it to him was an evil man and a thief, the thing that he gave him was stolen, and furthermore he was not in a position at the time to be entrusted with anything of value from anyone. And although he might be in a position to safeguard it, he should have thought it strange to be entrusted with it. For a trust is of such a nature that it must be kept completely just as the man who receives the money, and he must not use any of it without the consent of the one who places it in trust. If he does, it can be considered a theft because the use of it is contrary to the owner's will.

When they were taking the knave to be hanged, those who followed him felt great pity for him because he was a stranger, youthful, very handsome, and of gentle speech. He swore that he had not committed the theft but

---

1. A *sueldo* was a coin of Aragon worth approximately three cents.
2. At this point there is a break in the sense of the text.

rather he had been tricked by the one who had entrusted it to him.

While the knave was astride the ass at the base of the scaffold and the executioners were tying the rope to the gallows beam, the Knight Zifar, since he had not found his companion, asked his host the innkeeper to show him the road to the kingdom of Mentón. The host, feeling sorry for him because he had lost his companion, went out with him to the road. After they left the town, the knight saw a great crowd of people in the field gathered around the gallows and asked his host: "Why are all those people there?"

"No doubt they intend to hang a knave who stole a purse full of gold," answered the host.

"And is that knave a native of this land?" questioned the knight.

"No," replied the host, "he has never been seen here up to now—much to his misfortune they found him in possession of the stolen money."

The knight suspected that it must be his companion and said to the host, "O friend, as you trust in me, aid me as is right. That man is guiltless."

"Certainly I will gladly aid you if it is as you say."

They proceeded toward the gallows, where they were urging the ass to move. As the knight was approaching, the knave recognized him and shouted, "My lord, my lord, remember the service I rendered you three days ago when the thieves came to slit your throat!"

"Friend," asked the knight, "what is the reason why they have ordered you hanged?"

"Sir," answered the knave, "wrongly and without any reason, as God is my witness!"

"Wait a little," said the knight, "and I will go speak with the judges and the court, and I will request them not to execute you since you have given them no reason to."

"A lot of good that is for one who is in such a predicament as I am," answered the knave. "Can't you see, sir, that my life is controlled by this ass's feet! One quick 'giddyap' will move him, and you tell me you are going to the judges to ask an audience with them! Certainly they are righteous men who are reasonable and lawful, but they must not be hesitant or delay in the good they are to do; because tardiness sometimes is dangerous."

"Certainly, friend," replied the knight, "if you are speaking the truth, your life will not be so short as you say."

"Sir," said the knave, "For the sake of truth and the vow I owe you, I am telling you the truth."

The knight drew his sword and sliced through the rope from which he was hanging, for already the ass had started forward. When the lawmen saw this, they seized the knight and took both of them before the judges, and told them all that had happened. The judges asked the knight how he had the audacity to commit such folly as to break the laws of the kingdom so that justice could not be fulfilled. The knight, to exculpate himself and his companion, declared that, whatever his companion had said he had done in the matter of the theft, he would place himself at their mercy. He believed he would win, because he was truthful and his companion was guiltless of the theft they blamed him for.

60. Of how they arrested the one who had stolen the purse of gold and how they took him to be hanged

After he learned that the man to whom he had entrusted the purse was taken away to be hanged, the thief who had stolen the purse with the gold believed that the knave had been hanged. Thinking no one would recognize him, he went to the court which was in session. As soon as the knave saw him, he recognized him, and said:

"Lord, order the man arrested who just came here, for he is the one who handed the purse to me."

They ordered him seized. The knave then brought as a witness the person from whom he had bought the pheasant. On account of this and for other knowledge that they had of him, and many other things of which he had been accused—although they were unable to prove it—they put him to torture so that he had to confess that he had committed the robbery. Because they were in close pursuit to arrest him, he had given the purse to the knave to keep for him and had hidden until he heard they had hanged the knave.

"Oh, you treacherous scoundrel!" said the knave, "Where does one flee who is a spawn of hell? Surely you cannot escape the gallows, for the gallows is to be your hell and is awaiting you as its guest. And go cursed by God because you placed me in such great fear; for I am certain that never again will I hear a 'giddyap' that does not terrify me. I am very grateful to God because he is imposing the final punishment on you and not on me, and rightly so."

They took the thief away to be hanged, and the knight and his companion went along their way, grateful to God for the mercy he had shown them.

61. Of how the thief who stole the purse was hanged and how the knave departed with his master, the Knight Zifar

"Sir," said the knave, "whoever approaches a good tree finds himself sheltered in its shade. And by Heavens, I find myself well off because I am in your shade, and may it be God's wish that I repay you in a similar situation."

"Don't even mention it, friend," replied the knight. "I trust in God's mercy that He will not want to see us in such straits again. For I tell you that it seemed to me that this matter was more risky than the other danger through which we passed night before last."

"Surely, sir," said the knave, "I don't believe this will be the only danger we will escape from."

"And why not?" asked the knight.

"I will tell you," answered the knave. "Surely the one who has a lot of traveling to do, will be set to many tests, and we are sure to pass through even more dangerous situations."

As they were traveling to a city where they were planning to lodge for the night, it so happened that they came upon a flock of deer near a spring. Among the deer there were small fawns. The knave drew his dagger, threw it at them, and wounded one of the small ones. He pursued it, caught it, brought it back on his shoulders, and said: "What ho, sir knight! Now we'll have something to eat!"

"It would please me a bit if we had better lodgings and better hosts than those of last night," replied the knight.

"Let's go," said the knave, "for God will aid us."

As they were traveling, before they reached the city, they came upon the ruins of a tower, without gates, as high as the shaft of a lance, in which there were many good beds of straw made by others who had lodged there. There was a clear spring before the door and a pleasant meadow.

"Alas, my friend!" sighed the knight, "how shameful it is for me to pass through towns on foot! And how embarrassing when they observe me and ask me questions, and I can not answer them. I would spend tonight here in this tower, rather than endure shame in the city."

"Rest," said the knave, "for I will bring bread and wine from the city, and when I return, I will prepare something to eat with the firewood from this thicket."

And so he did, and after the food was cooked, he gave the knight his supper. The knight was quite satisfied and considered himself very lucky being close to the spring in the meadow. However, when they fell asleep, it was astounding how many wolves came to the tower! After the wolves had eaten all the meat scraps outside, they tried to enter the tower to devour them. The knight and the knave were hard put to defend themselves against so many wolves. The wolves were howling because the knave was wearing his tunic, which was smeared with the blood of the deer. They were unable to sleep or to rest during the entire night, as the wolves kept up a constant attack against them.

In the midst of the attack, a large wolf launched himself at the knight, who was standing directly in the doorway, seized his sword between his teeth, jerked it from his hand, and caused it to fall outside the tower.

"Help me Saint Mary!" exclaimed the knight, "that scoundrelly wolf has taken my sword from me and I have nothing with which to defend myself."

"Do not fear," said the knave, "take my dagger and defend the door, and I will recover your sword."

He went to the corner of the tower where he had cooked and gathered all the hot coals he found there. He put the coals into the straw and wood, went to the door, and scattered the fire among the wolves. They drew back from the tower, in their fear of the fire. The knave recovered the sword and gave it to the knight. While the coals from the fire lasted at the door to the tower, the wolves did not approach; instead their numbers began to decrease and they dispersed.

Truly the knave was very wise, because wolves fear nothing more than fire. However, daybreak was near, and when the dawn broke, not a wolf remained.

"By Heaven," said the knight, "it would have been better to endure shame in the city than to pass such an accursed night as this."

"Sir," said the knave, "that is the way a man goes to paradise, for first he has to pass through purgatory and through many terrible places before he arrives there. And you, before you reach the high estate which you will reach, will first have to endure and to suffer many harsh trials."

"Well, friend, stated the knight, "what is that high estate which I am to attain?"

"I truly do not know," answered the knave, "but my heart tells me that you are to reach high estate and that you will be a great lord."

"My friend," said the knight, "let us go joyfully and strive to accomplish good works. May God command and do with us what He in his mercy sees fit."

62. Of how the owner of the garden forgave the knave when he found him gathering turnips and putting them into a bag

They walked a long time that day until they reached a very small village that was half a league from the camp of the army commander. Before they entered that little village, the Knight Zifar saw a garden in a beautiful dell. There was a very large turnip garden there and the knight said: "Oh, friend! how greedily would I eat those turnips tonight if I had someone who knew how to prepare them for me!"

"Sir," replied the knave, "I will prepare them for you."

He arrived with the knight at an inn and left him there and proceeded toward the turnip patch with a sack. He found the gate locked, so he climbed the walls and jumped inside. He began to pull up the turnips and put the best ones in the sack. While he was pulling up the turnips, the owner entered the garden. On seeing the knave, the owner went to him and said: "For certain, you sneak thief, you will accompany me as a prisoner before the law. They will deal you the sentence you deserve for coming over the walls to steal turnips."

"Oh, sir," said the knave, "may God reward you, do not do it, for I was forced to enter here.

"And how were you forced?" asked the owner of the garden. "I don't see that anything has forced you to do anything, except your own wickedness."

"Sir," explained the knave, "I was walking along that road and a powerful whirlwind arose and lifted me by its strength from the earth and hurled me into this garden."

"Well, who pulled up these turnips?" questioned the garden owner.

"Sir," answered the knave, "the wind was so strong and so fierce that it raised me from the ground, and I was afraid that it would throw me into some rough ground, so I held on to the turnips and many were pulled up."

"Well, who put the turnips in that sack?" asked the owner of the garden.

"Well, sir, that's something that has puzzled me also," replied the knave.

"Well, you can be proud of yourself," said the owner of the garden, "you really are convincing. I'll pardon you this time."

"Oh, sir!" said the knave, "what need has a guiltless person of pardon? Surely it would be better if you would let me have these turnips for the trouble I had in pulling them up—although against my will—since it was the strong wind that made me do it!"

"I'm amused at the way you have defended yourself so well with such witty lies," said the owner of the garden. 'Take the turnips and go on your way, and watch out from now on that it doesn't happen to you again. If you don't watch out, you'll pay for it."

The knave departed with the turnips, very happy because he had escaped so easily. He prepared them expertly with some meat that he had bought, and he gave the meal to the knight. After the knight had eaten, the knave related to him what had happened when he went to pick the turnips.

"Surely," replied the knight, "you were very fortunate to thus escape, because justice is harsh in this land. Now I see what the wise man said is true—that at times it is advantageous for a man to lie with glib words. But friend, avoid lying, for seldom does a man come off well in such a predicament as you found yourself in, for you escaped through your wits."

"Certainly, sir," said the knave, "from now on out I would rather have money than be crafty, for now everyone understands tricks and dissimulations. The owner of the garden through his tolerance let me go, for he understood that I spoke in jest; and let no one be deceived in this, for men of this age, as soon as they are born, are more knowledgeable in evil than in good. And therefore now one man cannot deceive another through the tricks he knows, although at times they pretend that they don't understand one another. They do this in order to conceal from their friend or their master, who may speak deviously, that they do not understand him, although they may have a suitable reply. Therefore artfulness is of little advantage to a man since all men understand it."

63. Of how the Knight Zifar and the knave came to an agreement on how they would enter the town

And the knight asked the knave, "Friend, what does it seem to you that we ought to do, since we are already near the army?"

"Well," said the knave, "I will tell you. The king of Ester, who has the king of Mentón besieged, worries very little because he is the master of the battlefield. Honor and glory will be won by the one who takes the part of those on the inside, who are less powerful, and defends them, protects them, and relieves them of the predicament in which they are. Therefore it seems to me that it is better to join with those of the town and not remain here where there is no danger to you."

"And how will I be able to enter the town without hindrance?" asked the knight.

"I will tell you," said the knave. "You give me your clothes and you take these vile ones of mine, place a garland of grape leaves on your head, and take a staff in your hand, just as a crazy man does. And although they shout at you, don't pay any attention to it. In the evening, keep going to the gate of the town, for they will not be watching for you. If there is anyone on the lookout platforms, you will tell him that you wish to speak with the king's steward. As soon as they take you inside, go to the steward. They say he is a very good man. Inform him of your business as best you can, and may God guide you the best He can. I have told you what little bit of wisdom I understand. If I knew any more, I would tell you more, but I do not have any more wisdom to impart. Help yourself from now on with the wisdom God gave you. The sooner we set out the sooner we shall arrive at the royal camp."

64. Of how the Knight Zifar, dressed in the clothes of the knave, entered the town while the knave remained outside

"Friend," said the knight, "I shall take your advice because I don't have, nor do I see, any safer way to enter the town."

When morning came, the knight took off his clothing and the knave took off his. The knight dressed himself in the clothing of the knave, put a garland of leaves on his head, and proceeded toward the encamped army. As they made their way among the troops, the highest ranks as well as the lowest began to shout at the knight as to a crazy man, "Behold here the king of

Mentón without a flag or a pot to call his own." And so this commotion traveled all through the camp as some troops ran along with him calling him the king of Mentón. The knight, although he felt great shame, pretended that he was crazy and continued jumping and running until he reached a tent where they were selling wine and badly prepared food. The tent was located near the periphery of the army and almost against the walls of town. He went inside the tent and asked for bread and wine. The knave followed him at a short distance, telling everyone that he was crazy. He went to the tent where they were selling the wine and said: "Oh, you crazy king of Mentón, so here you are? Have you eaten today?"

"Certainly not," answered the crazy man.

"And do you want me to give you something to eat for charity's sake?" asked the knave.

The crazy man replied, "I would like that."

The knave touched the vendor of the rank food and told him to give the crazy man as much food and drink as he wanted. The knave then said, "Mad man, now that you are drunk, do you believe that you are in your kingdom?"

"Certainly," responded the crazy man.

The tavern keeper said, "Well, mad man, defend your kingdom."

"Let me sleep a while," answered the mad man, "and you will see how I will go throw stones at those who are behind those walls."

"And why do you wish to attack your kingdom?" asked the tavern keeper.

"O stupid one," babbled the insane one, "don't you know that I ought to know those who are against me and not attack any others?"

"What does that mean?" asked the tavern keeper.

"Leave him alone," said the knave. "He does not know what he is saying. Go to sleep, for you are already delirious."

They ceased to talk and the crazy man slept for a short while. And as the sun was setting the knave arose and whispered in his ear that he should go find the gates of the town. He took two stones in his hands, and with his sword under the ragged clothing he was wearing, departed. When the men saw him, they shouted at him calling him king of Mentón. As soon as he reached the gates of the town, he called to the one who was on the lookout platforms, "Friend, let me have refuge here, for I come with a message to the king's steward."

"And why did the troops permit you to pass through the army?" asked those soldiers who were on the platforms.

"I pretended to be a crazy man while among them, and all shouted at me, calling me king of Mentón," replied the knight.

"You are very welcome," the one on the platform said, and he admitted him. As soon as the knight entered the town, he asked for the location of the lodgings of the king's steward, and they pointed them out to him.

When he reached there, the steward was preparing to mount his horse. The knight approached him and said, "Sir, I would like to talk with you if it is convenient for you."

And he went aside with him and said: "Sir, I am a knight of the nobility from a distant land, and I have heard much good of you. I come to serve you, if it pleases you."

"You are very welcome," replied the steward. "I am pleased with you. By the way, are you ready to put your knighthood to good use?"

"Yes," answered the knight, "with the aid of God, if I had the equipment."

"Of course, I will give it to you," said the steward. He ordered him given fine vestments, a good horse, keen weapons, and all the other equipment essential to a knight. After he was dressed, the steward was very pleased with him, for it seemed obvious that from his actions and his speech he was a man of great intelligence and of the nobility. One day while alone with the steward in his house, the knight said to him: "Sir, what is this all about? From the other side of the army two men ride forth side by side to ask if there is anyone who wants to challenge them. There are many good men here and no one goes out to meet them."

"Truly, sir," responded the steward, "ours are taught by hard experience. Those two knights you see who come forth side by side are the king's sons and expert with their weapons. They have already killed two counts and that is why no one dares to challenge them."

"Are you to be defamed and humiliated by them?" asked the knight. "For certain, if you would like, I will go out there when one of them sallies forth, and I will fight him."

"I am very pleased with what you are saying," said the steward, "but first I will have to inform my lord, the king." Then the steward mounted his horse and went before the king.

"Sire, a strange knight came to me the other day and told me that he wanted to live with me under your protection. I welcomed him and ordered him given vestments and outfitted with a horse and weapons. Now he has asked to be allowed to go forth to fight those challengers from the other side. I told him that he could not do it unless you knew about it."

"And how does this knight strike you?" asked the king.

"Sire," answered the steward, "he is a very handsome knight, well mannered, and prepared to do everything well."

"Let us see him," said the king.

"With pleasure," replied the steward and sent for him. The knight entered the palace and proceeded toward the king, who was attended by his daughter and the steward. He entered with a firm step and serious countenance, so that the king and his daughter knew that he was a man of substance. The king questioned him: "Knight, where are you from?"

"Sire," he replied, "from the land of India."

"And do you dare to fight with those who come forth seeking combat?" asked the king.

"Yes," said the knight. "With the help of God, I will challenge one fighter at a time, for I am not inclined to commit a reckless act."

"Go with God," the king rejoined, "and may He help you."

65. Of how the Knight Zifar killed a son of the king of Ester, who had them besieged

Early the next morning, the knight prepared his horse and his weapons for combat, so that he lacked no item of weaponry. He advanced toward the gate of the town. The steward sent a man with him and ordered those men at the gates of the town to permit him to leave and to admit him again whenever he wished. As the sun began to rise, a son of the king of Ester came forth to challenge, and a man who was on the platform began to shout, "The challenger has already sallied forth from the enemy army and is approaching here."

When the Knight Zifar heard this, he told the gatekeeper to allow him to leave. The gatekeeper said that he would not do it unless Zifar promised to give him a reward if he was victorious. The knight said that if God helped him to win the contest he would give him the horse of the other knight, if he were able to catch it. The gatekeeper opened the gate and let him go forth.

When the Knight Zifar met the other on the battlefield, the son of the king said to Zifar, "Knight, you have been ill-advised to dare to do battle with me. I believe you would have done better to remain at home."

"You don't scare me," retorted the knight, "any more than I already am. Do what you are to do."

They gave their horses free rein and charged. They struck with their lances so violently that they penetrated deeply into the shields. But God chose to protect the knight for He turned aside the lance of the king's son, and the lance of the Knight Zifar penetrated the armor of the king's son, hurling him backward, and killed him. He took the horse of the king's son and led it away. He gave it to the gatekeeper just as he had promised, and then he proceeded to his lodgings to remove his armor.

66. Of how the king of Mentón learned that a strange knight had killed a son of the king of Ester

The noise and lamenting was very great throughout the army for the king's son who was dead. This selfsame news circulated throughout the town; however, no one knew who had killed him. Each of the counts claimed he had killed him. The king sent for his steward and asked who had killed the king's son.

"Sire," replied the steward, "your knight who came here yesterday to see you killed him, and we have sure knowledge of it. He gave the horse of the king's son, whom he killed, to the gatekeepers, and they and those who were in the towers and at the doors know it for certain."

"May he be blessed in the name of God," said the king. "Perhaps God brought this man here for his own good and ours. And what is the knight doing?"

"Sire," replied the steward, "after he took off his armor, he did not leave his dwelling. He secludes himself and does not wish to be recognized."

"We are pleased that he does," said the king. "We should let him rest, and tomorrow we shall see what he will do."

"Sire," added the steward, "I am sure that tomorrow he will come forth, for he is a man of courage and good common sense."

The princess, daughter of the king, had a great desire to see him, and said, "Sire, you would do well in sending for him, praising him, and exhorting him to do his best."

"And if he does the best he can," said the king, "how will we be able to improve him? Let's leave him alone and may his good fortune continue."

67. Of how the Knight Zifar killed the other knight, who was the nephew of the king of Ester

The next morning before dawn, the knight armed himself, mounted his horse, and headed for the gates of the town. He requested the sentinels on the towers to let him know if some challenger should come forth.

And not a single challenger sallied forth from the enemy army, and one of the sentinels on the towers spoke: "Sir, no one comes forth, and you may go out as you please."

"I am pleased," answered the knight, "since God thinks it well."

And as the knight was going out, the sentries on the towers spied two armed knights come forth from the enemy army. They proceeded toward the town, challenging any two knights to contend with them. The sentinels on the towers shouted to the knight to turn back. He came to the gate and asked them what they wanted, and they told him, "Sir, you need another companion."

"And why?" asked the knight.

"Because they are two heavily armed knights and they are asking for any two knights to challenge them."

"The truth is," said the knight, "I do not have a companion, but I will take God as my brother-in-arms. He aided me yesterday against the other, and He will aid me today against these two."

"What a great companion you have chosen!" replied the sentinels. "Go in the name of God, and may He in His mercy aid you."

They opened the gates and allowed him to go out. When he entered the battlefield, the other two knights very haughtily and scornfully said: "Knight, where is your comrade?"

"He is here with me," answered the Knight Zifar.

"Is he invisible?" they asked.

"He does not appear to you," said the knight, "for you are not worthy of seeing Him.

"How can he be invisible if he can be seen?" retorted the others.

"He is invisible to evil sinners," responded the Knight Zifar.

"And why do you consider us greater sinners than yourself?" asked the enemy knights.

"It is my belief that you are," said the knight, "because you in your great arrogance have besieged the king in this town. He has not wronged you nor does he merit this action from you. I believe if you lift the siege you will be doing right and fairly, and therefore God will reward you."

"Really," replied one of the other knights, "this knight thinks we will lift the siege of this king on account of his smooth words. You may well believe that we shall not do so until we have seized the king by his beard."

"Those are words of pride," said the Knight Zifar. "Pay heed, for God will hold you accountable."

One of these two knights was the son of the king of Ester, and the other the king's nephew. They were the two most powerful knights in the army, and the most capable with weapons. All the enemy soldiers and those in the town were watching what these knights were doing and wondering what was delaying them. It seemed to them that they were talking, and they believed that the knights were debating some issue. The king of Mentón, who was in the fortress tower with his daughter and with his steward watching them, also believed they were bargaining. The king said to his steward, "Is that our visiting knight?"

"Sire," answered the steward, "it is he."

"And is he planning to challenge both those knights?" asked the king.

"I do not know," replied the steward.

"Lord God!" said the king, "aid him on our behalf!"

"Yes, He will grant it through His grace, because He knows we do not merit the evil they do us," said the princess.

The two knights from the enemy army turned again toward the Knight Zifar and said, "Knight, where is your comrade? You are mad if you fight us alone."

"And I have already told you," said the knight, "that my companion is with me, and I believe He is closer to me than both of you are to each other."

"And are you, sir knight, the one who killed our relative?" inquired one of the other knights.

"His arrogance and his folly killed him," replied the knight, "and I believe it will also kill you. Friends, don't underestimate anyone else because you are knights of noble blood. Surely you ought to know that in this world there are some men of nobler blood and higher station than you."

"You are not the one," retorted one of the knights.

"Nor would I take on such airs as you give yourself," said the knight. "I know perfectly well who I am; and no one can judge another well nor know another well if first he does not know or understand himself. However, I say that he who fears his enemy and knows how to be on guard against him is wise, although his foe may not be a strong, or a very powerful, knight. A small dog is accustomed to attack a very large deer, and a very small thing at times moves the very largest and causes it to fall."

"Well, do you consider us to be defeated?" asked the king's son.

"Certainly not by me," said the knight, "for I would be unable to overthrow you nor would I dare so much on my own account."

"I would like to know," said the king's son, "on whose strength you depend, since you don't dare anything on your own behalf."

"Certainly," said the knight, "on the strength of my companion."

"He will be of little help to you when you are in our power," one of the other knights replied.

"You must know that the devil has no power over that person who commends himself to God. Therefore you will not overcome me," answered the Knight Zifar.

"You are very insulting," said the other. "Let us attack this knight." Sinking their spurs into their horses, they charged toward the knight as he charged them.

The knights each struck blows with their lances on the shield of the Knight Zifar, so that they broke their lances on it. They were unable to unhorse him for he was a skilled horseman. The Knight Zifar struck with his lance at the nephew of the king. He ran his lance through his side, piercing his armor, and hurling the dead man to the earth. Then the knight and the king's son drew their swords and struck each other great blows on the crests of their helmets and their armor, so that the king of Mentón, who was in the top of his tower, could hear them. And what a good advocate the knight had in the princess, for if he had been her brother, she could not have made her prayers more devoutly to God in his behalf. She continually asked the steward, "How is my knight doing?" The steward came to tell her the news of how he had slain one of the two knights and was still struggling with the other.

"Oh, our Lord God," she said, "blessed be Thy Name for the help and grace Thou art giving this knight. And since Thou hast granted such a good beginning to his feat, I ask through Thy mercy that Thou grant him a successful conclusion."

And then she returned to her prayer as before, and the knights continued fiercely attacking each other on the battlefield with their swords until not a particle of their shields remained.

68. Of how the Knight Zifar killed the other son of the king and took away his horses

Seeing that neither was able to damage the armor they wore, for it was tough and very strong, the Knight Zifar drew his dagger, reached out for the king's son, put his arm around his neck, and held him to his own body, although he was very strong. He cut the straps to his helmet and the armor cloth that he wore underneath it. He threw them away and began to strike savage blows with his dagger at his chain mail headgear until he broke his dagger. Then he seized the mace he carried and struck him countless blows on the head until he killed him.

69. Of how the knave accompanied the knight into town with the horses

While the fight was in progress, the knave, who was following the route the Knight Zifar had taken, was watching with the soldiers of the enemy army to see how the struggle would end. He heard the voice of the knight who represented the people of the town, and it seemed to him that it was his master's voice. When the voice cried out, he was completely sure of it. As an excuse to go find out for sure, he said to the troops: "Sirs, the horse of the king's nephew is straying through the battlefield and I'm afraid that he will go into the town if some one does not catch him. If you think it right, I will go for him."

"Of course, that makes sense," answered the soldiers, "go after him."

The knave proceeded toward the place where the two knights were struggling, and when he neared them, the Knight Zifar recognized him in the clothes he had given and said, "Friend, you are here?"

"Sir," replied the knave, "here at your service. How are you doing with that knight?"

"Very well, of course," answered the knight. "Wait a little until he dies, for he is still breathing."

"Well, then, what do you order me to do?" asked the knave.

"Fetch that horse that is straying on the battlefield," said the knight, "and come to the town with me."

The knave went to catch the horse and climbed into the saddle.

As soon as the Knight Zifar saw that his opponent was dead, he let him drop to the ground. He took his opponent's horse by the reins and headed for the town, accompanied by the knave. When they reached the gate, the knight called the gatekeeper and told him to take them to a house where they could remove their armor and he would give him the horse he had promised. They entered a house and closed the gate. He gave the gatekeeper the horse which belonged to the king's son. They stripped off the knight's armor and that of the horse the knave was riding. The knight asked the gatekeeper to lend him some clothing until he could reach his own lodgings, since he did not want to be recognized and the gatekeeper complied. He mounted his horse and the knave the other, and they went secretly through another gate to their quarters.

70. Of how the king sent a messenger to learn who the other knight was who had entered the town with the Knight Zifar

All the people, the counts as well as the nobles, were sitting at the gate through which the knight had entered in order to salute him when he came out. They considered that no other knight in the world could have accomplished a greater feat of arms than Zifar had done that day. When they were told that he had gone secretly through another gate, they were deeply concerned and they asked the gatekeepers if they had recognized him. They replied they had not as he was a strange knight and they did not believe that he was a native. The counts and the other citizens departed with grave misgivings because they did not realize he was there. They acclaimed his gallantry and praised him. The struggle of these two knights had lasted well until eventide. The king, the princess, and the steward, seeing the fight had ended and that the knight had returned, wondered about the identity of the other person who accompanied him on the other horse. The king ordered his steward: "Go to his lodgings and find out from the knight how the battle went and who the other one is who came with him. Meanwhile we shall dine, for it is already supper time. You will return later with the news that you learn from him."

"With pleasure," answered the steward.

71. Of how the king told the princess, his daughter, that it suited him for her to marry that knight

"Truly, sire," said the princess, "you have dined well today. You have had Our Lord God as a host who has not abandoned you, but rather aided you against your enemies. You have had a great victory over them, and blessed be the name of God for sending such a knight here to you. I have faith that in His mercy He will act through this knight to lift the siege of the city and deliver us from our unhappy lot."

The king sat down to eat and told the princess to come to dinner. She answered that she would not do so until she heard news that the knight was unhurt. She believed he had received such heavy blows in battle from one opponent or another that perhaps he was wounded.

"And do you love him so much that you ache for him?" asked the king.

"Truly, sire," she replied, "I do right in loving him with all my heart, for he fights for you and to defend your kingdom. Moreover, he fights for me, for I will be heir to the kingdom after you pass away."

"Daughter," said the king, "do you want him to conquer the enemy and lift the siege of this city and deliver us from our predicament?"

"Sire," she answered, "I would like this very much, and soon if it please God."

"And do you believe that it would be suitable for you to marry him, my daughter?" asked the king.

"Truly, sire," she answered, "God willing, it is better to marry a nobleman who is wise and a gallant knight-at-arms, so that he will be capable of preserving the kingdom in your lifetime and after you have passed on, than to marry a prince or other nobleman who would not know how, or be capable of defending himself or me."

"By Heaven, daughter," said the king, "I am glad you speak so sensibly. I really believe this fine knight is as great as we had thought."

72. Of how the steward brought the king news of the knight and his companion

And while they were conversing, behold the steward arrived with all the latest news. When the princess saw him, she said, "My knight, is he wounded?"

"No," replied the steward, "Praise be to God, he is happy and in good health."

"And who was the other man who came with him?" inquired the king.

"A servant of his who accompanied him along his way," said the steward; for the Knight Zifar had informed him it was his servant who had come with him as far as the enemy lines. "And the knight even told me a thing that I did not know before—that this servant of his had advised him before they entered the enemy lines that if he wanted to enter the city, the knight should give him his clothes and take his shabby ones and that he should pass through the enemy army acting like a crazy man and harming no one, and that in this way he would be able to come to the city without hindrance. And the servant added more, saying that when the knight was passing through the enemy lines the soldiers shouted at him as at a crazy man, calling him the king of Mentón, and so he entered the city."

The king said, "God does not want these words spoken in vain. He has some great honor planned for this knight.

"May God grant it to him," said the princess, "for he truly deserves it."

The king began to smile and told the steward he wanted the knight well cared for. The steward withdrew and ordered his servant to take good care of the knight. Then he sat down to dine for he had not eaten that day.

73. Of how the king of Mentón said that those whom the Knight Zifar had killed were the two sons of the king of Ester and the other was his nephew

The next morning the counts and the other noblemen came to the king's dwelling and the king asked them: "Friends, who was that valiant knight who did so well yesterday? For the love of God, present him to me and let's show him all the honor he merits, for it seems to me that he used his weapons in a clearly superior fashion."

"Truly, sire," answered one of the counts, "we don't know who he is. It seemed to us that no knight in the world could handle weapons better than he. We went to the gate of the city to find out who he was, and we found that he had entered a house to take off his armor. While we were waiting at the gate to greet him, he secretly left through another gate. He went away, so that we were unable to find out his identity."

"I truly believe he may be a knight sent by God to defend us and fight for us. And since we are unable to identify him, let's be grateful to God for the help He sent us. Let us ask Him through His grace to continue it from now on; for the Knight of God has slain the two most arrogant knights in all this world. Moreover, they tell me the third one is the nephew of the king, who greatly resembled him in his arrogance."

"That is the truth," replied one of the counts. "When we went to the gate of the town we never heard such great laments for any man as they were making for those two last night and still are this morning."

"May God give them lamentation and sorrow, and happiness to us," said the king. "They have caused us enough evil and sorrow, without any provocation on our part."

"May God so grant it," said the others. And from then on they called the Knight Zifar the Knight of God.

"Friends," said the king, "God has given us a great boon in eliminating the two best arms that the king of Ester had, as well as his nephew on whose strength he relied. Let us plan how we can escape this predicament in which he holds us."

"Very well," they all agreed. "Let's do it."

74. Of how the Knight of God asked the steward why they had not sallied forth to attack those troops of the royal encampment

While the Knight of God was alone with the steward, the steward asked him in what way they might be able to escape the siege they were under.

"Truly," said the Knight of God, "nothing ventured nothing gained. Fortune smiles on the brave and God helps those who help themselves."

"And how?" asked the steward. "Already we have seen many such deeds as these attempted, and they have turned out badly."

"I am not talking of the reckless, but of the valiant, for there is a great difference between recklessness and prudence, for recklessness is committed through madness and calculated risks are taken through good native sense," replied the knight.

"Well, how can we get the strength to escape the predicament in which our enemies hold us?" asked the steward.

"I will tell you," answered the Knight of God. "The best cavalry of the king's army should be divided into two groups of five hundred knights each. Before dawn, they should set out from two different sections of the town and strike the enemy while they are in their deepest rest. By doing this frequently they will defeat the enemy forces or the enemy will be forced to disperse. They will be weakened by the great blows they have received and they will have to leave, for while you desire your sleep and rest, so the enemy desires the same thing. And moreover I tell you, if you let me choose five hundred knights of the cavalry that is here, I will strive to accomplish this task with the grace of God."

75. Concerning the council the king of Mentón held with the counts about what the Knight of God had told his steward

"I approve of what you are saying," said the steward. And then he proceeded toward the king's palace. When he arrived the king asked him what the Knight of God was doing.

"Sire," said the steward, "he is acting in the manner of a competent knight and man of wisdom. It seems that he has always participated in war and the practice of chivalry, for he knows so well how to explain all the maneuvers pertaining to war."

"Well, what does he say about this war we are engaged in?" asked the king.

"Well, considering how many knights and noblemen are here, he thinks we are remiss in our duty," said the steward. He related all that had passed between them.

"It is well that we keep to ourselves the things that the Knight of God said, and we shall see what the counts, the nobles, and all our other men who will gather here tomorrow with you will respond," the king added.

"I consider it all good and to your advantage," said the steward.

Early the next morning, the counts, the nobles, and all the people of the city arrived at the palace of the king. And when the king came out, he asked them if they had come to some agreement through which they might be able to escape the oppression of their enemies. Alas! They hadn't spoken about it nor had it crossed their minds. One arose and said to the king, "Sire, give us time to hold a council and we will come up with a solution." The king scornfully replied: "Sir knight, take all the time you wish; but while you are holding council, if it's all right with you, I will choose five hundred knights from among yours and mine. We shall begin to organize and afterward we may learn better how to attack the problem."

"We agree," responded the counts. "Let the steward go and select them."

The king sent for the steward and the Knight of God. And as soon as they came, he commanded them to choose five hundred knights from among his troops and the others. And so they did. As the Knight of God pointed them out, the steward wrote down their names, so that the five hundred best knights of the cavalry were listed. The steward ordered them to assemble in the plaza early the next morning to stand review in full military dress with all their weaponry.

76. Of how the Knight of God and the townsmen routed the king of Ester, who had them besieged, and how they vanquished him

The next day all those armed knights assembled there. It seemed to the king to be an excellent group that could fight well and could undertake a great enterprise if they had a good leader.

One of the knights among them said, "Sire, whom will you appoint as leader?

"My own steward," answered the king, "who is a hidalgo and a valiant knight, as you all know."

"We are pleased," a spokesman replied, "and for Heaven's sake, sire, what we have to do, let us do quickly before the enemy learns of us and is forewarned."

"I am very grateful to you," said the king, "for your response. Assemble early tomorrow before dawn at the gates to the town. Be prepared, and do whatever my steward commands."

"At your service," they replied.

Very early the next morning, before the dawn, they gathered at the gates of the city—five hundred knights in full armor and three thousand foot-soldiers also well armed, for the steward had equipped them. The Knight of

God dressed and took his horse and weapons. He was wearing the helmet plume of the steward. He accompanied the steward to the gates of the town. The steward addressed the knights: "Friends, that is my nephew up front who wears my helmet plumes. I want him to lead. You follow and protect him. Wherever he goes, all go. I will go in the rearguard and will return with you. Do not follow anyone except him."

"In the name of God!" said the knights. "We will follow him and guard him with our lives."

The gates of the town were opened and all sallied forth briskly, rank following rank. The Knight of God placed the infantry in the advance guard and turned to the cavalry and said: "Friends, we have to strike directly at the royal headquarters where the king is. If we rout him, all the rest will be vanquished."

He instructed the infantry not to engage in looting, but to kill all the horses as well as the men, until God brought success to their enterprise. These orders he gave them under threat of the king's ire. They promised to carry out his command. And when they started their advance, the steward returned, for the king had commanded him to do so.

Slashing and killing savagely, the Knight of God engaged the enemy with his own forces. The infantry set fire to the tents, so that the flames climbed to the sky. When they reached the encampment of the king, the turmoil was great amid the press of slaughter and the assault on all they encountered. Dawn had not yet broken and consequently the enemy soldiers had not been alerted to arm themselves. Reaching the king's tent, they stormed it, cutting the ropes that supported it, so that the king could not be helped by his own troops nor did he dare to hold his ground. He mounted a horse his troops brought him and fled. The troops of the Knight Zifar pursued him at a distance of about three leagues, striking and killing. When the king's retainers came to the tent seeking the king, they were told he was gone. In bewilderment they took to their heels to save themselves, each man for himself. Seeing them retreating, the Knight of God, leading his soldiers, fell upon them, giving no quarter. Then they returned to the royal headquarters where they found immense wealth and booty. The enemy could not carry it away nor did they have time to, and when day broke and the townsmen saw the Knight Zifar's army returning, they went forth and followed them.

77. Of how the Knight of God conquered the royal encampment, and the king of Mentón asked his daughter if marriage would please her

The Knight of God sent word to the king to order security placed over the booty in the royal tents, in order that it not be lost. The king sent his steward, who was already quite wealthy and owned a palace. He was affluent, possessing great wealth. However, with advice from the Knight of God, he gave the major share of the plunder to the five hundred knights and the three thousand infantrymen who participated in the great victory. The Knight of God went to his lodging surreptitiously so that they would not recognize him, while all the rest went to their lodgings to disarm. The king was in his royal apartment giving thanks to God for the mercy He had shown them. He said to his daughter, the princess, "What did you think of the great victory?"

"By Heaven, sire," she answered, "it seems to me that God has been good to us and it does appear His doing and not that of an earthly being, unless God wanted His aid to manifest itself through someone He loves."

"Well, daughter, who can it be? We are about to have to decide who broke the siege of the town, and we must give you that person as a husband."

"Oh dear father!" she said, "There is no reason for you to doubt that the Knight of God did all these deeds. If it weren't for him and God wishing his success, we would not have been freed so quickly."

"And you believe that, daughter?"

"Truly, I do believe so, sire," she responded.

"And you will be happy to marry the Knight of God?" asked the king.

"It pleases me since it is God's will."

Then the king sent word then to the counts and all the other noblemen to come to the palace the next morning. They came the next day to the palace of the king, and he gave thanks to God for the victory. Then he thanked the five hundred knights who had participated in the victory.

78. Of how one of the five hundred knights said to the king that the Knight of God and no other had raised the siege of the town

A valiant knight arose from among the five hundred. "Sire, you do not have to be grateful to anyone for this accomplishment except primarily to God and to a knight whom your steward appointed to lead us. He said the knight was his nephew; and it truly seems that in all my life I have never seen a knight so handsomely armed nor so well suited to the saddle. I have never seen deeds of arms such as he won in this victory. He inspired his own people as he inspired us; for when he uttered his first word to us, it truly seemed the inspiration of God. I tell you, sire, in truth, he led us into places with his daring that if I had two thousand knights, I would not have dared to enter. And if you believe that I am lying about this, I beg those knights who were there to tell you that it is true."

"Sire," declared one of the others, "he has told you the truth about everything. You may believe, sire, that all the good deeds we have seen this knight do can not be related in the short time we have been here."

"Well, what will it be?" asked the king. "Who shall we say broke the siege of the town?"

"Don't be in the slightest doubt, sire, that the one we are discussing now broke the siege, through his good fortune," stated the spokesman of the five hundred.

"Well, according to this," said the king, "it seems to me we are to give him the princess, my daughter, as his wife."

"You would be doing wrong," declared the knight, "if you did not give her to him, for he truly deserves her."

79. Of how the son of a count told the king that he had their agreement if he would give the princess to the Knight of God

A son of one of the most powerful counts who was present stood up: "Sire, you know that many counts and good men of noble blood came here to serve you and to study carefully to whom you gave your daughter. Conceivably you could give her to a man of common birth, which would not be a credit to you nor your kingdom. Think more about it and don't be led by emotion."

"Truly," replied the king, "I have never thought of reneging in the slightest degree on what I promise, nor would I break my word to the least significant man in the world."

"Sire," said the son of the count, "find out first from the princess if she wants to marry him."

"I am sure she wants what I want," stated the king, "especially in regard to keeping my word."

"Sire," they all agreed, "send for your steward and have him bring the knight he said was his nephew."

The king sent for the steward and the Knight of God. They entered elegantly dressed, and although the steward was a very handsome knight, the Knight of God completely outshone him.

When they entered the palace, all the people present were so anxious to see him that they all stood to greet him and said in resounding voices: "Welcome to the Knight of God."

He entered a pace before the steward, for the steward in order to honor him, allowed him to enter first. The knight nodded his head to all and greeted them. When he arrived where the king was seated on his throne, the king said: "Knight of God, I beg you, by the faith you owe to God Who sent you here, to declare to me in the presence of all if you are a nobleman."

"I tell you the truth, sir," answered the Knight of God. "I am a nobleman, the son of a legitimate lady and knight."

"Do you come of royal blood?" the king asked.

The knight was silent and did not answer.

"Do not be modest," said the king, "say it."

The knight replied: "Sir, it would be a great shame for anyone as poor as I am to say that he came of royal blood. If he did, he would defame and dishonor himself."

"Knight," said the king, "they say here that you broke the siege of this town."

"God broke it," replied the knight, "and those good people whom you sent."

"Shall we all agree that this is true?" asked the king. "Go for the princess and have her come here."

The princess returned attended by numerous duennas and handmaidens to stand there in the presence of the king. She and all the others who accompanied her were elegantly dressed. She wore on her head a tiara studded with rubies and emeralds that illuminated the room.

BOOK TWO

The King of Mentón

80. Of how the Knight of God was married to the daughter of the king of Mentón and how he succeeded to the throne on the death of the king

"Daughter," questioned the king, "do you know who broke the siege of the town?"

"Sire," she said, "you should know him, but I do know this much about yonder knight; he killed the son of the king of Ester, who was the first to challenge him, and I truly believe he killed the others and lifted the siege."

When the son of the count heard this, he said, "Sire, it seems to me that this is all God's doing, and since it is so, with God's blessing, let them be married."

"We agree," the others said.

Then the story relates how they sent for the chaplain and the chaplain came. He took their vows, and the Knight of God received the princess as his wife and she took the knight as her husband. And you can truly believe there were none present to gainsay them. Moreover, all the citizens of the kingdom present accepted him as their lord and future king. However, the Knight Zifar had to bide his time for two years, because the king considered the princess too young for marriage. Through this knight's efforts, many towns and castles that were lost during the reign of his father-in-law were recovered. He ruled the land fairly and made many good laws and established many good customs, so that the rich and poor of the kingdom were devoted to him. The king, his father-in-law, died before the two years had run their course, and he became king and defender of the kingdom. He was a fair, just ruler and a powerful defender of his country, so that each person was treated impartially and lived at peace.

81. Of how the king of Mentón told his wife that because of a sin he had committed, he had been ordered to maintain celibacy for two consecutive years

One day while the king was resting in his bed, it suddenly occurred to him that he was married to another woman and had sons by her, and he recalled the circumstances of losing his sons and wife. Moreover there came to his mind the words his wife had spoken to him at the time he had related to her what had transpired between him and his grandfather. While deep in thought, he began to weep because his wife would not be pleased with this embarrassing situation. According to his faith he could have only one wife. He was thus living in mortal sin. And while he was in the aforementioned dilemma, the queen came and saw him sorrowing and sad. She questioned him: "Oh, my lord, what is the matter? Why are you weeping? What is troubling you? Tell me."

"Certainly, my queen," he replied, trying to conceal his thoughts, "What I was thinking is this: I sinned greatly against our Lord God, and I made no amends to Him, nor did I carry out the penance that was assigned to me for this sin."

"And can it be rectified?" the queen asked.

"Yes, it can be by great penance," he answered.

And she spoke to him: "Do you think you will be able to endure and suffer this penance?"

"Yes," he said, "with the grace of God."

"Well, let us share it," she responded. "You take half and I will take half, and let us finish it."

"God does not want the just to suffer as if they were sinners. Only the one who committed the sin should suffer the penance, because this is only right."

The queen answered: "According to the words of the Holy Church, are we not both as one from the day we married? Surely you ought not to suffer an ordeal which I can not share, nor should you enjoy pleasure that I may not share either. If you are hurt by a thorn in your foot, I suffer in my heart, because our flesh is one and we are both one body. Thus you will be unable to have or to feel anything in this world that I will not feel also."

"That is the truth," stated the king, "but I do not want either you or I to do this penance now."

"Well, will you be in mortal sin?" asked the queen.

"Yes, I would live in mortal sin and even worse for the love of you," declared the king.

"For the love of me, do not do it," said the queen. "May you know that you will not take any pleasure with me until you make amends to God and extricate yourself from this sin."

"Since that's the way it is," said the king, "it is fitting that you know the penance I have to do. The sin I committed against our Lord was so great that it cannot be rectified unless I maintain chastity for two years."

"What!" exclaimed the queen. "You failed to do penance in order to please me? For Heaven's sake, it would please me body and soul but would worry me to death. As it is, I would have had you as a sinner and outcast in the eyes of God, and now I shall have you clean and spotless before God.

Since you have waited two years for me, I can wait two more years for you because I love you."

"You have my gratitude," replied the king, "for your goodness in returning me to God's favor."

The king was very happy and pleased with their conversation and so was the queen. They lived together very discreetly. The king was grateful to God, for through the goodness of the queen, God was guiding his way; for his intent was to wait for a period of time in order to learn whether his wife Grima was dead or alive.

82. Now the story ceases to tell of the king and the queen and again tells of the knight's wife, and what happened to her after her departure from the kingdom of Orbín

According to the story of this good lady, as you will now hear, she was traveling in a ship guided in His mercy by our Lord Jesus Christ. They traveled a long distance and at last reached a port in the land of the king of Ester. The good lady asked people on the shore what land that was and if it was a land of justice where men could live without fear. A certain man, who was leaving the country with all his company, came to the lady and said:

"My lady, are you asking if this is a land of justice? I say to you it is not, because it does not have a good foundation."

"And why not?" inquired the lady.

"Because it does not have a good ruler," answered the man, "and the good foundation of a castle, a town, or a kingdom is not the stones nor the towers, although they may be built into good and solid walls, but a good governor who rules it in justice and in truth. Instead there is a very arrogant king here, cruel and merciless, who confiscates the property of those who are wealthy. He crushes his people with taxes unjustly under the pretext of doing some good with them. But alas! he does not, and he executes men without giving them a hearing, and he does many other evil things which would be too long to relate. And if the man had good sense, he should have already taken warning of doing these evil things, for God punished him through his two sons, whom he no longer has."

"And how was that?" asked the lady.

"I will tell you," he replied.

83. Of how the man related to the lady all the deeds of the king of Ester, and in addition those of the Knight of God

"A short time ago the king of Ester had arrogantly surrounded the capital of the king of Mentón. This king of Mentón was a very good man, but was old and unable to command well, and for this reason the king of Ester dared to undertake aggression against him. He had sworn never to lift the siege until he had seized the king of Mentón by his beard. But man proposes and God disposes. And so it happened that in two days a certain knight killed his two sons right before his eyes. He also killed his nephew, a son of his brother. After the fourth day he was overwhelmed and annihilated on the battlefield where he had established his siege. All the country rebelled and pursued him, killing all his soldiers. He lost all the enormous treasure he owned, for he was forced to leave it behind. Surely this was only fair, for they were ill-gotten gains. Therefore they say that 'when the sheep come from bad stock, the wool is also bad.' And still the wretch learned nothing from all these things, for now he does worse than before. But God, all-powerful, who destroyed his two sons, will crush him, so his evil doings will cease and the earth will rest. It is my advice that you go live in the kingdom of Mentón, where there is a virtuous king. Men consider that he was sent by God; for he rules his land in peace and in justice, and he is a gallant knight-at-arms and very wise. He defends himself easily against those who wish to do evil. He is the one who killed the two sons of the king of Ester and his nephew, routed the king and broke the siege he had established. For this reason, they gave him the princess, daughter of the king of Mentón, as his wife. After the death of the king his father-in-law, he became king and ruler of the kingdom. Because of these commendable deeds I have told you of him, I and my company are going there to live under his protection."

84. Of how the wife of the Knight Zifar with all her company sailed away to reach the kingdom of Mentón

The good lady contemplated what that good man had told her, and an idea suddenly occurred to her. She wondered if that king was her husband, and she said, "Friend, I believe your advice is good. Let's leave in the morning in the name of God for that kingdom you speak of."

"For Heaven's sake!" said the good man, "if you do, you will be doing well, for those men you see on the shore all dressed in uniforms, are the king's men. They are waiting until you unload this ship. If they find valuable items, they will take them from you and carry them to the king under the pretext of purchasing them, and thereby pay you nothing. This is what they have done to others. God save us from evil hands henceforth."

The next morning they set sail and proceeded on their way. And so God favored them and guided them, for they covered in two days what they would normally have traveled in five days, arriving at a harbor in the kingdom of Mentón, where there was a large and rich city named Bellid. There they debarked and unloaded everything they had aboard the ship. They stored their cargo in a hostel that the king of Mentón had recently constructed. The king had placed a good man in charge of the hostel, and he welcomed the guests who came there and treated them very well. And thus he treated the good lady and all who accompanied her. He gave his own rooms to the lady Grima and separate quarters to the rest of the company. It seemed to the good lady that she should not keep all her retinue with her; so she gave them a large share of the vast wealth given to her by the king to be used as she pleased and which she carried in the ship. So they took leave of her rich and contented and set out for their own lands. And one of them said to the others:

"Friends, the ancient proverb is true, for 'whoever serves a good master loyally, receives nothing but a good reward.' We protected this good lady and served her the best we could, and she gave us a greater reward than we deserved. And may God permit her to be successful in this world and in the next in anything she desires."

The others responded, "Amen, through His mercy." Boarding the ship, they proceeded on their way.

85. Of how the keeper of the hostel related to the lady all the king's doings

The lady, who remained in the hostel, asked her host about the king of Mentón—what kind of man he was and what kind of life he was leading and where he dwelt most of the time. He told her that he was a very good man, a good Christian, and that it was obvious through all the things that God did through him. The people of the kingdom had never before been so prosperous or fortunate since he had become lord of the kingdom. He ruled it in justice, peace, and harmony, and each person controlled his own possessions and could do with his own wealth as he pleased, openly and without fear. And no matter how powerful or influential he might be, no man dared to take so much as one small coin from another against his will. And if anyone should do so, he would forfeit his head; for the law was enforced in the kingdom against the great as well as the small, so that it caused great uneasiness to the powerful, who were accustomed to committing many crimes in the land. However, so stringently did the king apply the law throughout all the kingdom, that all mutually abided by it. He pleased them all with this good law, for they were more secure than they had ever been. Therefore they say, "It is better for a man to be forced to be good than to allow him to have his own evil way."

"And certainly," said the host, "a man is known by his deeds, and if his actions are bad, his works cannot be good; and thus he falls from God's grace first and then from his lord's, and he is no longer secure in his person or his possessions. The one who wants to live a Christian life and practices good principles will earn the love of God, of his country's ruler, and of his fellow

man. He will have a peaceful life and will be secure in his possessions, unless
the lord does not punish the evil, for then the good men will lack security
and will be forced to take flight. And I will tell you more: this king leads a
good and saintly life, for he and his queen have maintained chastity for more
than a year, although they truly love one another, and the queen is one of the
most beautiful and best-natured women in all the land, and the king is in the
prime of life. All the people in the kingdom wonder greatly about this matter.
The king dwells most of the time in a very noble and delightful city, which
is called Glanbecque, where they have everything they need. And because of
the abundance of the land, and the justice, peace, and harmony that exist
there, he and his judges have very few lawsuits to hear. Hardly anyone comes
before them, as you can see in this city if you care to.

"It has been a month since a suit came before the judges. And thus the
king works at nothing except having books containing many good stories of
great deeds read to him. Otherwise, he goes hunting in the forest or hawking.
The counts and all the king's subjects are pleased when he happens to go on
their land for he does not take anything belonging to them nor does he
trespass against their laws nor their good customs. Instead he supports their
laws and does such favors for those people as he realizes he can do without
endangering his own dominion. And for all these aforementioned reasons,
the population of the land has increased a great deal; for people come from
all the other dominions to make their homes in this kingdom. It seems to me
that soon we will be unable to contain all of them in the kingdom."

The good lady smiled, and said: "By Heaven, my good man, good
attracts more than evil, and good welcomes men with pleasure and supports
them in comfort and in folly as if they were good souls in paradise; and evil
treats men miserably and holds them in misery and torment, just as hell
holds the souls of the wicked. From what you have said here, you must therefore believe the virtue of this kingdom can contain all the people of this
world if they should come here to dwell, for virtue will enlarge your
kingdom, converting more of the evildoers from nearby. God knows you have
made me happy by the many good things you have told me of this king and
of the kingdom. From here on I propose to live all my life in this kingdom
where justice reigns, for it is the base of every good thing and the shield and
protection of all citizens. The ruler who administers just laws in his land is
very fortunate; for just as he keeps it and has it kept, so will he be judged
before our Lord God. And I wish to go to that city where the king lives, and
I will build a hostel there where all the noblemen who chance that way may
find lodging. And I request you, sir, to guard for me all these things that I
have in this room until I come or send for them."

"With pleasure," her host answered, "and you can be certain I will
guard them for you as I would guard my own eyes from being stolen."

"And I ask you to find a couple of good women to accompany me, and I will give them animals for transportation, clothing, and whatever else they may need," the good lady requested.

"As a matter of fact," answered the host, "here in the hostel there are two such women as you need. I will get them to go with you and serve you." The good lady had horses purchased for herself and her maids, so they could travel more easily.

86. Of the king of Mentón, and how the queen learned about all the activities of the wife of the Knight Zifar, and how she traveled through strange lands

They mounted their horses and proceeded toward the city where the king dwelt. They had no need for anyone to guard the animals for them, because they were welcomed wherever they went, and the found someone to tend them. They did not fear they would be stolen or seized from them by force, as frequently happens where there is no law nor anyone who is inclined to abide by it. Woe betides the land where there is no justice; for lacking it, the land is destroyed and the people flee. Thus the lords become poor and destitute, which is not their fault for if the land is deserted, there is no one to serve them.

The next morning, after the virtuous lady reached the city where the king lived, she went to hear mass at a church where the queen was in the chapel and mass had already begun. She knelt and began to pray to God to guide her and to aid her in His service. The queen noticed the strange lady who was saying her prayers earnestly and with such great devotion. She wondered who she could be, for she noticed her strange clothing and that of the other two women who accompanied her. After mass was over the queen had her summoned, and inquired who she was and from what lands she had come. She replied:

"My lady, I am from a foreign land."

"From where?" asked the queen.

"From India," she answered, "where Saint Bartholomew preached the gospel after the death of Jesus Christ."

"Are you a noble lady?" queried the queen.

"Of course I am," she replied. "I come here to live under your protection. I would like to build a hostel here, if it meets your approval, so that wandering noblemen can find shelter when they chance to come here."

"Since you had the means to, couldn't you have built it in your own country?" asked the queen.

"No," she said. "We had a greedy king who confiscated whatever his vassals owned because he needed it for the great wars he waged against his neighbors and against the powerful vassals of his own land. Therefore I had to sell all the property I owned, and I took as much wealth as I could with me and came here to live in your dominion, because of such good things that I heard of the king and you, and especially because here the law is championed and enforced."

87.   Of how the king and the lady Grima recognized each other and they did not dare to acknowledge it

"For Heaven's sake, lady," said the queen, "I am very pleased with you, and you are quite welcome. I will speak to the king on this matter and arrange for him to give you a place where you may build this hostel dedicated to the service of God. I will help you with it, and it is my wish that you hear mass and dine with me every day."

"My lady," she answered, "may God grant you a long life for what you are doing for me and for what you promise me. But I ask you as a favor to first let me complete this work that I have carried in my heart so long."

"With pleasure," responded the queen. The good lady Grima then departed for her quarters. The king came to see the queen as he was accustomed to every day, and the queen related to him what had transpired between her and the lady. The king asked her from whence came the lady and the queen told him, just as the lady had told her—that she was from the lands of India where Saint Bartholomew had preached. From the statements he heard about her, the king wondered if the lady could be his wife, and he began to smile.

"Sire, at what are you smiling?" asked the queen.

"I am smiling about the lady who has come from such distant lands," replied the king.

"Sire," said the queen, "order her given a plot of ground where she may build a hostel dedicated to the service of God."

"I would be pleased to," said the king. "Have her come in later and I will order her given whatever she wants."

The queen sent for the good lady and told her how she had spoken with the king. And while they were conversing, the king entered through the doorway. And as soon as he saw her, he recognized that she was his wife. The color drained from his face when he thought she would reveal that she was his wife. And she was uncertain about his identity, because his speech had changed and he was not speaking the language to which he was accustomed. Furthermore, he was fatter than he used to be and his beard had grown longer. And whether she recognized him or not, because she was a prudent lady she did not want to expose him for he would then be dishonored. The king asked her to choose any plot of ground in the city she desired.

"Sire," she said, "if I should find some houses ready to purchase, would you think it right for me to buy them?"

"I would be pleased," answered the king, "and I will help you do do it."

"And so will I," said the queen.

"Then, good lady, go and carry out your plans," said the king.

88. Of how the good lady built the hostel for noblemen in the city where the king and queen dwelt

The lady searched through the town for a place she might purchase, and she found an abandoned monastery that some monks had vacated in order to move to another place. She bought it from them and converted it to a hostel, a very good one, and stocked it with many articles of clothing and many serviceable beds for deserving men who might chance there. She bought a great deal of property with which to endow the hostel. And when noblemen happened to come there, they were welcomed and given whatever they needed.

The good lady spent most of the day with the queen, because the queen did not want to hear mass nor eat unless she came. And at night, she went to her hostel and passed most of the night at prayer in a chapel she had established there. She asked God to let her see something of her sons before she died and especially the one she had lost in that city by the seashore. She had no hope at all of recovering the other son whom the lioness had carried off, for she feared the lioness had devoured him.

89. Here the story ceases to tell about the king and the queen and the lady and tells of their sons

The story relates that these two small boys were reared by that townsman of Mella and his wife. They were adopted, as you have already heard, and were so well cared for and educated that no children of their age could have been better. They tilted well and were proficient at throwing the spear, and no one could do it better than they. No one could play a game of backgammon or chess, or hunt with falcons, better than they. They were very resourceful and courageous and demonstrated it when their adopted father was kidnapped by some thieves while he was hunting in the forest where the lioness had carried off the older of the two. Mounted and armed, the boys pursued the evildoers, overtook them, fell upon them, and killed them. They rescued their father and three other men who were being held by the thieves and returned with them to the city. Everyone was surprised at the daring deed undertaken by these youths and considered that older men would not have dared to attempt it. It seemed to them that this strength and the good traits they possessed came to them naturally through inheritance. And many times their adopted father was told that he should have the boys trained to be knights, for according to signs God had shown in them, they were to grow into good men.

90. Of how the burgess and his wife sent their sons to the king of Mentón in order that he should train them to be knights

The father and the mother considered it seriously and it seemed fitting to do so. They had heard that the king of Mentón was an excellent knight, a just king, mighty in arms, and a Christian in character. Although it was far, they considered it right to send their two adopted sons to this king, so that he could train them to be knights. And they sent them well supplied with horses, weapons, and a fitting escort and gave them a great deal of money. When they were ready to depart, their father, in the presence of their mother, spoke to them: "My sons, I have reared you the best that I could, and I love you both more than words can tell, and now I am sending you to a place where you will receive honor and the beginning of a better life. I beg you to remember the training I have given you, no matter what happens to you."

They told him that God would never allow them to make such a mistake, for they would always be grateful to him—their father—for the advantages they had received. They prayed to God that the day might come in which they would be able to serve him and show their gratitude. And with that, they took their leave of the good lady and departed. Their father accompanied them with a number of their escort. Bidding them farewell, they proceeded toward that city where the king of Mentón lived. They were on the road for a month, for it was so distant they they could not reach it any sooner. They entered the city and went to an inn. A certain man asked if they were hidalgos and they replied that they were.

"Friends," said the man, "then go to that hostel near the entrance to the town. A lady built it for traveling hidalgos. There you will be welcomed and they will give you whatever you need."

They set out for the hostel, which was staffed by many women. They asked them if they could be admitted there. The women answered yes, that they would be welcomed if they were hidalgos. Responding that they were, they were accepted cordially and food was prepared for them.

91. Of how the good lady recognized her sons and fainted with joy when she saw them

A maiden who worked in the hostel paid special attention to them, because many times she had heard her mistress say that she had two small sons—

one who had been carried off by a lioness and another who had gotten lost—and she observed them as they stopped at the door of a house where there was a lion, and that one had said to the other:

"Brother, you would be making a mistake to stop here, for you should have learned through experience from the lioness who carried you off in her mouth. You would have been eaten by her except for my father's dogs, which came to your aid and forced her to let you go. You still carry the marks of her teeth on your shoulders, and it's true that only a fool fails to learn from experience."

When she heard this, the maid went straight to her mistress and related how two youthful pages had come to her hostel. They were the handsomest and the best dressed she had ever seen. She believed these two were her sons whom she had lost, because when they were at the house where the lion was she had heard one say to the other that he should be careful and that he should have learned a lesson from the lioness which had carried him away in her mouth when he was small.

When she heard this, the lady did not wish to tarry, and she came to the hostel. When she saw the pages, she was very pleased with them. She had their heads and their feet bathed and then ordered food for them.[1] After they had eaten, she asked them where they were from and why they had come. They told her they were from a city named Mella in the kingdom of Falit[2] and that their father and mother, who had reared them, had sent them to the king of Mentón to become knights.

"Son," inquired the lady, "why do you say your father and your mother who reared you? Of course, I know that parents rear their sons and send them out to be educated."

"My lady," replied one of them, "the reason we tell you that they reared us is because they are not our natural parents. They obtained us only through fate; and because they had no children, they adopted us. And fate favored us, for when a lioness carried me off in her mouth into the forest—for she had seized me near a spring where our mother and our father were—the man who adopted us was at that time walking through the woods searching for deer. When his dogs saw the lioness, they pursued her and attacked her so ferociously that she had to release me. Then the burgess arrived with his company and they killed the lioness. He had one of his squires take me in front of him on his horse, and they brought me to the city. I still have the tooth marks of the lioness on my shoulders. And my brother here, I do not know through what misfortune he was lost from our father and mother. He was wandering lost through the city, and the good lady—wife of the burgess who saved me—felt sorry for my brother and had him brought to her home, and so the townsman and his wife adopted him as they did me."

1. This washing of the head and the feet was a courtesy extended to travelers in medieval Spain.
2. The kingdom of Falit is also referred to as Falac and as Fallid.

When she heard these words, the good lady dropped senseless to the floor. The pages were astounded at this, and they asked the women what could be wrong. They told them that they did not know, except that they saw their mistress dying, and that the pages' arrival had caused them this evil misfortune.

"Alas, my lady!" cried one of them. "Why has our coming caused such evil for you? God knows that we did not believe we would cause any harm to your mistress or you, nor did we come to this land to harm anyone. Now we are deeply grieved on account of what has happened to your mistress. We wish to God we had not come to this hostel, regardless of the pleasure and honor we have received from you and your mistress."

92. Of how the pages recognized the good lady as their mother, and she recognized them as her sons

At this moment, the good lady came to her senses. She opened her eyes, tired and overcome with emotion. She went to their room and ordered them well cared for so they might rest. And after they had slept, she took them aside and convinced them that she was their mother. She related to them all that had happened—how she had lost her husband and in what manner she had spent her life until that day. And our Lord, choosing to protect them from error, so that they would recognize what was right and reasonable, did not allow them to doubt anything their mother said. They immediately and completely believed that it was so, and they kissed her hands and acknowledged her to be their mother. Garfín, the older son, asked her, "My lady, have you ever heard any news of our father?"

"I have not, my sons," she answered, "but I trust in the mercy of our Lord God. He considered it right that I should recover you and Garfín whom the lioness carried off, although I had already given up hope. He, through His great compassion taking pity on us, will consider it right to have us regain your father and my husband, to be happy with him, and to forget the worries and the troubles we have endured up to now."

"May God so wish it through His mercy!" said Garfín.

At night she ordered a large and comfortable bed made for them and a sumptuous meal prepared. And she dined with them, because she still had not eaten that day because of all the emotions she had experienced.

93. Of how the king's messenger found the lady sleeping with the pages, and how he went to inform the queen

After they had eaten, they went to bed. She lay down between her sons whom she had lost and newly found; for she had so much to say to them that she could not bear to leave them. She talked so much with them, and they with her, that they became weary and slept until the third hour of the next day. The queen, not wishing to hear mass, as was her custom, until the lady arrived, sent one of her messengers for her. When the messenger reached the lady's home, he found the doors open and approached the bed where the good lady was sleeping with her sons. As soon as he saw her lying between those two youths, he was astounded at her wickedness and returned to the queen and said, "My lady, I come to you amazed at the wickedness of the lady whom you trust."

"Silence, you scoundrel!" exclaimed the queen. "Do not say such things as these. It is not possible that you in your wickedness could see any evil in that good lady."

"Truly, my lady, I did see so much in her that it concerned me because of the great trust you have in her and because you believed her to be better than she is."

"You blackguard!" responded the queen, "What did you see?"

"My lady," answered the messenger, "you ordered me to bring the lady to hear mass with you, and I found her sleeping in a huge bed between two tall and handsome youths with a quilt of marten fur over them.

"That is an absolute impossibility," replied the queen. "You are lying like a scoundrel and you are full of wickedness, you have tried to slander that good lady."

94. Of how the king learned that what the messenger had told the queen was true and how he ordered the lady to be burned on that account

At these words the king arrived. He saw the queen was very pale and sad, and he asked her why.

"Sire," she answered, "if what this scoundrel told me is true, I think I am a most unlucky woman for trusting in so wicked and sinful a person as that foreign lady who came here. And I tell you that what that scoundrel says he saw in regard to that lady, I do not believe can possibly be true."

The messenger related to the king all the facts just as he had seen them, and when the king heard them, he was greatly surprised and angered at the ones who had stained his wife's honor. And he sent his constable there and ordered him to arrest them and her and bring them to him if he found them in the manner the messenger had described. The constable went to the lady's house and he did find them, just as the messenger had told the king. The constable shouted, infuriated: "Oh, you wretch! How could you let yourself lose your reputation and the high regard you had among all the good ladies of this land? Curse the hour in which these two youths came here, for so quickly did they betray you!"

The loud voice and what the constable was saying awakened the pages and they arose hurriedly and frightened. They tried to draw their swords to defend themselves, but they were allowed no movement, for they were seized then and so was the lady herself in her dress and fur robe, just as she had lain down between them. And so she was taken before the king, and the constable told the king how he had found them. The king was beside himself with an insane rage and did not know what to say, not wanting to pry any further into her business. Although it grieved him deeply because he knew she was his wife, he ordered that she be burned alive. And before they took the lady away, the king questioned the youths.

95. Of how the king recognized those were his sons and how he then ordered the lady set free

"Friends, where are you from and what was the reason you came to this land? You have ruined this lady's reputation by your wrongdoing."

"Sire," replied Garfín, "we are from Mella, a city in the kingdom of Fallid,[1] and our foster parents, who heard that you were a good and just king, sent us here under your protection to be schooled in knighthood. And yesterday, when we arrived at that good lady's home, through the words that we spoke to each other and through that which she told us, we learned we were truly her sons and she our mother. She had lost us when we were very small children, and God through His mercy wanted us to be restored to her and her to us."

"And how did she lose you?" inquired the king.

"Sire," said Garfín, "our father and she were walking along their way, and as they were tired, they sat down to eat near a clear spring which was in a very beautiful meadow. And after they had eaten, our father put his head in our mother's lap and fell asleep while she was picking lice from his hair. And I and my brother here, being children who knew little, were playing games in the meadow. A lioness came out of the forest which was on a hill nearby and drew near to where we were playing. She seized me in her mouth and carried me into the woods. And our foster father went out to hunt with his people and his dogs, and it pleased our Lord God that as the lioness was entering the woods with me, the dogs of the burgess gave chase. The burgess with his people, following the noise the dogs were making on the tracks of the lioness, came and rescued me. And our father and this lady, our mother, as soon as they realized that they could not recover me, went to the city where that burgess lived and took lodging in an inn near the entrance to the town. Our father went to look for something to eat. And while this lady, our mother, was in the inn lamenting because she had lost me, the horse

1. See note 2, chap. 91.

strayed from the inn. She went in pursuit of it. And this brother of mine, being a child too young to know better, went after his mother, crying, and she took one street and he took another. Feeling great pity because he was wandering lost, many good men and women went calling for him but no one saw him except a lady who was on her balcony. She soothed me in her arms, because I was crying from the pain of the wounds made by the lioness. She sent one of her servants down for my brother. When we were together again, we began to embrace and kiss, overjoyed as boys are who were raised together and know each other. And the burgess and the good lady adopted us, reared us, and cared for us. They sent us to Your Excellency to become knights, and we bring you his letters in which he requests this. Therefore we ask you please, sire, through the great virtues of understanding and compassion they say God endowed you with, to call off your order to have our mother, this lady, executed, for she has done nothing for which she should die. And may it please you to make knights of us, and we will serve you in whatever you consider proper."

96. Of how the king made his sons knights and gave them lands and vassals and ordered their mother freed

When the king heard these things, he was very grateful to God and believed that He had granted him a great boon. He had recovered his sons and the order he had made in anger in regard to his wife was not carried out. He sent word ordering that she not be killed. And therefore it is said that "God protects that person whom He wishes to protect." The king accepted them as his vassals and knighted them with great merrymaking according to the custom of that land. After the king had knighted the pages, he endowed them with the income from certain of his vast lands. As they were well educated, these pages labored hard to serve the king well and faithfully and without any complaining. When they saw that strong action was needed, and without being summoned, they rode out with all their troops and went to the place where they realized their service was most needed by the king. They accomplished so many great and outstanding feats that everyone was astonished and judged them to be superior knights. All said that there had never been two such youthful knights who had accomplished so many outstanding feats of chivalry so fearlessly. They never ceased to do great deeds. When all returned from army service, some had the desire to relate to the king the great deeds of chivalry of these two youthful knights, and the king was extremely pleased to listen, and he would smile and say, "I truly believe these two young knights will turn out to be good men, for they come from a good family."

And the queen loved them very much because of their gentility and innate qualities and because of the good things she heard about them. And she honored them in every way possible. And the more they were honored and praised for their good customs, the more they persisted in doing better. The more men of good family and wisdom are praised for their fine manners and good deeds, the more they strive with humility to improve.

But the more men of low estate and ill breeding are praised—if they should chance to achieve some good—the more they are swollen with pride and refuse to be grateful to God for the grace shown them, just as Count Nason was with the king of Mentón.

97. Of how the Count Nason rebelled against the king and how the sons of the king opposed him, and from there on the knave was dubbed the Knight Amigo

The story relates that this Count Nason was a vassal of the king of Mentón. Rising in revolt with his province against the king with a force of one thousand knights consisting of his kinsmen and vassals, he made forays throughout the land, causing great havoc. Messengers close upon each others' heels hurried to the king to tell him of the damage the Count Nason was causing in his lands. And while the king was sending for his vassals to rally against the count, these two youthful knights, Garfín and Roboán, prepared themselves and their soldiers well. They had three hundred of the finest cavalry as vassals. The king had chosen them from his own armed forces when he had given Garfín and Roboán the land-rents. He presented the knights to them, and among them was the knave who accompanied the king to the army of Mentón when he took leave of the hermit. The knave had been successful and had accomplished many daring deeds of chivalry, and for that reason the king considered him ready for knighthood and had endowed him with property and had arranged a good marriage for him. He was now called the Knight Amigo.

They set forth and advanced against Count Nason, so that when they had traveled one day's journey into his province, and the sun having set, they saw huge fires in the field where Count Nason was camping with his five hundred knights. And those who were traveling in the advance guard halted until the rest arrived and they formed into one large squadron. Roboán, the younger brother, said:

"Friends, it seems to me by the number of fires that appear there, there may be a great number of the enemy. I believe that God will aid us against them, for they are wrong and we are right. The king, our sovereign, did many favors for them and never did anything detrimental to them, and we know the truth through our lord the king, and they lie. If my brother Garfín approves, I will take the advance guard, and we will conquer them tonight through God's grace."

98. Of how Garfín and Roboán sent the Knight Amigo to spy on Count Nason's army

The Knight Amigo, who was very bold, said: "Roboán, sir, you are very young, and you have not thoroughly been tested, although God has favored you in feats of arms when the occasion arose. Therefore you ought not to attempt all deeds through courage alone. We are certain you are so daring that you would not hesitate to attack a larger force. However, you ought to plan in what way you should attack that would be more in your favor and your honor. If you approve, I will go there tonight to find out how many they are, and through which area you may have the best entrance. I have a good and swift horse, and if need arises, I will come very quickly to give you the information."

Garfín and all the rest agreed to the Knight Amigo's counsel, although it troubled Roboán that they were not going to attack then. The Knight Amigo then departed after he had eaten supper and hastened to the count's army as fast as he could, so that at times he was inside the picket lines. He walked ten times throughout the camp that night, estimating how many there were and which would be the best way to penetrate their lines. And as he was about the leave the enemy forces and head for his own lines, he heard a horn blow three times in the count's tent. This puzzled him, and he waited so that he might learn why the horn had sounded, and he saw the grooms get up to saddle the horses and put armor on them. Meanwhile he was walking among the patrols as if he were one of them, and heard a groom calling to another one, cursing him: "Get up, you son of a whore, and saddle and armor your master's horse."

"I certainly will not do it," retorted the other, "rather I want to sleep and rest because our master is not one of the one hundred fifty knights chosen to return to the camp this morning." And the Knight Amigo was well pleased when he heard this and said to himself, "Blessed be the name of God, for we have conquered one hundred fifty knights of this army without striking a blow and without injury!"

So he waited until those one hundred fifty knights set forth on their journey, and he followed the path they were traveling. And their course brought them to within a league of where Garfín and Roboán were with their troops; and when the knight saw that they were proceeding along the road where they had to go, he headed for his own troops. And when he was about a thousand paces from the enemy, his horse began to whinny very loudly at being separated from the others. And the one hundred fifty knights were puzzled when they heard the horse whinny, and some said that it was the king's troops, and others said that it was some horse that had broken away from the army and was straying through the fields. A bold knight among them, named Gamel, said that if they wanted him to, he would investigate the straying horse and meet them in the morning where they were going. They considered that a good idea. The knight headed directly toward the sound of the horse, and when he was near him, his horse began to neigh, and the night was so dark they were unable to see each other. Thinking there were many people after him, the Knight Amigo began to ride as fast as he could. The Knight Gamel believed that the horse was loose and began to call and whistle according to the custom of that land. Thinking it was a phantom trying to scare him, the Knight Amigo waited and heard only the thunder of one horse. He placed his lance under his armpit and charged the other knight, so that he toppled him from his horse, badly wounded. He took his horse and headed for his own troops, and he guessed that he must be one of the one hundred fifty. When he reached his own troops, they asked him how he was, and he told them he had defeated one of the one hundred fifty knights that had separated from the main part of the army. The knight lay wounded nearby, and they could send for him if they wanted to learn all the truth about the count's army. However, he related to them what had happened and how those knights were coming on the run only a league from them, and that only three hundred fifty knights or so were with the count.

99. Of how Count Nason was defeated and how Garfin took him prisoner

They held a council to determine whether they should attack the force of one hundred fifty knights first or the three hundred fifty. Some argued that it would be better to go against those who were separate from the main force and prevent their ravaging the land and not attack the three hundred fifty who were with the count, for he was a great fighter and very courageous. And the others said it would be better to go to the count's campground; and Roboán especially insisted on this, saying that if they should destroy the source, little strength would remain with the rest. They agreed with Roboán and mounted and proceeded toward the count's army. They found the wounded knight and asked him who had wounded him. He answered that an unknown knight had done so and if he were healthy and recognized him, he would roundly curse him because he had wounded him without a challenge first. They asked him how many troops the count had with him, and he told them approximately three hundred fifty plus the one hundred fifty he had sent on a raid.

"As a matter of fact," said the Knight Amigo, "one hundred fifty less one."

"True enough," agreed the Knight Gamel.

Just then the horse of the Knight Amigo neighed and he said, "Aha, sir knight, I believe that you are the one who wounded me."

The Knight Amigo responded: "Why did you come whistling after my horse, which you never saw nor knew of? I can truly say that when I heard the noise of your horse coming after me and you were whistling to my horse as if you had raised him, I really wondered what it could be. I was very frightened, believing that it was the devil who was trying to frighten me, for the night was so dark I could not recognize you. I say to you that if I wounded you, I did it more through fear than valor, and I cannot give you greater apology than this."

"Of course," answered the Knight Gamel, "you have no reason to make me any apology, because I was to blame in this matter. But if I had been wise, I would not have left my people, who were all selected for the mission. But 'whoever is sick in the head is a long time getting cured.' And this is not the first foolish trick that I have committed that turned out to my disadvantage."

"Sir knight," said Roboán, "are the troops with whom you were traveling going to be raiding through the king's land very long?"

"Two days," responded the knight, "and no more, and then they are going to return to the count."

"Truly, friend," declared Roboán, "God's favoring us, for these knights cannot be of any help to their master, and if God favors us tonight and tomorrow, we will have put an end to this affair and the count."

And as they were preparing to depart, the Knight Gamel said:

"Oh friends, if God should give you victory, I beg you not to leave me here to die, for I am very badly wounded. Therefore I say 'if God should give you victory,' for I am sure that if you are defeated, each one of you will be looking out for himself in escaping or defending himself."

"Why do you think that we will be defeated in this battle?" asked Roboán. "Only God knows it," answered the knight, "because after you are met on the battlefield, the decision will be God's"

"I am sure if the decision is up to God, in my opinion, God will be on our side," stated Roboán.

"How do you know that?" asked the knight.

Roboán answered: "I will tell you. You know that the count has done great wrong to the king and the king none to him, and the count is a hypocrite, and we who support the king hold to the truth."

"Then," said the knight, "if it is as you say, go in the name of God, and the truth will aid you."

The Knight Amigo dismounted and stripped him of his armor, for it was hurting him. He bandaged the wound as best he could and promised to come back for him if God gave him the time to do it. He took his weapons and armed one of his squires and had him mount the knight's horse, and they went in pursuit of the others. When they overtook them, the Knight Amigo spoke to them: "You are to proceed through here, and it is necessary to follow me closely, and when I shout 'Attack them,' head full speed for the tents, for the count is there. They have not posted any pickets for they are in their own land and suspect nothing. I shall place you so close to them that when I shout, you will fall upon them immediately."

When they topped a small hill and saw the count with his troops, the Knight Amigo shouted, "Attack, knights, for now is the time!"

Garfín and Roboán were in charge of over three hundred noble squires whom they placed before them, and they proceeded as fast as they could for the headquarters of the count. They began to attack and to kill whomever they found before them. When they reached the tents of the count, they found he was only dressed in a ganbax.[1] He held his shield before his chest and placed himself at the door of the tent. Several squires were coming his way, but they were unable to stand successfully against the others; so they were attacked, overcome, and slain. As soon as the Count Nason saw he was abandoned and that not a single knight of his army had rallied to him, he believed all were dead or wounded. He turned and fled through the flaps of his tent with his shield. He went out the other side where there were many tents and supply tents adjoining his. He found his men dead, wounded, and crippled in the tents. He did not find any of his men who could accompany him, except a wounded knight who followed him advising him to save himself, for all his men were wounded or dead. As the count and his knight were going down a ravine, a squire who was with his lord Garfín espied them and seeing that the count was badly wounded, said, "Sir, there goes the count on foot with but a single companion."

Garfín, who was searching for the count, heard him and spurred his horse in pursuit of him.

On reaching the count, he said, "Prisoner or dead, whichever you want."

"And who are you who wants me to be your prisoner?" asked the count.

"I am a knight whom you see," replied Garfín.

"And on account of your being a knight," said the count, "you think it right that I be your prisoner? There are many men who are not knights through their family line, but through their good training and through services they render their lords. If you are not the son of a king, or from a more noble family than I, I say to you that I do not care to be your prisoner."

"By heaven," said Garfín, "it would be better for you to be my prisoner than to die here."

"In truth," replied the count, "it would be better to die honorably than to live dishonored."

"Well, cover yourself with that shield," said Garfín, "for I am going to free you from this problem if I can."

1. A *ganbax* was a padded garment worn underneath armor.

"You do right to say 'if you can'; because saying and doing are two different things," replied the count. He drew his sword and covered himself with his shield, and Garfín let him advance and gave him a great blow with his lance on his shield, so that he pierced the shield and broke his lance, but he did the count no harm; for the count had his arm drawn away from his body. And the count swung his sword and struck Garfín's horse a great blow on the back. so that the horse was paralyzed. When Garfín saw this, he dismounted, drew his sword, and assailed the count. Striking a mighty blow, he sliced off the outer rim of his shield. The count struck back at Garfín in such a manner that he split his shield from top to bottom, cutting him slightly on the arm.

"How small the advantage is for you, even though you are wearing armor and I am not!" exclaimed the count.

"Of course," said Garfín, "you have forsworn the truth. How great a difference between the truth and a lie, for you hold to falseness and I to the truth."

"And how is that?" asked the count.

"In truth," replied Garfín, "you failed to be loyal to the king of Mentón, who is my lord, and you were untrue to the service you owed him, since you were his vassal. You did not sever your relation with him and he did not desert you. You raided throughout his land, and therefore you will die for being treacherous and disloyal."

"You lie in your teeth! because I sent another to take leave of the king and to kiss his hands on my behalf," the count retorted.

"Certainly," said Garfín, "that is no excuse for an honorable knight to take his leave and to raid throughout the land without his lord giving him a reason why. I believe that you would do well to give yourself up as my prisoner, and I will take you to the king and ask him to have mercy on you."

"I promise you, sir knight," said the count, "that you will not take me a prisoner this time, unless you grow considerably stronger."

"Why do you take me to be so fainthearted?" asked Garfín. "I trust in the mercy of God that you will yet know my strength before you depart here."

They charged each other, wielding their swords, for they were skilled in swordplay, and they struck each other great blows on their shields, breaking them to pieces. Count Nason thrust with his dagger and gave Garfín a great gash on the cheek and said to him:

"Surely, sir knight, it would have been better for you to have been satisfied with the booty God gave you on the battlefield, and not to have tried for everything. Therefore it is said, 'Whoever wants everything, loses everything.'"

"Do you believe yourself to be free of this duel with me because of what you have done to me? God would not want the devil, who is a supporter of treachery, to overcome one who abides by the truth."

"Certainly," said the count, "you know as much as is necessary and you should see that if you pursue me zealously you will not escape with just this wound you carry. Therefore it is said, 'Follow the wolf, but not into the thickets.' I consider it would be better for you and more to your advantage to return to your own troops and let me go in peace."

The count raised the arm holding his sword, and Garfín in great anger struck a great blow that cut through the sleeve of his ganbax, severing his hand, so that the hand holding his sword fell to the earth. And so strongly did Garfín strike that blow that he sliced a great piece from his haunch to his toes, so that the count was unable to stand and fell to the ground.

"Ha, count," asked Garfín, "would it not have been better for you to go willingly as my prisoner—and healthy—than to go unwillingly, handless and lame?"

"Unwillingly it may be," replied the count, "for someone strengthened your arm, for surely you are not man enough to conquer me or to manhandle me so."

"Haven't you given up hope yet?" asked Garfín. "Surely this lack of faith of yours has brought you to this plight."

While they were thus involved, Roboán and all the other soldiers, not knowing whether he was dead or alive, were searching for Garfín. They did not know what to do and were very worried. They were not disposed to return with the booty that God had given them, and they were not disposed to remain. They believed the count, who was gone, might perhaps fall upon them with many troops.

Garfín, seeing that he could not take the count from that valley and back to his army, climbed a hill where all his troops were visible and began to sound a horn he carried. When Roboán heard it, he said to the others: "Surely that is Garfín. I know him by the way he blows the horn. Let us go to him, for he is afoot."

An aged knight said to him, "Roboán, sir, you stay here with these troops, and about a hundred of us knights will go there and find out what is going on."

Roboán agreed to this. And when they reached Garfín, they recognized him and dismounted. They asked him where his horse was, and he told them that it had died, so that no one could aid it, that the count was wounded in that valley, and that they should fetch him and escort him to the king. Garfín rode on a horse they furnished him. The others accompanied him to the valley, where the count lay very weak, for he had lost a great deal of blood. They put him on a horse and took him back to the army. When Roboán and the others saw they were bringing the count as a prisoner, they were grateful to God and very happy and pleased to see Garfín alive, although he was badly wounded on the cheek and his face was swollen. However, they doctored him well, so that he would be cured in a few days, and they bandaged the wounds of the count. At midnight they mounted and went to the king with all the booty that God had given them. They gave the horses and weapons they had captured to the noble squires who had accompanied them and knighted them. From the three hundred they began with, their number had increased to five hundred fifty; and on account of this generosity of Garfín and Roboán to these noble squires, all the other squires in the land came to them, and not without reason. They believed that what Garfín and Roboán had done for their squires in return for the service they had received, so they would do for them for the services they might render them. Surely lords should strive to reward those who deserve it, for then others will endeavor, with this hope, always to serve and do their best.

As they were making their way along the road, they encountered those one hundred fifty knights of the count, who had been ravaging the land of the king. They were bringing a vast booty of animals and cattle, and were easily routed, made prisoner, or killed. Roboán's men took the booty from them and returned it to the land of the king. They had it proclaimed through all the land that each one should come to claim what was his. They did not desire to retain anything for themselves, being the kind of people they were. They had no wish to take something that belonged to another, as some do, for if the enemy is carrying away stolen property of the country and they are pursued and the booty taken from them, the pursuers say that it ought to be theirs. Surely this is unreasonable, since they are from one territory and one city and ought to be of one heart in the service of their lord, guarding and protecting each other so that none receives harm. And if some enemy should take from them what is theirs, they ought to aid one another, and with or without such aid they should recover it if they can. Otherwise it could be said of them what a certain man said to his companion, about the wolf that carried away his sheep.

His companion went in pursuit of the wolf and overtook him, then took the sheep and devoured it. When the good man saw his companion, he said to him: "Friend, they told me that you went in pursuit of the wolf that carried off my sheep. Tell me what you did with him."

"I will tell you," he replied, "I went with my dogs in pursuit of the wolf and we took it away from him."

"By Heaven, friend, I am very pleased and very grateful to you. And where is the sheep?" asked the good man.

"We ate it," said his friend.

"You ate it!" exclaimed the good man; "surely, friend, you and the wolf are all the same to me, for I was robbed by you the same as by the wolf."

And those who retrieve booty from the nation's enemies are as much robbers as the enemies, if they do not return the booty to its rightful owners. However, in some places it is the custom of the land to keep the booty recovered from the enemy who took it, because they say when the enemy carries it away and keeps it overnight, it no longer belongs to its original owner and has become the property of the enemy who captured it, and so they consider they should retain the booty. Certainly it is not lawful, but lords agree that it should be thus, because men will pursue an enemy more zealously when they believe they will profit thereby. They consider it better for their own people to take advantage of it than for the enemy to enjoy having it. And this is so through lack of virtue in men who are not prone to protect each other as they should. Since they are of one country and one dominion it is only right that they should protect and defend each other— their persons as well as their properties. Therefore Garfín and Roboán, as good and unselfish knights trying to set a good example, had the booty given back to its rightful owners and afterward went directly to see the king.

100. Of how the Knight Amigo arrived with the message from Count Nason to his lord the king

The king had already gone with most of his army and was camped in very beautiful meadowlands called the Valley of Paradise. He was concerned about Garfín and Roboán, who had not accompanied him, and he inquired anxiously about them. He did not find anyone who could tell him anything about them, except that they told him it had been two weeks since they had sallied forth with all their troops from the city where they were staying and they did not know where Garfín and Roboán were. Fearing that they had run into some problem, the king was very worried and unable to rest or to calm himself. And surely, just as it worried the king because they were not there with him, so did it worry all those in the army, because they esteemed them for being such fine knights, well mannered, and proven in battle. And at this juncture, one of Roboán's knights entered the king's tents. This was the Knight Amigo whom the king had knighted and had assigned to Roboán as a vassal. He went and knelt before the king. He kissed his hand and said to him:

"Sire, Garfín and Roboán, your loyal vassals, sent me to kiss your hands and to commend themselves to your favor. They send word to ask you as a favor to remain here, for tomorrow morning, if God is willing, they will be here with you and will tell you some very good news, which you will hear with great pleasure."

"O Knight Amigo!" exclaimed the king, "by the faith that you owe me, tell me if they are alive and well."

"Of course," answered the Knight Amigo, "I tell you, sir, they are alive."

"But are they well?" asked the king.

The Knight Amigo did not want to answer, because his lord Roboán had forbidden him to tell that his brother Garfín was wounded or that they were bringing the count prisoner, but only to tell him they would be with him the next morning. The king insisted that the Knight Amigo should tell him if they were well, and the Knight Amigo told him:

"Sire, do not insist, because I will not tell you. I was forbidden to; but in order to set your heart at ease, I want you to know that they walk and ride as upright as you."

"And you are most welcome!" exclaimed the king.

101. Of how Garfín and Roboán reached the king, accompanied by Count Nason, a prisoner and badly wounded

The next morning Garfín and Roboán reached the king together with all their troops, except for fifty knights they left to escort the count prisoner. They followed them about one mile and no more, always having them in sight, for if some unforeseen attack should befall, they could then come to their aid. When they reached the king, they knelt before him and kissed his hands. The king arose and greeted them effusively, as those whom he loved sincerely. Looking at Garfín, he saw the bandage he was wearing on his right cheek over his battle wound, and the king said to him:

"Garfín, what is that? Were you wounded on the face?"

"Sire," Garfín replied, "no, it is only a tumor that has been there since birth."

"Certainly," answered the king, "such a large tumor could not have been in such a place at birth. May the one who did it to you get such a lump!"

"Sire," said Roboán, "I believe you are a fortune-teller, for so did it happen to the one who did it, and he couldn't possibly have a larger swelling or be in worse condition than he is now."

"Surely it was some recklessness Garfín started," said the king.

"It was not recklessness," said Roboán, "but a mighty deed."

"And how was that?" asked the king.

"Sire," said Garfín, "let us leave this now, because if nothing is ventured, nothing is gained. It is proper for young knights to prove themselves in some matter of chivalry, because that is how they obtain knighthood. Surely no one can be said to be a knight who hasn't first proved himself on the field of battle."

"That is true if he learns from it," said the king.

"And so I understand it," replied Garfín. And at this point the king remained quiet and ceased to ask any more questions on the matter.

"Sire," said Garfín, "Roboán and I, together with these good knights—the vassals that you gave me—and with your good fortune and the favor of our Lord God, bring Count Nason here a prisoner for you; however, he is wounded."

"And who wounded him?" inquired the king.

"His audacity, his misfortune, and his inherent treachery," answered Garfín.

"By Heaven, Garfín and Roboán," exclaimed the king, "you bring me an excellent gift, and I am grateful. Around here we shall take all the fortresses he owned, for be has no son; and may God give him none, for we would take that hope from him." And he ordered the count brought before him. They had him brought in and seated on a bench. He leaned against some cushions for he was unable to stand. When the king saw him without his hand, and all the toes of one foot severed, and wounded very badly in the hip, he said to him: "Count, I don't believe that you will threaten me with that right hand of yours henceforth."

"Truly," answered the count, "nor with the left hand either, for I am wounded all over."

"Blessed be the name of God, for He gives to each his just deserts," replied the king.

"Count," said the king, "the one who crippled you was taking plenty of time, for he wounded you all over your body."

"Sire, it was only one blow that caused what you see," replied the count.

"Indeed?" said the king. "I believe the sword was of hard steel and the knight was very strong and quick, for he struck such a terrible stroke. Tell me, count, who wounded you?"

"Sire," answered the count, "that young knight near you at your feet, the one they call Garfín."

"By Heaven, his youth has been well spent, and I believe that he will continue to do deeds such as these from now on; and may God guide him through His grace," said the king.

"So be it," said Roboán.

"Truly," said the count, "it did not go well with me, and I regret that he was so fortunate."

"Count," said the king, "I know well that it grieves you, but you will admit his superiority this time."

"Of course," said the count, "and even forever, for he left me in such a condition that I could not hinder him in anything."

All present marveled at that mighty blow. They believed that Garfín among all the others would develop into a great and powerful knight, for he was yet a youth and his beard was scarcely beginning to show.

The next morning the king held a council with all the counts and noblemen who were present to decide whether he should go with his army to take possession of the count's land or should send some one in his stead. Those not desiring to take over the count's land so hastily advised him to remain and to send those whom he thought best. The others, desiring to serve the king and understanding that the deed would be expedited more easily by the king, advised him to go there in person. Considering the advice good, he set out with all his army for the count's land.

102. Of how a nephew of Count Nason prepared himself with his people against the king of Mentón, his lord

However, a nephew of the Count Nason, the son of his sister, an excellent knight at arms, was left by the count in command of five hundred knights. Together with the three hundred who fled from the campgrounds of the count when he was defeated and those who were transporting the booty from the land of the king, there were in all over eight hundred knights gathered together. They swore to stand together to defend the count's land. A company of the king's cavalry advanced into the count's land, raiding and burning and destroying everything they encountered. The nephew of the count, with four hundred knights, was in a nearby town. He saw great fires caused by burning farm houses and the havoc the enemy had wreaked throughout the land. He consulted with his knights and said:

"Friends, now you see the damage those troops of the king are causing throughout the land. I believe the first place they will come to fight will be where we stand. After careful consideration, my decision is to seek them out and let us leave these noble squires and our infantry, together with the local citizens, to guard the town. And perhaps we will encounter some of the king's company and it will be their bad fortune that we shall defeat them, so that they will not have the audacity to invade here as they so audaciously invaded the country."

The knights answered that he should command as he saw fit, for they were all ready to go where he wanted and to avenge the count's honor, since it would be better for them to die fighting on the battlefield than to be held under siege. The count's nephew commanded that the next morning they should all proceed under arms from the town, and so they did.

103. Of how Roboán asked his lord the king to let him lead a cavalry raid

Garfín and Roboán were proceeding along the road with the king, discussing many things, and the king was questioning them about their role in the defeat of the count. When they told him what had happened to them, he was greatly pleased. He was instructing them and advising them in many ways as to how they should behave when they happened to be in some battle in the field. They should not let their enemies attack them first, rather they should attack the enemy. The fear the enemy tried to instill in them, they should instill in the enemy, for certainly those being attacked are more afraid than the attackers, who charge fiercely and strongly against them. When Roboán heard the king say these things, he considered it a special favor to him. He went to kiss his hands and said to him:

"Sire, neither Garfín nor I will be able to repay you for the many favors you have done us and are doing for us every day, which is more than you do for anyone of your dominion because you not only command us as lord, but you instruct us as a father does his sons."

The king answered very happily: "Roboán, my friend, you are doing well in what you are doing, and I believe you will do even better. I trust in God that you will recognize that I love you truly as a father does his sons. And may God grant me no honor in this world if I do not also desire it for you."

Garfín and Roboán fell at his feet and kissed his hands many times, declaring that he was doing them a great and very special favor in speaking such noble and heartfelt words to them. They asked him as a favor to allow them to accompany the cavalry advance guard in order to see some action.

"Garfín," said the king, "I don't want you to go, for you are still not well from your wound."

"Sire," replied Garfín, "I do not have any wound that would prevent me from accomplishing a deed of valor."

"Garfín," said Roboán, "the king says correctly that you should rest and get well, for a great fire springs from a small spark if a man is not careful. And although that wound of yours may not be large, if you do not treat it as well as you can, you may find yourself in great danger. Moreover if you think it right, I will accompany your troops and mine together with the advance guard to win some great feat of arms."

"And what feat?" asked the king.

"Sire," answered Roboán, "I could not win a greater honor than my brother Garfín has won, for he won it at great glory and great cost to himself. By that feat, men will know and recognize the great deed that he performed, asking about it, and they will easily see and understand that he did not win it by fleeing."

104. Of how Roboán defeated the nephew of Count Nason and split him down to his eyes with one blow

The king was very pleased with what he heard and he said to him: "My brave son, may God give you His blessing and I do give you mine. Go in God's name, and I trust in His mercy that you will accomplish successfully all you wish."

Roboán rode forth and took his brother's troops. Together with his, there were three hundred fifty knights. They invaded the land of the count, being careful to protect the farmers in every way from damage and from harm as much as they could. They took only what they needed to eat. Roboán had so ordered it, realizing that the farmers had no blame for the malfeasance of the count. Truly Roboán was always close to God in doing the best he could, and God showed He was close to him in all his deeds, so that one morning, as they were leaving a little wooded area, they saw the nephew of the count approaching with four hundred men on horseback; however, they were at a distance of approximately six miles.

"Friends," said Roboán, "shall we hear mass on this field before those knights arrive? In all our acts we should keep God before us."

"Sir," said a chaplain, "you will be able to hear it easily, for I will hold a private mass for you."

Then the altar was prepared in the field quickly and the chaplain dressed in his robes over his own clothing. He performed the mass well, for he was a good and virtuous man.

When they had heard mass, they saw the other knights approaching, who hesitated and came to a halt. Roboán spoke:

"Friends, fears are equally shared, so it seems to me. Let us attack them, for only five days ago I was instructed that the enemy would instill fear in us by attacking. We should instead put fear into them by attacking savagely and without hesitation."

The knights, being men of great strength and having the desire to do well, agreed that he had spoken sense. So they did as he said and increased their pace until they approached the enemy. Then Roboán ordered them forward and they fell upon them fiercely. The enemy considered this a good move and in the manner of good knights wheeled about, and the armies fell to striking at one another. There you can see many knights thrown to the ground and riderless horses galloping about the battlefield.

And at the first blows, lances on both sides were shattered. They drew their swords. The press of battle was so great and so heavily were they engaged that none could easily recognize another, except when someone called out on his own behalf. Roboán performed in that battle in the manner befitting a noble and mighty knight, shouting, "Mentón for our lord the king," and the enemy were shouting, "Hold for Count Nason!" But whoever encountered Roboán had no need for a surgeon—for by then he was dropping to the ground either dead or badly wounded. Roboán was dealing such mighty and fearsome blows with his sword that he struck one knight a blow on top of his helmet and split his head in half. Half his head fell on his shoulder and the other half continued erect, and thus he rode among the troops for a long time, so that those who saw him were astonished. They were amazed as such a mighty and strange blow. He refused to fall from his horse and rode upright, holding his sword in his hand and spurring his horse among them.

Roboán saw the nephew of the count and made his way toward him, saying, "Nephew of a scoundrel, defend yourself, for I am coming for you. And you can be sure the sins of your uncle the count are going to fall on you."

"You lie," said the count's nephew, "for I am not the nephew of a scoundrel. There was never a better knight in all the kingdom of Mentón than he."

Then they charged against one another and struck each other mighty blows with their swords. However, they were unable to penetrate the superlative armor they were wearing. Then they made another turn and charged each other and struck powerful blows. The nephew of the count wounded Roboán with his dagger on the point of his chin and almost made him lose his teeth. Roboán struck the nephew of the count a slanting blow with his sword through the visor of his helmet. He cut through the helmet-grid. His sword penetrated into his face and gouged out both his eyes. So deep and so bad was the wound that he could not stay on his horse and fell to earth. Afterward, Roboán turned to his own troops to encourage them, saying, "Strike them, for the nephew of the count is dead."

Those on the count's side who heard this retreated from the battlefield and dispersed, and so the battlefield remained in the control of Roboán and his troops. No more than fifty of the count's men escaped and all the others were dead or prisoner. However, one hundred fifty knights of Roboán's company were dead or badly wounded. On both sides they fought like gallant knights who have the zeal to conquer each other.

105. Of how the Knight Amigo reached the king of Mentón with the message of how Roboán had won the battle

Then Roboán ordered the knights on his side who were wounded to be treated and their wounds examined, and to be placed on their horses. Then he returned to where the count's nephew was lying and ordered him disarmed. They found that his eyes were lacerated from the wound Roboán had given him. They put him on a horse and then proceeded on their way to the king. The Knight Amigo, although he was wounded with two sword cuts, went in advance to the king with the news. When he related it to him, the king called together the men of his army and told them:

"Friends, since Garfín brought us incomplete news, Roboán brings us what was missing. This is the nephew of the count who organized all his people and thought he could stand and defend the land against us. However, both his eyes are hurt, as the Knight Amigo will tell you."

The king noticed that the Knight Amigo had been wounded twice and said to him:

"Knight Amigo, I believe you found some one who christened you."

"Certainly, sire," responded the Knight Amigo, "we did find some one. King Arthur wasn't in greater trouble or in greater danger with Paul the Cat[1] than we found ourselves in with those accursed troops; for when we scratched them, they scratched us so fiercely that we could scarcely endure it. You may well believe, sire, that for a little while the battle was in doubt for our side. So fiercely did they press us that on our side there were up to one hundred fifty knights dead or wounded."

"And what about the other side?" asked the king.

"Truly, sire," replied the Knight Amigo, "there remain no more than fifty of the original four hundred knights. All the rest are dead or prisoners."

"In truth," said the king, "where so many were killed, the battle must have been fierce."

"You may believe, sire," said the Knight Amigo, "that being present at the hottest point of fighting in that battle does not sit well with me."

"Oh! Knight Amigo," exclaimed Garfín, "does my brother Roboán return in good health?"

"He is surely as healthy as you," he replied.

"What! is he already as marked as I am?" asked Garfín.

"Truly he is," said the Knight Amigo.

"Where does he have the wound?" asked Garfín.

"Below his mouth," replied the Knight Amigo, "you may believe me, if it were not for the gorget[2] he was wearing high, he might have lost his teeth."

"And who wounded him?" asked Garfín.

"The nephew of the count wounded him with his dagger," answered the Knight Amigo.

"These soldiers take great pride in attacking with the dagger," said Garfín. "And Roboán, did he wound the nephew of the count?"

"By Heaven, said the Knight Amigo, "he wounded him with a mighty stroke. He struck him with a sword-thrust over the grid of his helmet in a crosswise manner and thrust his sword into his face and slashed both his eyes. And he also struck another knight an odd stroke. He struck with his sword on top of his helmet and split his helmet in two with half his head falling to his shoulder and the other half staying upright. And thus he made his way among us on the battlefield for a long while staying upright in the saddle and refusing to fall from his horse. Everyone fled before him as from a phantom."

---

1. The Spanish phrase here is *el Gato Paul* which I have translated as "Paul the Cat." *Gato* in Spanish could also mean a "caitiff" or a person of the lower classes or of the criminal element, such as a petty thief, pickpocket, or robber. I cannot find the relationship to King Arthur.

2. A *gorget* was a high linen collar or a piece of armor to protect the throat.

"Let him be," said the king, "for he has killed his first man, and I believe that he will not hesitate from here on out to fight again when the occasion arises. Truly, I believe he will be a fine man and a noble knight-at-arms."

106. Of how Roboán reached the king with his prisoner, accompanied by the others who were escorting the prisoners and wounded

And while they were talking, Roboán appeared with all his troops. The king mounted his horse and accompanied by the stalwart men went forth to greet him. He was welcomed heartily by the king and all the others. When the king saw a great number of the troops of his company with their heads bandaged and others with their ribs bandaged, he was deeply moved, but smiling he said to Roboán to console him, "Roboán, where did you find a bishop to confirm[1] your troops for you so quickly?"

"Truly, sire," said Roboán, "they can be said to be bishops, for each soldier was his own bishop."

"And what did they confirm them with?" asked the king; "Did they carry their own baptismal oil and holy water with them?"

"They carry their own stoles around their necks and their own maniples[2] in their fists, and their own blood; however, sire, we got even with them, we gave as good as we got."

The king said, "But the bishop who confirmed you did not touch you on the forehead. I believe he was an old tired man and could not raise his hand high and so struck you on the chin, or he was very arrogant and had no shame, for your chin was uncovered." And the king said this because Roboán had no sign of a beard.

"Surely, sire," answered Roboán, "what was done was because neither was bashful or had fear of the other."

"And was there anyone who repaid him for the dishonor he showed you?" asked the king.

"Yes," replied Roboán.

"And who was it?" asked the king.

"The treachery that lived in him," said Roboán.

"Truly he is the vilest man in the world. There is no need for such a person to appear in the plaza because there are no logical words with which he can be defended. However, bring him in and we shall see if he wants to present an argument in his defense. A good judge ought not to rule unless he hears both sides."

1. The Spanish verb *crismar* means "to christen" or "to confirm," but it also has the colloquial meaning "to split someone's head."

2. The Spanish word *manípulo* means a maniple carried by a priest, but it also refers in a military sense to a division of soldiers.

Then they brought in the nephew of the count, on horseback and his face completely exposed. He arrived before the king, and his face was so disfigured by that fearsome blow across his eyes, that it was horrible to look upon.

However, the king said, "Poor devil of a nephew! I believe that henceforth you'll not be much of a lookout."[3]

"I will tell you; the blow split me all the way to my ears, and so I have lost my sight and my hearing."

"It must have been a good bishop who gave you such a blow. I truly believe whoever confirmed you did not wish you well."

"Of course," he said, "I was under no deception, for I would have done the same thing to him; and damned be the bishop's hand which is so heavy that it deafens and maims the one who is being confirmed."

And they all began to laugh.

"In truth," said the nephew of the count, "all of you may laugh, but it's no laughing matter to me, and in such suffering one may take pleasure if it pleases him."

And the king said, "I would still say this even if I were your prisoner."

And they sent for the count to come see his nephew, and he was brought there.

107. Of the things that Count Nason and his nephew said to each other in the presence of the king and all the knights of the court

When the count saw his nephew with his lacerated face, his sorrow overwhelmed him and he fell senseless to the floor. When they lifted him to his feet, he said, "Alas, my nephew! How did you merit this terrible thing happening to you?"

And he answered, "Truly sons are made to suffer for the sins of their fathers and so I suffered for your sins."

"That's not so," said the count. "You are the one who urged me into this undertaking."

"In truth," his nephew answered, "I could not dissuade you and I was forced to follow wherever you cared to lead. You had the power over me and not I over you. The truth is that you did not fear anything because of your overweening arrogance. You made yourself feared and you did not care to follow any one else's advice. And remember that at the door of your castle on your return, and before the gates of the town in the presence of all your relatives and your vassals, you stated arrogantly that you would not leave the

3. The Spanish word *atalaya* is used here. It means a "lookout post or watch tower." It is a pun referring to the nephew's eyes being wounded.

king any place in the world where he could escape and that you would expel him from the kingdom."

"Now," the king declared, "we have heard enough. It really seems the parable is true that says, 'When thieves fall out, honest men profit.' And certainly enough has been said on each side for a good judge to make a decision."

"Count, order the towns and the castles of the county given over to me," said the king.

"Sire," replied the count, "the castles as well as the towns all pledged allegiance to my nephew here."

"Of course it is true," said the nephew of the count; "but with such a proviso that if you should return here upset or pleased, healthy or sick, dead or alive, with few men or with many, they would welcome you back, and if they did this for you, they would be free of the pledge they had made me. And therefore, count, you are the one who can give the towns and castles back to the king."

"Indeed," exclaimed the king to the count, "is what your nephew says true?"

"Sire," replied the count, "what he says is so. But sire, why would they return the towns and castles to me, since they can see that I am not free but held under duress?"

"Count," said the king, "you are mistaken in all the rest, for you should know that those who pledge allegiance to a traitor are not bound by their pledge."

"They pledged it to a loyal master," answered the count.

"Yes," the king stated, "and while his loyalty lasted, they were obligated to keep their pledge; but as soon as he became a traitor, they were given their release by God and by men from the pledge they made to him. They are not obligated to keep their pledge to him in any manner, as he is not the peer of any other man, no matter how low that man's station may be. They may renounce him in any trial that they may wish to enter with him by lawsuit or by combat. And those who pledge allegiance to a traitor knowingly, aware that he is a traitor, or hearing of it and knowing he has done nothing to exonerate himself, should avoid him as a traitor or one branded as a traitor. Since he was not cleared of his treachery and they pledged homage to him, they are guilty of the sin of treachery just as the one who committed it."

"And it is judged similarly, if some one talks with or has dealings knowingly with a known excommunicated person in contempt of the sentence of excommunication, that he is excommunicated just as the other is. And therefore the one who condones treason is guilty of treason just as the one who commits it, since he has the power to prevent it and does not. The evildoers and their consorts equally deserve punishment, especially since they willingly conspire with the traitor and aid him in his treachery. Therefore it is rightly said, "Oh, how dearly is hell purchased" for the one who buys hell exchanges many good things for the doing of evil. The evildoer loses the favor of God and the love of men and lives discredited and always in fear of suffering punishment in this world for the evil that he does. And above all, he has bought hell at a dear price by giving up all these noble things in exchange for such a vile and wicked place. And the one who does good has the favor of God, earns a good reputation, and fears no one, because he has done nothing for which he need fear anyone. And afterward he goes to the paradise that he has earned with so little effort, gaining the favor of God, the love of men, and a good reputation and having no fear of anyone.

Thus the one who shuns evil and adheres to good is very fortunate, for a man can obtain honor by doing good and rendering service in this world and the next. And from evil one can have dishonor and harm for the body and the soul, just as the one who commits treachery gets his just reward. The traitor is similar to the snake, which never travels in a straight line but in a crooked one; and to the rabid dog, which does not bite in a straightforward way but furtively; and to the pig, which fails to bathe in clear and clean water and goes to bathe in the most putrid quagmire it can find. And he is even similar to the fly, which is the filthiest thing in the world, for instead of satisfying itself on fresh meat, it goes to gorge itself on the rottenest meat it can find. And so the traitor, when he wants to recruit aid for his treachery, does not speak directly or straightforwardly about the deeds of his master, but in deceitful ways, defaming his lord and speaking evil of him secretly and with malice. In his presence he speaks with flattery and pleasantry; and thus he bites him with no warning as the rabid dog does, slandering his good reputation and his honor. Moreover he leaves the road of goodness and takes the road of evil, and thus he travels crookedly as the snake; because he is doing wrong against his lord, not protecting him with the truth or with loyalty as he should. Moreover, he ceases to strive for a good reputation, which is as clear as a good mirror, and he proceeds to earn the infamy of treachery, which is abhorred by God and by all men; and thus he is similar to the pig, which shuns the clear water and bathes in the mud. And furthermore he leaves the good reward for punishment, and he leaves honor for dishonor, just as the fly leaves the fresh meat and goes to the rotten. Wherefore if men were disposed to know treachery for what it is, they would flee from it as from leprosy; for just as leprosy inflames and corrupts unto the fourth generation descending through the direct line, so does the treachery of the one who commits it stain those who descend from him unto the fourth degree of kinship, because they would be called sons and grandsons and great-grandsons of treachery, and they would be dishonored among men. They will not be welcomed in service unless their lord absolves from infamy the ones who are descended from the traitor, so that they may be able to have the use of his land. And all ought to flee from the traitor as from a leper and corruption, and his kinsmen, however close they may be, ought to disown him and declare that he is not their relative nor of their lineage. Moreover his vassals should abandon him, for he is no longer their lord.

This parable proves in a similar way that they should do so, for it is right for men to shun the excommunicated, neither talking to them nor associating with them in any manner because they sinned against God by laying violent hands upon sacred things or the keepers of those things, or in some other fashion. Then they should shun even more whoever transgresses against God by committing an act of treachery, for the traitor does not abide by the oath he swore in God's name and his pledge to serve his lord loyally, and he does not keep the word he pledged to serve his lord to his benefit, which is the oath a loyal vassal should make. And surely it is right to flee from so corrupt a thing as this, for so wickedly did he sin against God and men and himself.

The one who swears to keep the truth and faith and loyalty to his lord ought to do six things: first, he must the protect the person of his lord in all natural and joyous things, and without any harm whatsoever; the second is that he must so act that his lord may trust in him at all times; the third, that he protect his home and his sons as well as his wife, and accordingly respect the virtue of the other women of his house; the fourth, that he not conspire to diminish his lord's holdings; fifth, that he in no way in speech, deed, or counsel present any hindrance to his lord's gaining anything which he can gain rightfully, easily, and quickly, because he may not gain it as quickly as he would if he were hampered; the sixth, that whatever his lord should say or do in regard to his honor, he not hinder him or allow any other to do so, for it will dishonor him. And still there is a seventh thing, namely, that when his lord asks his advice, he give it to him honestly without any deceit whatsoever according to the good natural intelligence with which God endowed him. And the one who fails in any of these things whatsoever is not worthy of honor or of loyalty, nor ought he to be said to be loyal. And these things the lord respects in regard to his vassal as well as the vassal in regard to his lord."

108. Of how the king of Mentón in the presence of all declared the Count Nason to be a traitor and ordered him taken away to be burned

"Wherefore, since you, count, were my vassal and in possession of your family's property in my kingdom, holding from me great lands for which you were in my debt and from which you received great wealth each year for which you were beholden to serve me, and having made a sworn oath and pledge to be faithful and loyal to me, just as a good vassal must do to a good lord, and having failed me in everything, and I not having said or done any-thing to give you justification, and you not legally breaking your pledge of fealty, and having coursed through my lands, robbing and burning—and even holding that you did not do all these things, you made many arrogant and reckless statements against me personally, threatening that you would pursue me and expel me from my kingdom, just as your nephew accused you before all my court just now, of which accusation you never chose to repent or ask pardon, although you are in my prison. . . ."

"Sire," said the count, "if I could find forgiveness in you, I would ask for it."

"And why would you ask it, if you had done nothing to be pardoned for?"

"Sire," said the count, "because of what my nephew said that I said."

"And was it true that you said it?" the king asked.

"To my misfortune, it was," said the count.

"Reprimanding with smooth words is sometimes a good thing by which a man may learn the truth," said the king.

The count would not have received any harm for what his nephew had said if he had not confirmed it; and therefore the king said:

"Count, since you confessed with your own mouth what your nephew said, and because of all the things that you committed against the trust and loyalty that you promised me to keep and did not keep, and I standing before God preparing to mete out justice, which I hold in trust from my Lord Jesus Christ to whom I am held accountable, and having my council and my advice with my court, in the presence of these good men here, I declare you to be a traitor and also all those who might choose to aid you and go against me for this decision. And because you may corrupt the land with your treachery wherever you go, I do not choose to banish you from my kingdom, but rather I order your tongue to be torn out through your neck for the words you spoke against me and your head cut off because you caused the deaths of others by raiding through my land, and that you be burned to ashes for the fires you set in my land, so that neither the dogs nor the birds may eat you, for they would be infected by your treachery. Instead I order your ashes thrown into that lake which is near the border of my kingdom, which they say is a sulfuric lake, where never a fish nor any living thing in this world could live. And I truly believe that that place was accursed by God, for I am made to understand it is the tomb of a great-grandfather of yours who committed another deed of treachery just as you did. And go from here and may God never take you from there."

109. Of how the Count Nason was cremated and his ashes thrown into a deep lake

They took the count there and carried out sentence on him according to what the king had ordered, and afterward they collected his ashes and went to throw them into that lake, which was a dozen miles from the king's tent. Truly the number of people was great who went there to see them throw his ashes into that lake. When they threw them, those present heard the most fearful voices in the world come over the water, but they were unable to understand what they were saying. And so the water commenced to boil as an amazingly fierce wind arose, and all present believed they were in danger and that they would be blown into the lake. They fled toward the king's camp and reported it to the king and all the others. They were all greatly astonished by it. And if great wonders appeared there that day, so do many more appear there now, according to what those who have seen it relate. And they say that to this very day many go there to see these strange events. They see many armed men fighting around the lake and they see cities and towns and mighty fortresses at war and castles and cities aflame. And when those visions appear and they see the lake, they find that the water is boiling so fiercely they dare not look at it. All around the lake for at least two miles, everything has turned to ashes; and at times a very beautiful lady stands in the middle of the lake and calms it, and she calls to those present in order to deceive them; just as it happened to a knight who went to view these wonders and was deceived in this way, as you will now hear.

110. Here the story ceases to tell about the king's campaign and tells of a daring knight, of how he came there and entered that lake

The story relates that a knight from the kingdom of Porfilia heard of these wonders that appeared in that lake, and he went to see them. The knight was fearless in the extreme and very daring, and he did not hesitate to test the fortunes of the world, and therefore he was named the Bold Knight. He ordered a tent pitched near that lake, and he was there both day and night seeing those marvels; but his men could not stand to be with him when those visions appeared, and therefore they withdrew. Thus one day that beautiful lady appeared in the lake and called to the knight. The knight went toward her and asked what she wanted, although she was quite far away because he did not dare approach the edge of the lake. She told him that the man she most loved was himself because of his great strength and that she did not know another such mighty knight in the world.

When he heard these words, it seemed to him that he would be demonstrating cowardice if he did not do what she wanted, and he said:

"My lady, if that water were not so deep, I would come to you."

"It is not deep for I am walking on the bottom, and the water reaches only to my ankle," she said.

She raised her foot from the water and showed it to him. And it seemed to the knight that never had he seen so white, so beautiful, or so well-turned a lady's foot, and he believed that all the rest would be according to what had appeared, and he approached the edge of the lake. She went to take him by the hand and entered the lake with him. And she led him through the water to the depths below. She took him to a strange land, and it appeared to him very beautiful and delightful. And he saw numerous knights and other men strolling through that land, but they did not speak to him or say anything.

111. Of how the Bold Knight took the lady of the lake as his wife

The knight said to the lady:

"My lady, why don't these people speak?"

"Do not talk to them," she said, "nor to any lady although she might speak to you, because by doing so you will lose me. And do you see that great city that appears yonder? It is mine, and you may have its wealth and be lord of it if you want to marry me, because I wish to marry you and not look at any other man except you, and so you will be one with me and I with you. May God keep you from wanting to lose me, or I you, and as a mark of good true love, I make you lord of this city and of what I own."

And certainly she was offering him a great deal if her love was as true as she was showing him.

"And I thank you very much for your good gift," he said, "and you will see, my lady, that I will serve you faithfully with it."

And because all this deed was the work of the devil, God did not want it to endure, as you will hear from now on.

112. Of the marvels that the Bold Knight beheld beneath the lake, of which he was greatly astonished

But before they reached the city, many knights and other folk came forth to welcome them with great merrymaking and gave them two magnificently saddled and bridled horses on which to ride. They entered the city and headed for the mansions where that lady dwelt, which were large and very beautiful. And they seemed to that knight so magnificently ornamented that in all the world there could not exist finer, more splendid, or better built places than those, for above the doorways of the houses, it seemed that there were rubies, emeralds, and sapphires, all the size of a man's head, so that at nighttime all the houses were lighted and every room and corner was illuminated as if they were full of candles.

The knight and the lady proceeded to sit on a high dais that had been constructed for them of silk and fine gold. And as their names were called, many counts and dukes came before them, followed by many other people, and they kissed the knight's hand at the lady's command, accepting him as their lord. Afterward tables were placed throughout the palace, and the most magnificent table that man could see was set before them, for its feet were covered with emeralds and sapphires.

And each of them was high as a cubit or more, made of rubies so brilliant that each ruby seemed a glowing coal. And on another table nearby were many ornate cups and glasses of gold studded with many precious stones, so that the three richest kings on earth would be unable to purchase even the least of them.

So spacious was the floor that it was sufficient to contain all the knights who were dining in the mansion. The knights who were eating there numbered ten thousand; and it seemed obvious to the Bold Knight that if he had so many knights in his land and so well outfitted as they looked to him, there was no king, however powerful he might be, who could stand against him, and he could be master of the world.

Some of the most beautiful maidens in the world and the best dressed, or so they appeared to him, brought foods prepared in many different ways; however, they neither spoke nor said anything. The knight considered himself to be very rich and extremely fortunate, with so many knights and the great wealth that he saw before him. However, he considered it a strange thing that no one spoke, for all were so silent it seemed there was no one in the palace. When he could no longer endure it, he said:

"My lady, what is the reason these people do not speak?"

"Don't wonder about it," said the lady, "because it is the custom of this land that from the day they accept someone as their lord, for seven weeks they are not to speak, and not only to the lord but to one another. However they must walk very humbly in the presence of their lord and be obedient to him in all those things he would command them. And so do not be impatient, for when the time limit expires, you will see that they will talk as much as you want, and when you order them to be silent, they will be silent, and when you order them to speak, they will speak, and thus it will be in all things that you desire."

And after they had eaten, the tables were very quickly cleared, and a great number of minstrels arrived; some played instruments, and the others did acrobatics, while some others sang and some climbed the sunbeams to the windows of the rooms which were very high, and slid down them as if they were descending by ropes with no harm to themselves.

"My lady," said the knight, "how can those men climb so easily and descend so easily along a ray from the sun?"

"Truly, they know magic incantations in order to do such things as those," she answered. "And do not be impatient to learn all these things in an hour, but watch and be silent, and so you will be able to know and learn things better; for things that were accomplished over a long time and with great study cannot be learned in a day."

113. Of how the Bold Knight had a son by that lady of the lake in seven days

When night fell, all the knights and the maidens who served them left, except for two maids, one of whom took the knight by the hands and the other, the lady. They escorted them to a room that was as bright as if it were day because of the huge rubies inset in the ceiling. They put them in such a magnificent bed that in all the world there could be none better. Then the maids left the room and closed the doors and that night the lady became pregnant.

Early the next day, the maids came for them and gave them clothing, and afterward, some water in two basins to wash their hands. The basins were both adorned with beautiful emeralds and the water pitchers with beautiful rubies. And afterward, they came to the main room and seated themselves on a dais. Many fakirs came before them and planted trees in the middle of the room, and then the trees sprouted and grew, and flowered and bore fruit, which the maids picked and brought in basins to the knight and the lady. And the knight thought that the fruit was the most beautiful and tasty in the world.

"Oh, Lord!" exclaimed the knight, "what strange things are in this land which aren't in ours!"

"Truly," said the lady, "and even stranger will you see, for all the trees and herbs in this land sprout, and flower, and bear new fruit each day, and the animals give birth in seven days."

"Why then, my lady," said the knight, "if you are pregnant, will you give birth in seven days?"

"Of course," she replied, "It is true."

"Blessed be such a land!" said the knight, "for it produces everything so abundantly and so quickly."

And thus a time of seven days passed very delightfully and the lady bore her son. And in seven days he was nearly as large as his father.

"Now I see that everything here grows quickly; but I wonder why God does it in this land and not in ours," the knight said.

And he thought to himself that he would stroll through the city and ask others how this could be, and he said:

"My lady, if you think it proper, my son and I will go horseback riding through the city."

She answered, "I am very pleased."

114. Of how the Bold Knight was then deceived by a woman as he was going through the city

Then they brought them each a palfrey on which to ride, very handsome horses finely saddled and caparisoned. When they went out the door, they found a thousand armed knights who went before them protecting and guiding them throughout the city. And as they were passing along the street there was a very beautiful lady, much more beautiful than his wife, in a doorway. Although she was a courtesan, he could not refrain from speaking to her: "Would it be possible for me to talk with you privately?"

"How is that?" asks she. "Aren't you the knight whom we took as our lord the other day, and don't you have our mistress as your wife?"

"Certainly, I am," he answered.

"Before you entered the city, did not our lady forbid you to speak to any other lady, lest you lose her?" she asked.

"It is true," he said.

"Well, how did you dare overstep her commandment? Certainly you behaved badly toward her."

"My lady," said the knight, "don't be so surprised at it, for I was forced by love."

"Love for whom?" she asked.

"For you," he replied.

"Alas, my lady," said one of her attendants, "you would be committing a great sin if you sent him away without letting him talk to you! Don't you see how handsome and elegant he is, and how he reveals he loves you so much?"

And at these words, another wicked woman, who did not prize any less than the first woman such naughty tricks as these, came up and said very quickly:

"Alas, madam! What has become of your image, your elegance, your good manner of speech, and your cordiality? Is this how you receive one who shows such great love for you? And can't you see that espying you he fell in love with you? And no wonder, for God gave you such personality there isn't a man who sees you that does not become a prisoner of your love. And surely you would be doing wrong in being stingy with what God bestowed on you so generously. By Heaven, madam, do not punish him by delaying the favorable answer he awaits."

And alas! there are many women in the world such as these, who work at nothing else but this, paying no heed to the honor or dishonor of those whom they advise, or making them lose their reputation and their good name. They do it in order to be entertained and to be able to bend to their will those who they know will be seduced by these naughty tricks. Wherever they go by day they may be sheltered and protected by being with them and accomplishing their wicked intentions in this world.

Because there is nothing that evil men desire so much as license, they can easily have it with those who are fond of the same thing. And therefore they say, everyone to his own taste; and alas! some, who believe it so willingly, take pleasure in what they are told, because wickedness is pleasing to them and they consider it admirable to go from hand to hand and to have many lovers. And certainly such women as these do not really love any man, nor do lovers really love women when they tend to love many, for it is not true or lasting love except at the moment. Therefore, Saint Jerome wrote a parable about such loves as these, which are godless, of how a good man asked his daughter some questions in which it is revealed if the love of a woman who loves many men can be true or not.

115. Of the questions that a father asked his daughter on the love affairs of women

And the parable says: a good man had a very beautiful daughter who was well-read, pleasant of voice, and very personable. She liked very much to talk to and listen to others, and for all these reasons she had frequent visitors. She was an intimate of many ladies when they made pilgrimages to shrines because of the many delightful things she knew how to say to them. Therefore, the good man wanted to know if the love she showed to all was sincere; and he said to her: "My dear daughter, many people love you, and you are very popular and knowledgeable of many things, and you are a pleasant conversationalist. Would you like for you and me to play a game of questions and answers in which we could find amusement?"

The daughter answered: "My father and lord, know that everything that pleases you, pleases me, and God knows I would enjoy joining you in any amusement in order that you may see if I possess some knowledge."

"Dear daughter," said the father, "will you answer me truthfully the questions I ask you?"

"Certainly, I will answer you according to whatever knowledge I have. I will hide nothing from you, although you may not approve of some of the answers I give," she replied.

"Now," said the father, "let us begin with my asking and your answering."

"Now is the right time to begin," said the daughter, "for I am ready to answer you."

"Well, my incomparable daughter, answer me this first question. The woman who loves many men—which of the lovers does she love?"

"Truly, dear father," replied the daughter, "she cannot love all of them at once, but now one and then another; because the more lovers she has, the more she wants; because the desire for new things is never satisfied, and always wanting a new man, she loves one and then another; for as quickly as she thinks of something new, just as quickly are they lost and forgotten. And thus the more she loves, the more she wants to love, treating all lightly except the last, and still ready to leave him and forget him as soon as a new one comes along.

"My clever daughter, since the woman loves many, which does she really love?"

"Dear father, whomever she sees directly before her."

"Alas, daughter, how long does the love of such a woman as this endure?"

"Dear father, for as long as the talk between both of us lasts in this questioning and answering, and as long as they are in each other's presence, and no longer. And dear father, there is no love at all in the love of such a woman as this, for at times when she is with one of her lovers, she sets her heart on another whom she sees passing by. And so showing that she loves each one, she loves no one. Her love is not lasting for one or the other, except for as long as she is in their company and as long as the love-talk lasts between them. At the hour that these things die, then the love that is forgotten between them dies. And it is proved in this way: the woman who loves many men is like the mirror, which pictures the many forms of the men who may stand before it, and as soon as the men withdraw from it, it retains no form of the man in itself. Therefore, dear father, a man ought not to join in love with a woman who was a mistress and intimate friend of many men, for she never keeps faith with him or is truthful. Although she may swear by the Holy Gospels, her heart can not bear to belong to just one man. Such women have no place for God in their hearts, although they pretend to be His servants, going on pilgrimages, and they go only in order to see and to be seen, and not for any devotion they have."

"Now my faithful daughter," said the father, "tell me when did you learn these things, for you answered them so easily and so surely?"

"Dear father," replied the daughter, "while I could examine them and see them."

"Now my daughter," asked the father, "is there a school and a teacher to instruct so that these things can be learned?"

"Certainly there is," replied the daughter.

"And where?" the father inquired.

"In laxly guarded convents," answered the daughter. "Such deceitful women as these are inclined to go out, to see and to make themselves known. If some men come to visit them or to see them, or through their folly go aside to talk and to bargain with them, or if they cannot meet them secretly, their words may reach them lewdly in a wanton way so that the man may well think they are trying to tempt him. And they are like that from childhood, having had the freedom to talk and do whatever they wished, and so they cannot break long ingrained habits, just as a jar can only late or never lose the taint imbued in it, no matter how much washing it may get. And certain of these women who know how to write and read have no need of go-betweens to procure visitors and caterers for them, for their hands work at whatever their minds desire. However, they are not displeased with those men who come to them with new things. And certainly, dear father, some women go to these convents in order to be protected and disciplined, and they hurt the women by greater scandal and emotional confusion."

"Dear daughter, did you tell me the truth in all these things I asked you?" said the father.

"Certainly I did," said the daughter, "and I did not refuse to tell you anything I knew to say to you, notwithstanding some of the things I told you hurt me deeply, for some applied to me and therefore I felt bad."

"Dear daughter," said the father, "I am very grateful to you, and now our game is over. There has been enough said on each side, and may God allow you to live a good life."

And thus the father and the daughter were happy and very pleased, but not the Bold Knight with his son, who was awaiting the reply of the lady, for he could not get a reply from her, because she held herself too dear. But finally another of her close friends in mischief, cleverer than the others in the same profession, came out and said:

"Madam, take care that God does not punish you for the discourtesy you have shown this knight, for I have already seen others who have lost their feet and their hands and their speech for tending to be niggardly of speech and of all the rest that God gave them."

"However," said the lady, "I will gain little in these love affairs and less. . . .[1] Certainly I will not go from here rudely treated."

And he took her by the hand and led her into her house and remained with her talking for a long time.

116.   Of how the Bold Knight and his son were suddenly both ejected from the lake at the same point where the knight had entered

Later, the knight mounted his horse and proceeded to his lodgings. The mistress of the city learned what had transpired between the knight and the lady and became exceedingly angry. She sat down on a dais and placed one arm around Count Nason, whom the king of Mentón had denounced as a traitor, and the other around his great-grandfather, who also had been declared a traitor, as you have already heard.

When the knight and his son passed through the gate of the palace on their palfreys, they saw an ugly and frightening devil on the dais with her arms around the two counts. It seemed that she was tearing out their hearts and eating them. The devil screamed loud and strong, saying:

"You reckless and daring knight, take your son and leave my land, for I am the Mistress of Treachery!"

And then an earthquake shook so that it seemed all the palaces and the city would fall to the earth, and a tremendous whirlwind took the knight and his son and rapidly carried them up and cast them out of the lake near his

---

1. At this point there is a break in the sense of the text.

tent. And this quake shook the earth for a distance of two days' journey all around the lake, so that many houses in the city, and towers on castles, came crashing down.

117. Of how the terrified squires of the Bold Knight found him on the lakeside

The knight's troops came back each day to the tent to see if their lord would appear in the lake. The next day, after the knight had arrived at his tent, his squires came there. They were extremely frightened by the quaking of the earth on the day before. After they saw their master they were very happy and pleased, and said: "Sir, we ask you please to leave this place, because it is very dangerous."

"Without fail," said the knight. "It is necessary for us to leave, for I have never come out of an event so weakened as from this venture. But do we have any horses on which we may leave? As soon as we dismounted from the two palfreys on which we left the lake, they fell into the lake, one in the shape of a pig and the other in the form of a goat, screaming in the loudest voices I ever heard."

"Certainly, sir," said a squire, "we have all our own fine and handsome horses, but they are frightened by the great earth tremor that happened yesterday."

"How's that?" asked the knight. "Did the earth tremble here above?"

"It certainly did, so that we believed we would all perish," replied a squire.

"Sir," said a squire, "who is that person with you?"

"He is my son," replied the knight.

"And how is that, sir?" asked a squire. "Were you in this land once before, that you have such a large boy?"

"Truly," replied the knight, "I have never been in this land except right now."

"Then how could this boy be your son, since he is already taller than you?"

"Don't consider it a wonder," said the knight, "for weeds grow quickly. He is of such a nature that in seven days he grew to the size you see. In that land where he was born, all creatures give birth seven days from the day they conceive, and all the trees turn green, leaf out, and bear fruit again every day."

"And who is his mother?" asked the squire.

"A lady who seemed to me the most beautiful lady in the world when I first saw her," answered the knight. "When we parted just now, I saw her turned into another form, and in my opinion, there is not a blacker or uglier devil than she in all hell. I truly believe that he is the son of the devil on his mother's side, and may God allow him to turn out all right, but I cannot believe he will, for all creatures return to their own nature."

And he told them all that had happened, and they were consequently very astonished that he had escaped alive and well.

"And what shall we call that son of yours?" said the squire.

"Really, I don't know," responded the knight, "but I believe it would be good to baptize him now and give him a new name."

And they agreed to baptize him, and they named him Albert Devil. He was a valiant knight-at-arms, daring and fearless in everything. There was nothing in the world he feared and that he would not undertake. And even today there are knights descended from him in that kingdom of Porfilia who are very clever and daring in all their deeds. And I told you the story of this Bold Knight so that no one should believe or place himself in the power of a person that he doesn't know, although that person may speak flatteringly or make wild promises, for by chance one may wind up scorned and in a dangerous place. Avoid dubious things, and especially if one sees some danger right in front of his eyes, just as those people of the kingdom of Mentón did. As soon as they saw the danger from that lake, they departed and went to their lord. When the king learned of the miracles that occurred in that lake and what had happened to the Bold Knight, he said:

"Friends, I truly believe that place is accursed by our Lord. Therefore, all those who fall into the sin of treachery ought to be cast into that place."

And so he ruled that it should be done from that time on.

118. Of how the king gave Count Nason's earldom to Garfín, his son, and how the queen died

The story then tells that the king gave Count Nason's earldom to Garfín and ordered Roboán his brother to accompany him with a large number of the knights of the army who were present. He ordered them to take Count Nason's nephew who had now made a pledge to yield all the land to the king. He ordered them to give the count's nephew a place where he could live honorably attended by ten squires. And so they did, and the land was delivered into their hands without any hindrance whatsoever, and all were very pleased and returned with Count Garfín to the king.

At this time, the king was living with the queen in a noble city called Toribia. Seeing that only eight days remained of the time limit that he and the queen had pledged to remain chaste, the king was disturbed and sad for fear he would have to live in sin with her. However, our Lord God, protector of those who wish to follow in His path and keep themselves free of sin of any kind, refused to let him live in sin, and before the time limit expired, He made the queen grievously ill, so she knew in her heart she was about to die. She reflected on the virtue that God had instilled in her husband, the king, and she thought of those four years in which they both had maintained themselves celibate. He had waited two years until she was of age and two other years to complete his penance. She thought of the king's youthful appearance and how he had no son to inherit the kingdom after his death, and the thought crossed her mind that the king's subjects might not be as obedient to him as they ought to be. And these things worried her so much that they made the pain of her illness increase. One day she called the king and told him what she had been thinking. She begged him to be kind enough to marry some high born lady of the kingdom without delay if God should ordain her death. She had commended her soul to Him, and the people of the kingdom had to have some one to respect and obey, and there was no heir, since God had not seen fit to grant her this boon. The king, very sad and worried, consoled her as much as he could, but his consolation was of no benefit. Before the eight days expired, the queen died and God received her soul in Paradise, for she was His servant who had led a virtuous life and performed pious acts. When the king realized God had done him such a great favor, he did not know what to do—whether to approach that good lady who was in the city and recognize her as his wife, and to recognize Garfín and Roboán as his sons, or not to do so.

119. Of how the king presented his wife and sons to his subjects and all received them as their lords

He continued thinking about this for a long time, and one night while he was in bed, he implored our Lord God through his holy compassion to deem it fit to reunite his wife and his sons with him in his present situation, and then he fell asleep. As morning was breaking he heard a voice saying, "Arise and send for all the people of your land, and reveal to them how you were previously married to that lady and not to the queen, and that you had those two sons by her, and that you and the queen lived celibately until God in His wisdom took her away, and they may welcome your wife as queen and Garfín and Roboán as your sons. And you may be sure they will welcome them with great joy."

The king arose very quickly and sent for his chancellor and all the court scribes, and ordered them to write letters to all the counts, dukes, and other noblemen, and to all the cities, towns, and castles in his whole dominion. The letters commanded them to send to him from each place six of their best men with letters empowering them to act and to dispose of those things that the court should decide ought to become law. All were to be present by Pentecost, which would be a year from the date of the letters.

The letters were then sent throughout the land very hurriedly, so that before the set time limit, they were all present in his largest chamber. Sitting on his throne, a magnificent crown on his head he sent for his wife and for

Garfín and Roboán, his sons. When they reached the room, the king said: "Friends and loyal vassals, I hold this kingdom through the grace of God, who saw fit to guide me here, to direct me, and to endow me with wisdom, power, and good fortune whereby I was able to lift the siege of this city where the enemy had surrounded the king who preceded me. I had his daughter as my wife, but God through his mercy did not want me to live with her in sin, for I had been married before to another woman. I did not know whether she was dead or alive, and until I could know with greater certainty about her fate, I told the queen, my wife, that because of a serious sin that I had committed, penance had been imposed on me to remain celibate for two years. And she being a saintly person, said that she would live chastely with me, and that I should be celibate. Moreover, she wanted me to keep close to God and fulfill my penance, so I would not live in mortal sin and dare God's anger. When the time limit of two years was over, God saw fit to take her away for Himself, since she was His servant and lived a Christian life as you all know. And during that time, I saw my first wife here with my two young sons. I recognized my wife quickly, although she did not recognize me. Because my sons were so young when lost, it was difficult for me to recognize them, until the good lady told me how and where she had lost them. And these are Garfín and Roboán, my sons and the good lady's whom you see here. While the queen was alive, may God forgive me, I did not dare to speak about it through fear of creating a scandal and raising doubt in the population. Therefore I implore you, that since God ordained that the queen and I should not live in mortal sin and saw fit to bring my first wife and my sons here to me, that it please you to allow me to reestablish my family as I should."

All his subjects were surprised and much amazed at what the king said, and they began to talk and murmur among themselves. Greatly surprised at their talking and whispering, and believing they were planning to refuse his request, he said:

"Friends, why don't you answer? Does what I ask you please you or not? But I want you to know for sure that I would leave the kingdom before I would live without my wife; because living without her and not as I should, I would be living in mortal sin, and for this reason I believe it would bring God's wrath against me and you."

Count Nafquino, who was the oldest and most influential man in all the land, arose and spoke:

"Sire and courageous king, may God not wish for any reason in the world for you to have to leave the kingdom, especially because of something we fail to say or to do for you. Because, sire, you are that one whom God chose, to your good fortune, to have the kingdom to protect us, defend us, and honor us, above all others in the world through you and your strength and wisdom. And if we were to lose you through our folly and especially our fault, we would be lost and destroyed, and rightly so, because we would be guilty in the sight of God and our neighbors would destroy us. However, we consider it right and proper that you acknowledge your wife and live with her and that you recognize and accept your sons as you should. And we shall welcome your wife as our mistress and as queen and your older son as your heir after your death."

And the count began to talk to all the others.

"Do you consider this agreeable?"

They all answered with one voice, "We consider it proper and we are pleased."

And then they took his wife to a private room and dressed her in elegant clothing and placed a magnificent golden crown on her head. They proceeded to seat her on a throne equal with the king's, with their two sons at their feet. One by one they went to kiss her hands and to pledge allegiance to the queen and the older son of the king. They arose with great happiness and pleasure and all went to dine with the king, for he had invited them to be his guests that day. And after eating, great celebrations were held that were beyond description, and after those who had come as special emissaries returned home, the same occurred throughout the realm.

120. Of how the king sent the Knight Amigo with his gift to the hermitage

The king was very happy and pleased with his wife and his sons. He related to his wife how he had passed the time after he had lost her and how God had done many favors for him, as you have already heard. And what is more, the knights, his sons, told him about the townsman and the many good things he and his wife had done for them. They asked the king and queen as a favor to grant their foster parents a good reward for the education they had received from them. And in truth, the king was deeply pleased because these youths were grateful for favors received, and he ordered them given magnificent gifts to be sent to their foster parents, and so they did. Then what he had promised the hermit suddenly came to the king's mind—that if God would give him victory or raise him to the high estate he was striving for, he would remember that hermitage. He then sent for the Knight Amigo and asked:

"Knight Amigo, do you remember the hermit when I first met you?"

"Certainly I do," responded the knight.

"Well, take this splendid crown of mine, which is extremely valuable, and ten mules loaded with silver. Take it to the hermitage and offer it to him. If you find the hermit alive, give it to him, and tell him to build a monastery for monks there and to buy lands on which they may support themselves."

The Knight Amigo went and all was accomplished as the king had ordered, so that to this day the monastery is very rich and abundantly provided for, and it is called the Monastery of the Holy Spirit.

121. Of how the Knight Amigo benefited the fisherman— the master with whom he formerly lived

After that was all finished, the Knight Amigo had it proclaimed that all who attended the Festival of the Holy Spirit would be given gold coins and something to eat. Among the vast crowd of people that arrived was the fisherman whose servant the Knight Amigo had been. The Knight Amigo recognized him and had him lodged in his quarters. He took off the fine clothes he was wearing and gave them to the fisherman and ordered him to dress. The fisherman, not recognizing him, said:

"Sir, I beg you please not to be so hasty as to make me dress in these clothes, for those who know me will believe that I stole them; and although they may learn you gave them to me, they will think I am crazy to dress in such garments."

"How is that? Is it madness for a man to dress elegantly and properly?" asked the Knight Amigo. "It is surely a greater madness for a man who has them not to wear them, especially if they cost him nothing. And if you can't give me another reason why you feel strange dressing in them, I will consider you of little sense."

"Certainly, sir, I will speak according to the little sense that I have," replied the fisherman. "You know well, sir, that such garments as these are not fitting for a poor man, but for a very rich and handsome man, and when he takes these off, he can make others as good or better."

"And do you believe you will be able to reach such a level in the future that you might be able to do this?" asked the Knight Amigo.

"Sir," said the fisherman, "I believe with the aid and mercy of God it may be possible."

"Now I tell you that I consider you have better sense now than when I took my leave of you, for you said that you saw no indication in me as to why God should do better for me than for you, and I answered that I commended you for your little sense, and so I said goodbye to you," said the Knight Amigo.

"Sir," said the fisherman, "I never said such a thing, for it would be extreme madness to say to such a powerful lord as you that you could not be better than I."

"And don't you recognize me?" asked the Knight Amigo.

"No sir," replied the fisherman.

"Well I am your worker who lived in the hut hear the seashore," the Knight Amigo said.

Looking at him carefully, the fisherman recognized him and fell on his knees at his feet. The Knight Amigo made him get up and said to him: "Friend, do not hold God's power so lightly, for He is powerful enough to do what no other can do; and I give you these garments in exchange for the old tunic that you gave me when I left because you had nothing else to give me. And for the reply you just gave, like a man of wisdom, I order one thousand gold coins to be given to you out of the bounty God has granted me and from which you can have other such garments made every year of your life, and another one thousand coins for the upkeep of your house. And if you ever need anything, I command you to come to me in the kingdom of Mentón, where I will supply whatever you might need. And furthermore, I think it proper for you to become overseer and steward of all the affairs of the monastery under the abbot, who is the hermit from the hermitage and was host for the king of Mentón. The king considered it proper to make him the abbot because of the many favors he received from the hermit."

And for such people as these, the ancient proverb says, "Every man has it within himself to improve his own fortunes." And from being extremely poor, these people became very prosperous—especially the Knight Amigo, as you will hear henceforth. And afterward, the Knight Amigo returned to the king of Mentón and related to him what he had done. The king was pleased to his very soul because he had done so well and was grateful to him for it. He felt especially pleased because the hermit, who was a virtuous and honorable man, was now an abbot.

122. Of how Roboán asked his father to permit him to go in quest of honor and fame and how the king granted his request

And then the king called his sons to come before him, and he said to Garfín: "Son, God has been very good to us, more than we deserve, and therefore we should be grateful to Him. We ought to show our gratitude to Him for all time by good service. You know that you are to succeed me as king; therefore, it is necessary for you to give a good portion of the kingdom to Roboán, your brother, so he may share the honor and bounty that God has granted us."

Garfín went to kiss his hands for this favor of which he had just told him, and said that not only would Roboán have his just share, but since the king was completely their lord and master, it would greatly please him if it were possible for both to be named king.

"Son," said the king, "you are very generous, and I am sure that if you treat Roboán fairly, he will always be at your service and will endeavor to increase your honor."

"Dear father," said Roboán, "I truly trust in the grace of our Lord God, who favored you by making you king and my brother your heir, not to abandon me or forget me. I hope that God will not give me a part of the kingdom, for I might discredit Him in some way; but I, serving God, will endeavor by working and accomplishing so much that He, through his mercy, will raise me to as honored estate as my brother, or perhaps, to greater. Furthermore, I ask you and my brother to grant me some of your wealth and give me three hundred knights with whom I may go search for adventure, come what may."

The king was truly and deeply concerned over these words of Roboán, for he believed that Roboán would persist in this request and perhaps would leave them, and he said to him:

"Roboán, for the love of God, please don't plan to leave this land where God has been so good to me and to you, for a man exposes himself to many troubles and many dangers in traveling through unknown lands, and here you lead a pleasurable life and everything will be done and arranged in the kingdom just as you wish."

"Sire," said Roboán, "I leave you and my brother free from care and with the kingdom at peace, just as you now hold it. Praise be to God, I ask you to have pity on me, for everyone has to die and return to dust, while nothing remains in this world except his good deeds, which live after him and endure forever. For what would it profit me to remain here and to lead an idle and pleasurable life, without accomplishing anything good? Surely on the day I die, all the idleness and all the pleasure of this world will die, and I would leave nothing behind me for which men could give praise. I say to you plainly, sire, that it seems to me the greatest faults that a knight can have are idleness and failure to use his chivalric talents as befits him; for in becoming idle, he hides himself and abandons all the goals in which he could attain greater honor than what he holds. Surely and rightly so, honor is not given to anyone except to that man who strives for it. And therefore I beg you—do not make me give up the quest I have set, because I truly aim to strive hard and to win honor."

"Well so be it," said the king. "God through His grace will guide you and aid you. And I trust in Him. And in my opinion, I am sure, and I hold no doubt, that you are to attain greater fortune than we, for your goal is so lofty. However, I want you and Garfín to come to me early tomorrow, for I want to counsel you in matters of chivalry as well as how to protect your fortune and honor when God may grant it to you."

Early the next day Garfín and Roboán went to the king and heard mass with him. When mass was over, the king ordered all those present to leave, because he had much business to dispose of concerning his house which was of benefit to the kingdom. Entering the room with Garfín and Roboán, his sons, the king sat on his throne. He ordered them to be seated before him, with their faces turned toward him, just like a teacher who prepares to instruct scholars. This is how the king began.

BOOK THREE

The Instructions of the King of Mentón

123. Of how the king took his sons aside and taught them how they should maintain their homes

"My sons, it is very true that whatever good and perfect quality we possess, we received from the almighty God. From Him we received our being, and it is the most noble being that we can receive, since we are made in His image and His likeness, which confers on us the quality of grace to attain that goal for which He created us, which is eternal glory; and since we owe so much to Him, for we received all good things from Him, let us place all our love in Him. Thus before all other things, you will follow my advice as I now will tell you: first, you will love and serve and fear God who created you, as He gave you reason and understanding to do good and to know how to avoid temptation. For it is said in the Holy Scripture that the beginning of wisdom is the fear of God. Therefore the one who always fears God is saved from sin; as a result you will keep his commandments through fear of breaking any of them, and especially you will keep that one in which he commands that a man should honor his father and his mother if he expects a good reward on earth. But, alas! There are many who are more inclined to follow evil counsel, since that is their nature, than to follow good; but the man of wisdom, when he perceives good and evil and understands it, will choose the good first, although it may carry danger, rather than the evil, which may be pleasurable and more to his liking; just as happened to a youthful king of Armenia, although he lived doing as he pleased."

124. Of the parable that the king gave to his sons about a king who was going hunting and met a preacher who was discoursing to the public

"The story tells that this king was going hunting and met a preacher on the road who was discoursing to the people. He said to him:

"'Preacher, I am in a great hurry to go hunting, and I can not be present at your sermon, for you talk too long; but if you want to shorten it, I will stay to hear it.'

"The preacher replied: 'The deeds of God are so many and varied that they cannot be told in a few words, especially to those who are more concerned for the vanities of this world than for the teachings and words of God. And Godspeed to you, and leave the sermon to those who desire to hear it and are grateful to God for His favor of giving them the intelligence to listen to sermons and to learn from them. Remember that for one sin alone, Adam was cast out of Paradise; and will God be inclined to accept in it one who has committed many sins?'"

125. Of the parable that the king gave his sons about the king and a doctor who was examining some chamber pots

"The king went away and as he walked he considered what the preacher had said, and he turned back. Entering the town he saw a doctor who had many chamber pots before him, and he said:

"Doctor, you who believe you can cure all those sick people whose chamber pots you have, would you know any medicine to cure and heal sins?'

"The doctor thought that he was a nobleman and said to him:

"'Sir, will you be able to bear the bitterness of the medicine?'

"'Yes,' said the king.

"'Well, write this prescription,' said the doctor; 'first, the preparation which you are to take to change the nature of your sins, and after you have drunk the syrup, I will give you the medicine to clear away your sins. Take the roots of the fear of God and the substance of his commandments and the bark of determination to keep them, the essence of humility, the essence of patience, the essence of chastity, the essence of charity, the seed of *costanca,* which means constancy, the seed of shame, and put them all to cook in the kettle of faith and truth, and set the fire of justice to it, cool it with the wind of wisdom, and cook until it raises the fervor of contrition. Skim it with the ladle of penance, and you will draw out in the foam the drosses of vainglory, pride, envy, greed, lust, anger, avarice, and gluttony. Place it to cool in the air that tempers the vices of the world, and drink it for nine days in the glass of charitable behavior, and the hardened fluids of the unyielding sins of which you have not repented or made amends to God will ripen. As you eat and drink and involve yourself in the vices of this world, they will try to take away from you the control of your feet and hands with each seductive drop in order to make you lose your soul, from which you gain your reason and wisdom and the five senses of your body. And after you take this preliminary syrup, you will take one dram of the pure rhubarb of God's love, weighed on the scales of faith in the One who will forgive you your sins with compassion. And drink it willingly with the medicine in order that you may not return to your sins. And thus you will be cured and healthy in body and soul.'

"'In truth, doctor,' said the king, 'this medicine of yours is very bitter, and I would not be able to tolerate its bitterness. From the kind of lord that I am, you wish to make me a servant; and from a happy man, a miserable one, and from a rich man, a poor one.'

"'Why do you think that you will be a servant just because you should fear God and fulfill his commandments?' asked the doctor. 'And by being humble and patient, you believe that you will be unhappy, and by being generous and circumspect you believe that you will be poor? Surely your line of thought is wrong, for God will preserve the one who fears Him and keeps His commandments from the misery and servitude of the devil and set him free; and He will relieve the humble and patient from misery and care and exalt him; and He will increase the wealth of the one who is generous and liberal with his wealth.'

"'Sir,' continued the doctor, 'Note that the punishments of Hell are more bitter than this medicine, and perhaps you will be able to endure them. There are few who know how to bear good fortune or ill fortune easily, but they endure both, although they may not wish to. Therefore if you do not wish to take good advice, I am afraid you will have to take bad advice that will cause you harm, and what happened to a hunter who was catching birds with his nets will happen to you.'

"'And how was that?' asked the king.

"'I will tell you,' said the doctor."

126. Of the parable that the doctor gave the king about the hunter and the calender lark

"The story tells that a hunter went hunting with his nets and caught a calender lark and nothing else. Returning to his own house, he drew a knife to behead it and to eat it. The calender lark said to him:

"'Alas, friend, what a great wrong you are doing in killing me! Don't you see that you can not satisfy yourself with me, for am I not a tiny dinner for such a large body as yours? Therefore I consider you would do better to set me free and allow me to live; and I will give you three pieces of good advice, which will be of advantage to you if you make the proper use of it.'

"'All right,' said the hunter, 'I agree to that, and if you give me one good piece of advice, I will set you free.'

"'Well, I will give you the first,' said the lark. 'Do not believe that what you know is impossible could be true; the second, do not grieve over what you have lost, if you realize that you can not regain it; the third, do not undertake a thing that you realize cannot be completed. You asked one piece of advice from me and these three items are all considered as one.'

"'Truly you have given me three good pieces of advice,' replied the hunter.

"And he loosed the lark and set him free. The lark continued flying over the hunter's house until he saw that the hunter was going hunting with his nets. He flew there directly above him in the air, wondering if he would remember the advice he had given him, and if he would make use of it. And while the hunter was walking through the fields setting his nets and calling to the birds with his sweet songs, the lark was traveling in the air and said:

"'Oh, you wretch, how you were tricked by me!'

"'And who are you?' asked the hunter.

"'I am the lark that you set free today in exchange for the advice I gave you.'

"'In my opinion, I was not deceived because you gave me good advice,' said the hunter.

"'It is true if you understood it,' replied the lark.

"'Well, tell me in what way I was tricked by you,' the hunter said to the lark.

"'I will tell you,' replied the lark. 'If you had known about the precious jewel that I have in my stomach, which is as large as an ostrich egg, I am certain you would not have freed me, for you would have been rich forever, and if you had taken it from me, I would have lost the magical virtue of speech that I have, and you would have gained the great ability to obtain whatever you wanted.'

"The hunter, when he heard this, was very sad and dejected, thinking what the lark was saying was true. He followed her in order to trap her again with his sweet songs. The lark, as she had learned by experience, was careful and refused to alight, and said to him:

"'You foolish man, how poorly you learned the advice I gave you!"

"'Truly, I remember it well,' said the hunter.

"'Perhaps,' said the lark, 'but you did not really learn it, and if you did learn it, you did not know how to make use of it.'

"'And why not?' asked the hunter.

"'You know that I told you in the first piece of advice not to believe anything that you saw, but realized was impossible?'

"'That is true,' said the hunter.

"'Well, how could you believe that in such a small body as mine there could be room for a jewel as large as an ostrich egg? You should understand easily that it is impossible. The second piece of advice; I told you not to strive to recover a thing lost if you realized that you could not recover it.'

"'That is the truth,' said the hunter.

"'Well, why did you persist in thinking that you might be able to catch me again in your snares with your sweet songs? Don't you understand that those who are deceived once learn from their experiences? Surely you should easily understand that since I escaped once from your clutches, I would be careful to stay out of your power. It would be quite correct for you to kill me as you wanted to the other time if I had not saved myself from you.

And in the third piece of advice I told you not to undertake anything that you realized you couldn't complete?'

"'That is true,' said the hunter.

"'And then you see that I fly wherever I wish to in the air, and that you cannot climb up to me, nor do you have the power to do it for it is not in your nature. You ought not to undertake pursuit of me, since you can not fly as I can.'

"'Certainly I will not rest until I catch you, by hook or by crook,' said the hunter.

"'You are speaking from pride,' said the lark. 'Watch out, for God makes the proud fall from on high.'

"Mulling over how he would be able to fly in order to catch the lark, the hunter took his nets and headed for town. He met a fakir who was performing before a large crowd and said to him:

"'You, fakir, you who show all your magic and make men believe the impossible, could you make me like a bird and able to fly?'

"'Yes, I could,' answered the fakir. 'Take the feathers of birds and stick them to you with wax. Stick feathers all over your body and your legs, even in your nails, and climb a high tower. Jump from the tower and flap the feathers as much as you can.'

"The hunter did so. When he jumped from the tower thinking he could fly, he could not, nor did he learn, because it was not natural for him. He fell to the earth, crushed his body, and died.

"And he received his just deserts, for he refused to believe the good advice that was given to him, and he believed bad advice that for natural reasons could not possibly be.

"When he heard this the king considered that the doctor had given him good advice and he followed his instructions and drank the syrup and the medicine, although it seemed to him so bitter that he could not tolerate it. He changed his dissolute ways and became a very good and just king. He was esteemed by God and men. By taking the bitter medicine the doctor gave him, and making advantage of it, he avoided the bitterness of the punishments of hell."

127. Of how the king of Mentón told his sons they should always act as well-born men

"And you, my sons," said the king of Mentón, "always pay attention to the advice that those whom you realize are reasonable give you and which will be to your advantage and your honor. Receive it willingly and use it to advantage and do not accept advice from those who are witless and which you know is contrary to reason. Know that men can be loved and honored and esteemed by God and by man in two ways: the first is to learn good manners; the second is to use them. One without the other is worth little to the man who desires to achieve high status and recognition. And, my sons, you are to know that in good breeding there are seven virtues, and they are these: humility, chastity, patience, abstinence, generosity, compassion, and charity, which is to say true love. Of them you will hear henceforth, and you will learn the qualities of each one in its place. You can believe that the person who is master of these good traits in which these virtues reside can be said to be noble; for the wise man says that the only nobility is that which adorns and honors the gentle heart. And another wise man says, 'A man is said to be noble not through his father or his mother, but only through the virtuous life and character that he possesses.' and another wise man said to his son, 'Do not think that you are noble because of the high status of your family or through their virtues, but only through your own good qualities, if you have them.' And therefore they say the elegant woman has no need of cosmetics, for if she is not good inwardly, she will be little improved by adding false colors to her complexion."

128. Of how the king of Mentón instructed his sons that they might always be noble

"Therefore no one can be praised for some one else's goodness but only for his own. And thus, my sons, learning moral precepts and using them advantageously, you will be respected, loved, and esteemed by God and by men. But you should know that the nobleman must possess these seven virtues we spoke of previously, and in addition he must be a lover of justice and truth.

"The higher in rank a nobleman is, the more humble he must be, and the more noble and powerful he is, the more he must be forbearing. Certainly the one who aspires to attain nobility will have to endure many annoyances, for he has to be generous to those who petition him, patient with those who misjudge him, and respectful to those who come to him. Therefore it is fitting for whoever aspires to nobility to have good traits and to make good use of them. He should forgive all those who err against him, and he should do something for those who ask it of him. He ought not to pay any heed to the stupidity of the dull; because the wise man says, 'Strive to be charitable to whoever would not give anything to you. Return good for evil, for by your returning good for evil he will realize and understand that he did evil and will repent, and thus you will make a good man of a wicked one.' And know that two things are necessary to the person who wants to be magnanimous: one is that he must be moderate in his speech and his deeds; the other is that he must be generous to those who are needy. And my sons, when God does you a great favor, it will last forever if you take advantage of it properly. If you do not, know that you will lose it; for God does not bestow his gifts on one who does not deserve them nor can make proper use of them. It is correctly written that the one who makes improper use of God's gift will lose the generosity and privilege bestowed on him.

"And avoid conversing with a person who you know will dissemble, and do not ask for anything from one who you believe will not give it to you. Do not promise what you are unable to do or know in your heart that you cannot give, and do not undertake a task that you know you cannot finish. And strive to associate with men of good faith, for they erase from their hearts the stain of sins. He who desires to be one of the good is good inwardly, and he who does good works gains esteem. And if you wish to fulfill the commandments of the faith, do not do to another what you would not want done to yourself. Know that all good qualities are joined together in the love of God."

129.   How the king of Mentón instructed his sons to always maintain chastity and to keep themselves pure

"Furthermore, my sons, you must know that the first and the most prized of good qualities is chastity, which means moderation, through which man attains God and reputation. And know that chastity means that a man should subdue and suppress his desires for vices and the delights of the flesh and other things that oppose chastity, and that he should maintain a pure body and soul. No soul can enter Paradise until it is purged and cleaned of its sins just as it was when it was placed in the body. Certainly a man can easily restrain himself from these vices if he wishes, except in that which is ordained by God, such as in marriage. However, stupid men say that it is not a sin, since God made male and female, because, if it is a sin, then God ought not to have consented to it since He has the power to prevent it. They are sadly mistaken, because God did not make man like the other dumb beasts to which he gave neither reason nor understanding, and the beasts do not know or understand what they do. However, they have their times to mate, and they abstain the rest of the time. And therefore God gave wisdom and reason to man whereby he could avoid evil and could do good. God gave him his free will in order to choose what he might wish; so that if he does evil he will receive no reward. And truly if a man's wisdom could overcome his nature, he would always be good. And following this argument, some men of little faith say that each one is judged according to his birth: therefore listen, my sons, to this parable that I will now tell you."

130. Of the parable of a philosopher that the king of Mentón told his sons about the birth of men

"The story tells that there is a parable that says thus: that Filemon, a philosopher, arrived in a city and founded a school of physiognomy there. This is a science to judge men by how many different types of features there are. A certain citizen who disliked Filemon summoned several of those scholars and asked them: 'According to what you have learned, what does it mean to have such and such a forehead?'

"They answered that it must mean enviousness.

"'And to have such and such eyes, what does it reveal?'

"They said that it must mean lust.

"'And to have such and such eyebrows, what does it signify?'

"They said that it must show mendacity.

"And he told them: 'Well, your teacher has all of these signs, and according to what he teaches you, he must possess all of these evil traits.'

"They went then to their teacher and told him, 'Master, according to what you have taught us, your own countenance shows these evil traits.' They continued courteously. 'However, master, we do not see this in you, because we ourselves see that you are so respectful and virtuous in every way that it is apparent this information is not true, for we would rather doubt this science than to doubt you.'

"Filemon, their teacher, answered like a wise man:

"'Sons, know that my face reveals all those things. I still lust after evil things, and they come unbidden to my mind. I forced myself in such a way to resist continually the inclination to do what my nature demanded, and I struggle still to strengthen my soul and to aid it, so that it may fulfill the many good things it should. And for this reason, I am such as you see, although my body shows the signs you spoke of. And know that when they asked a wise man what he found in the faces of the signs in astrology and what they signified, he said that in each face there appeared many varied forms. Whatever appears in the face first, which is in the degree of ascendancy, a man always loves and takes pleasure in more than anything else. And know you that in the face of my ascendant star two small negroes appeared. I do not know what I craved more to see before my eyes every day than those two and because I knew it was not proper, I asserted my will and ordered that no negro man should ever enter my house or appear in my presence.

"'And furthermore, know that a certain man asked a wise man, if a man's horoscope revealed that he was to kill a man or violate a woman, and if he did as his stars foretold, would they have to kill him or punish him, since he had been born under a star that had forced him to do it, and it seemed to him he was not to blame. The wise man responded, "Because man has a free will, he has to pay for the evil he does."

"'And what free will could one have who is born under an evil star?' the other asked.

"'The wise man refused to answer him because a crazy man can ask so many questions that all the wise men in the world could not answer them. However, he could have answered this one very easily if he had wanted to: celestial things influence elemental things, and it is obvious that the bodies of men are made from the elements and are worth less than mud when they are soulless. The soul is the spirit of life which God bestows on those men whom he wishes to live, and when the soul is joined to the body, then a man becomes alive and rational and mortal. And the soul without a body and the body without a soul are worthless in this world, for the joining of the soul to the body is life and its departure signifies death. Because the soul is spiritual and the body elemental, the soul has the virtue of guiding the body; and although the appearances of the stars indicate some things about the birth of a man, his soul has the power to defend him from them if it wishes to, for it is spiritual and is higher than the stars and outranks them. They are under the ninth heaven and the soul comes above the tenth heaven, for so the astrologers state, and here it is proven that it is in the power of a man to do good or evil; and this is fitting, so that he may have a reward or punishment for what he does. Wherefore by this, my sons, you should know that it is in the power of a man to overcome the temptations of the flesh and to strengthen the good inclinations of his soul; because free will is given to man to do good or evil, for which he may have a reward or punishment.'"

131. Of how the king of Mentón instructed his sons that they should always fear and love their earthly lord

"And therefore, my sons," said the king of Mentón, "you must believe and be certain that no evil is pleasing to God because He is good and virtuous, and it is not possible for anything base to come from Him. And those who say or believe anything else are badly mistaken, for they are unbelievers and are disobedient to God, nor do they fear the punishment that they should receive in this world from the kings who abide by the faith. Therefore every man who wishes to enhance his reputation and rise to high estate, ought to be primarily obedient to the commandments of God and then to their earthly lord. For obedience is a virtue that is owed to great lords, and especially to those who are in power, for obedience and respect is due to them. Not a man lives in this world without another greater than himself, except the Holy Father, who is greater than all others in spiritual matters. However, God is above him and he is accountable to Him for the office he holds in trust.

"And know that service means that a man truly love his lord and be loyal and true to him in all matters, that he advise him without deceit, that he strive to serve him well and loyally, that he speak well of him each time the occasion arises, that he be grateful for the good he does for him, that he submit his will to his lord's and receive patiently whatever instructions he may give him. On this matter, the wise men have said that a man should be as obedient to his king as to God; for he who is not obedient to his king is not capable of true religious feeling. And therefore they said, 'Fear God because you ought to fear him, and obey the king, because you ought to obey him.' And know that through obedience, a man avoids all evil and saves himself from all suspicion of evil, for obedience is the protector of whoever wishes it, the teacher of whoever pursues it, giving perception to its possessor; because whoever loves God, loves His things, and who loves the things of God loves God's law and therefore must love the king who maintains the faith. Those who are obedient to their king are sure of having peace in the kingdom and do not allow greed to flourish among them, which might upset their society. They will be sure of living under law and order. No subject of the realm should censure the king for how he directs the affairs of the kingdom, and all subjects should be guided by the king. And know that through obedience all contention is avoided, the roads are safe and the good are favored. And there never existed a man who labored in disobedience to the king and searched for ways to do him wrong, to whom God did not bring misfortune before he died—such as happened to Rages, nephew of Fares the king of Syria, as you will now hear."

132. Of the parable that the king of Mentón gave to his sons about King Tabor and his favorites of the palace

"The story relates that Fares, king of Syria, was a good king and much beloved by his subjects. He was married twice, having no children by his first wife and only one by his second. This son was named Tabor. And the king loved Rages, who was his nephew, the son of his sister, as much as if he were his own son. He bestowed more favor upon him than upon all his subjects, promoting his fortune as much as he could. And it came to pass that Fares, king of Syria, became very ill and was at the point of death. Before he died he commended his son and the kingdom to Rages, this nephew of his, and requested him to protect and defend the kingdom, and to rear his son and show and teach him to be virtuous. Rages promised him with his hands between his that he would do so, and he, together with all the other subjects, accepted Tabor as his king and as his only lord after the death of Tabor's father.

"But the devil, who does not hesitate to place evil in the hearts of men, and evil thoughts, inspired this Rages, nephew of the king, to strive to take the kingdom for himself. Being ungrateful for all the good bestowed on him by King Fares, father of this King Tabor, Rages, thinking he would be successful because of his power, did so strive. Rages was the most powerful man in the kingdom, for he strove to have all the noblemen of the kingdom on his side as well as the commoners. He told them the entire kingdom was being destroyed by the negligence of King Tabor, who rather than desiring to do justice, taxed the public more than was just and trampled upon every one's rights. And all this was true, but the blame and the cause of this evil was not King Tabor's, but Rages', in whose care and power the king was after the death of King Fares, his father. King Tabor was only eight years old when the king, his father, died, and he did not possess sufficient wisdom to govern the kingdom properly, nor did he do anything except what Rages ordered or advised him to do. He showed his youth and prankishness in all things, for he had no one to instruct him or to hinder him from doing the contrary, and Rages was pleased with all this, for it suited his evil plans to gain control of the kingdom. When on occasion the king tried to sentence someone who deserved it, Rages prevented it, saying that it was his prerogative. Pleading for the evildoers, he thus prevented justice from being carried out. With the great power he had, and believing he had many supporters, he frequently attempted to carry out his wicked plans. He was strongly supported by Joel, a great and very powerful knight of the kingdom.

"But Our Lord God was deeply concerned over such ingratitude and did not want him, nor did He allow him, to be successful in his wicked plans and designs. It was God's will that any one who deserved it should receive punishment for wrongdoing in the kingdom, as you will now hear. God is the guardian of those who do not merit evil, and He inspired King Tabor, although he was a youth of only fifteen years, to observe and understand the evil and treachery of those who should have been protecting and defending him. They were now close to completely fulfilling their wicked plan of overthrowing the king and leaving Rages lord of the kingdom. Some friends of the king who were faithful to him were deeply concerned over what they saw and understood. They told the king in secrecy to pay attention to what was transpiring and warned him to be attentive to his affairs. They alerted him and made him aware of the problems.

"One night while in his bed meditating over these things he had been alerted to, the king thought to himself that in order to remain king and lord, with God and His aid, he would have to take action against those who planned to overthrow him. It seemed to him that there was no other way except this, and he fell asleep. As he was falling asleep, he saw as though in a dream a small youth who stood before him and said:

"'Arise and carry out your plan to remain king and lord, for I will support you with my people.'

"Early in the morning he arose, and thinking that it might have been one of his pages who was still standing guard, called them and asked if one of them had said anything to him that night. They told him they had not.

"'Well, so be it,' said the king. "Promise me that you will keep secret what I tell you.'

"They promised and the king related to them the wickedness which Rages was planning to do to him, aided by Joel, his friend, and other of his subjects.

"He confided that he would be unable to be successful without aid and counsel from them. Since they knew already that everything the king said was true and fully understood it, one of them said:

"'Sire, for a man of your age, and considering who they are and how powerful they are, you are audacious to undertake such a momentous task.'

"Then another said, 'Sire, be careful and be sure the enemy does not hear of this, or you and we are dead and annihilated, for in a day they could throttle us here in this room like rabbits.'

"A third one joined in, saying, 'Sire, whoever plans to undertake a project ought to plan it painstakingly, in order to carry it out successfully and without harm to himself.'

"Another stated, 'Sire, it is necessary to seek diverse opinions in dangerous matters, just as in this affair, for it is very doubtful if it can be successfully undertaken.'

"And the next declared, 'Sire, whoever can foresee the conclusion of a plan and what possibilities exist seldom errs.'

"And the next said: 'Sire, it is better to delay than to have to repent of haste. Therefore, sire, we are prepared to serve you and take the responsibility for what may happen to us in defense of your person and your kingdom. However, as we are your vassals and have no other lord to provide for us except God and you, we ask you as a favor to consider this enterprise more carefully. Do not put your plan into action so quickly that the rest of the kingdom sides with them, and not with you. Alas! None sides with you and everyone has joined with your subjects in revolt against you.'

"And the king answered them on this matter in this fashion: 'Friends, I want to answer what each one of you has said to me. The first one said this deed was a very great and serious one to undertake because of my youth and their power, and I say that it is true. But, if a thing is never begun, it is never finished. And therefore it is fitting for us to begin with the help of God, for He knows the truth of the matter, and I am certain He will aid us. And as to what the next said—that I should be careful the enemy doesn't hear of the plan, for if so, in a day we would be throttled in this room—I answer that the true and all-knowing God inspired the plan in me. He originated it and considered it well; for you should readily understand that so great a plan as this could not come from my poor wisdom or strength, but it was God who inspired me. And as to what the next said, that whoever plans a great undertaking must plan carefully to complete the deed without harm to himself, I say that it is true. But what can one think about the planning of God and what can one do in order to improve it? Surely, no one; for what He gives or does is certain and sure, and therefore it serves no purpose to argue about it. And as to what the next said, that in dangerous matters, diverse advice was necessary, as in this matter, for it is doubtful whether it could be carried out, I say it is true. But in what God decrees, there is no doubt whatsoever nor should there be any attempt to improve on His judgment, for He was and is the guide and the originator of this plan. And in reference to the next, that whoever foresees the conclusion of what he plans to do and what may happen is sure of himself and can proceed confidently with it, I say that God is the beginning, the way, and the completion of all things. And therefore I am sure that He who was the creator of this plan foresaw the beginning and the end of it. And as to what the next said, that it was better to delay and succeed than to repent through hasty action, I say that when the results are certain, there is no reason for a man to hesitate, but rather he should hasten to achieve them; for once the opportunity is lost it may never come again. And to what all of you say, that this project should not be undertaken so quickly because all the people side with the enemy and none with me, I say it is not so. The truth always travels freely through the open plazas, and duplicity hides furtively in the corners. Therefore the voice of truth always has more followers than the sound of deceit; just as you will be plainly able to see with the aid of God in this undertaking. At the moment these traitors are killed, the rest of their followers and cohorts will flee in every direction stricken by fear because of the treachery they planned, just as a hundred night-prowling thieves flee and hide when one man stands against them. All the others who are not followers of the enemy will rally to the voice of the king, which rings true. And you should realize that greater strength and power echoes in the voice of the king who holds to the truth than in all the lying and treacherous voices of his enemies. And friends, do not be afraid, for you can be sure God will stand with us and crown our venture with success.'

"'Sire, the others agreed, 'since it is true and you are so determined, start now, and we will stand with you in life or in death.'

"'Let us begin tomorrow morning,' said the king. 'Here is the plan: do not let anyone enter my bedroom, and say that I have a fever and am sleeping. And those scoundrels Rages and Joel, being reckless with power and having free run of the court and being pleased with my sickness, will enter alone to ascertain if it is so. When they enter, bar the door and I will act as though I am getting up in order to honor them. Then we shall attack them, execute them as traitors and scoundrels against their natural lord, and cut off their heads. And two of you go to the roof of the palace with their heads, show them to all, and cry out, 'The traitors, Rages and Joel who tried to depose their natural lord, are dead!' Throw the heads before them and cry out, 'Syria for King Tabor!' And you can be certain that none of the enemy will fail to flee, for they will not stand together. The wicked never support their master after he is dead. Good people do, for they are grateful for benefits received in life and death from their benefactor. And all the rest will rally to the voice of the king just as bees come to honey, for they must come, since the king is the one who can dispense all patronage and favors in his kingdom, and no one else.'

"The pages agreed to follow their lord's wishes in such a way the deed was carried out just as the king had told them. Loyal men of the kingdom came at the king's voice, as was right and fitting, and when they learned what had happened, they were astounded at how youths as young as the king and his pages could carry out so great a task, because none of the pages was over eighteen years of age and some of them were even younger than the king. Therefore, the men of the kingdom realized that this deed had been inspired by God; for when they asked the king and each of the pages how it had happened, they answered they did not know, but they had seen the room full of men dressed in white garments, swords in their hands, and a child among them dressed the same as those aiding them, who urged them to fulfill their task. Therefore every man ought to avoid speaking evil, doing evil, or searching for evil without cause against his natural lord; for whatever a man may do, he can be sure of being extremely unfortunate before he dies. And the lord owes this same obligation to the vassals who serve him loyally, dispensing benefits and favors for them as he is obliged to do. And by so doing, he may be certain that God will fight for him against those who serve him treacherously, just as God fought for this king of Syria."

133. Of how the king of Mentón instructed his sons in what manner they were to behave toward a king if they lived with him

"Furthermore, my sons, avoid making your king angry; for whoever angers the king does harm to himself and whoever keeps his distance from him will not be noticed by him. Likewise avoid disagreement with the king, for they customarily count the smallest error as a large one, and although a man may have rendered great services to him over a long period of time, all is forgotten in a moment of anger. Whoever becomes very privy to the king, may anger him, and if he considers his own safety, should keep his distance from him, except if he thinks the king has need of him. For kings have a way of becoming angry with those who become too familiar with them and of wishing harm to the ones whom they esteem the most. And therefore the closer the king draws you into his service, the more you have to be careful; for you should know that there is no greater or more dangerous anger than that of the king, for while laughing, the king may order an execution and while in an exuberant mood may deal out destruction, and he often decrees a heavy punishment for a small crime and at other times allows many crimes to go unpunished. Consequently a man ought not to become angry with the king although the king mistreats him. Although he may be the king's favorite, he should not allow his anger to show; for the king contains great anger and unleashes it like a lion. The king's love can be painful, for at times when he is suddenly angered, he kills with the first spear he can seize. Also he places the unworthy in the seat of the noble, and the coward in the seat of the brave, and is pleased with his actions because it suits his disposition. And know that the king's grace is the best earthly good with which a man can be favored, but he should not do any wrong or be vain or bold while basking in the love of the king, because a king's love is not a piece of land that bears fruit nor does it endure forever. The king is similar to the grape vine, which seizes hold of the nearest trees, whatever they may be, and wraps itself around them and does not look for better trees which are farther away.

"And my sons, next you will consider yourselves first, for true love begins in one's self, and afterward you will extend your love to others by sharing your resources with them and seeking advantage for them by interceding with your lord. But although you are his favorites, avoid angering him, for whoever is closest to him should be careful not to anger or annoy him, because fire burns what is near it more quickly than what is far away. And if the time is not propitious to seek advantage for yourself or for another with him, do not bother him.

"All the seasons in the world, good and bad, have a time limit and the days that they are to last are circumscribed. Then if a bad season comes, endure it until its days are completed and its time limit expires; because the best times in the world are the days in which men live under the protection of a lord who loves truth and justice and moderation. The best chance for the bettering of the times lies with the king. For know that the world is like a book, and men are like letters, and the written pages are like the seasons; for when one is finished, another begins. And be assured that the people's fortunes are a reflection of the king's and depend upon his fortune. And when the time in which they live under his rule expires, great company, weapons, or tumultuous crowds hold no advantage for them. And those men, although they may be small and weak, who begin projects at a propitious time always succeed in whatever they undertake. And they have this good fortune when God sees fit to aid them because of their good virtues. And the best time to live in is that time when the king is good and merits God's love. Those people whom God decides to aid are always fortunate.

"And therefore, my sons, you ought not to be forward with the king in any matter, except when you understand the time is propitious to ask him for what you want; otherwise he may react to your detriment."

134. Of how all people should love one another, but ought to love their own people and instruct them properly

"But, my sons, afterward you will extend love to others, welcoming them and honoring them in words and in deeds and not preventing anyone from obtaining whatever he might need, nor should you speak ill of anyone. First you will love your own people, and afterward you may be charitable with love toward strangers, which means true love; for charity means to truly love one's neighbor and to feel compassion for him and to do good to him as much as possible, but first you should do so to your own, for the Holy Scripture says that charity begins at home.

"All men should honor and treat their kinsmen well, because by doing good and honoring their relatives, their family ties are strengthened and their family increases. However, they ought not to do so if it causes harm to another, for it would be a sin to adorn one altar by stealing the cover from another. And a man acts properly by fearing God and treating his own people well. The greatest charitable act that a man can perform is to treat his poor relatives well, for it is said that three voices can be heard in Heaven: the first is the voice of mercy; the second is the voice of one's conscience; and the third is that of the kinsmen. The voice of mercy says, 'Lord, they created me and they showed no gratitude to me for what they received.' And the voice of conscience says, 'Lord, they did not place loyalty in me, for they did not expend it on me as they should have.' The voice of the kinsmen speaks thus: 'Lord, they do not love us as before and we do not know why.'

"And know that it is a sad state of affairs for a man to give charity to strangers and not to his own kinsmen. Whoever ceases to love his kinsmen without any reason, commits a great wrong unless they do not deserve his love. And therefore they say that all disaffection for God is not a hatred of God, and furthermore that all love for God is not love. And know that a man ought not to hate his own people, however rich or poor they might be, and should do nothing through which his kinsmen might be dishonored.

"It is right that an evil person should not profit from his wickedness, but there are times when a man ought to cover up the sins of his own parents, when they fall into sin accidentally and not through wickedness or premeditation. He should not expose or shame them, for it concerns God when some people expose their own parents who sin unintentionally, just as He showed His concern when Canaan,[1] son of Noah, found him stark naked, and he told his brothers of it in a derisive manner. And when his father learned about it, he cursed him, and God approved of what he said. And therefore, my sons, always love and protect everyone in general, but primarily love and keep your own people. Do not harm anyone, although he may deserve it, unless it be a man whom you have to judge and punish. It is a mortal sin to conceal the deeds of evildoers and to fail to punish them when one can and ought to do so. Certainly a man should first punish his own relatives rather than strangers, and especially should he punish his own children. You owe it to them to correct them without pity. The father who is very

---

1. The author has mistaken Canaan and Ham. It was Ham who uncovered his father's nakedness. Canaan was Noah's grandson.

lenient will never have well-bred children, for as a consequence they will be foolish and reckless. And there will be occasions when the father will be punished for the wickedness of his ill-bred children and rightly so, since he is guilty for failing to punish them when they transgressed. The parents receive the punishment for the sins of their sons, just as happened to a lady from Greece in this manner."

135. Of the story that the king of Mentón told his sons about a lady who never punished her sons and of what consequently happened to the lady

"The story relates that this lady made a good marriage with a good and very rich knight, who passed away and left only a small son that he had by this lady. The lady adored this son, because she had no other, and whatever he did, good or evil, she praised him and let him know she was pleased. And after the boy grew up, he did not cease to do the devil's works, for he wanted to experience them all. He committed highway robbery and killed many men senselessly and violated women wherever he found them to his liking. Whenever the officers who had to enforce the law arrested him for any of these reasons, the lady his mother then took him out of prison. She bribed those who had ordered his arrest and brought him to her home, not saying a single word of reprimand for the evil he had done. Instead she seemed pleased with him, and she invited knights and squires to dine with him, just as if he possessed all the good qualities that every man should have.

"So it was that after he had committed all these crimes, the emperor came to the city where that lady lived. Then those people who had received dishonor and mistreatment from that lady's son came to the emperor and complained to him about it. And the emperor was astounded at these ugly and evil deeds committed by the squire, because he had known his father who had been his vassal for a long time, and he had spoken very well about him. He sent for the squire in regard to these complaints, and he asked him if he had committed all those wicked deeds that the plaintiffs said he had. They related everything to him, and he acknowledged it all, but still excusing himself that he had done it as a youth of little wisdom.

"'Clearly, friend,' said the emperor, 'any one of a thousand men would be put to death for the least of these things, if it were true. And even if he were my son and had committed these crimes, I would order him executed for them, since I must enforce the law and mete justice to each who deserves it. And since you have openly confessed what you did, it is not necessary for us to make any other investigation here and no other proof is needed for what is self-evident.'

"And he ordered his constable to have him taken away to be executed. And as they were taking him away to be executed, his mother was following after him, screaming and tearing her face with her nails and crying as loud as possible, so that there was not a man in the city who did not feel great pity for her. Some good men of the city went to ask the emperor to pardon him, and some of the plaintiffs felt compassion for the lady; but the emperor, as one who always lives by the law, refused to pardon him, and instead ordered him to be executed without fail. And as they arrived at the place of execution, the mother asked the constable as a favor to permit her to embrace her son and to kiss him on the mouth before they executed him. The constable ordered the executioners to detain him and not to execute him until after his mother had arrived and embraced him. The executioners detained him and told him his mother wanted to embrace and kiss him on the mouth before he was executed. He was very pleased and then said in a loud voice:

"'Let my mother be welcome for she wishes to make me see that justice is carried out as it should be. I well believe that God would not want anyone else except the person who deserves it to suffer punishment.'

"All were amazed at those words that the squire was saying, and they waited to see what could possibly develop. And as soon as the lady reached her son, she opened her arms, grief-stricken, and went to him. They had released his hands, although they were guarding him very closely so that he could not escape.

"'Friends,' said the squire, 'you can be sure that I will not run away, for I desire, and am pleased, that justice be carried out. I consider myself a terrible sinner for doing so much evil as I did, and I want justice to begin with the one who deserves it.'

"And he reached his mother as though he wanted to kiss and embrace her, and he took her by the ears beneath her hair with his hands,[1] and he placed his mouth against hers, and began to gnaw and eat away her lips so that he did not leave her anything up to her nose, nor of her lower lip to the point of her chin, and all her teeth were exposed and she remained very ugly and disfigured.

"Everyone who was present was horrified at this great cruelty that that squire committed, and they began to curse and attack him. And he said:

"Gentlemen, do not revile me or restrain me, for it was God's justice and He ordered me to do it.'

"'And why against your mother?' asked the others. 'Is she to be mutilated for the evil you committed? Tell us what impelled you to do it.'

"'Indeed not,' answered the squire, 'I will not tell it except to the emperor.'

"Many went to the emperor to tell him of this inhumane deed that the squire had done, and they told him how he did not want to tell anyone

---

1. This strange way to hold by the ears while kissing was referred to as a "Dutch kiss."

except the emperor why he had done it. The emperor ordered them to bring him into his presence and refused to sit down to dine until he had found out why he had committed this astounding and cruel deed. And when the squire arrived in his presence, and the lady his mother came before him, horrid and loathsome, the emperor said to the squire:

"'Speak, you treacherous scoundrel, were not all the wicked deeds you committed in this world sufficient to satisfy you? As to your mother who bore you and raised you extravagantly and lost everything she owned on your account by paying fines for the evil and wicked deeds you committed—why did you mutilate her in such a manner that she is unfit to appear before men? Did you have no compassion for your own blood in shedding it so outrageously? Didn't you fear God or the hatred of men, who consider it a wicked and extremely cruel deed you perpetrated?'

"'Sire, said the squire, 'let what God considers right be fulfilled. None can prevent it from being done. And God who is of all the justices in the world, the sternest, intended that justice be applied to that one who was the cause of the wickedness that I committed.'

"'And how can this be?" asked the emperor.

"'Certainly, sire, I will tell you. This lady, my mother whom you see, although she leads a very saintly life, doing good to those who are in need, dispensing her charity very freely, and praying very devoutly, considered it proper not to punish me in word or in deed when I was small or after I was grown. She praised me for whatever I did, whether it was good or bad, and she gave me everything she owned for me to spend, and alas! I spent it more on evil works than on good. And just now when they told me she wanted to greet me and kiss me on the mouth, it seemed that Heaven inspired me to devour her lips with which she could have disciplined me and had not. And I did it considering that it was the judgment of God. And He knows well that she is the thing that I love most in this world; but since God wanted it to be so, it could not be otherwise. And sire, if greater justice is to be carried out here, order it done to me; because I greatly deserve it on account of my great misery.'

"And the plaintiffs present felt great compassion for the squire and the lady his mother, who was grief-stricken because the emperor had ordered him executed. Seeing that the squire acknowledged the error of his ways, they asked the emperor's grace in pardoning him, because they had forgiven him.

"'Truly,' said the emperor, 'God has bestowed great mercy on me in this matter in determining that justice should fall upon that person whom He knew for certain was the cause of all the misdeeds of this squire. Since God desired this result, I release him and pardon him from the judgment I ordered carried out on him, because I did not understand the truth of the matter as God did. Therefore, blessed be His name!'

"Then the emperor made the squire a knight and received him as his vassal, and he was from that time on a very good man and highly esteemed. And the lady got the justice she deserved, as an example for those who have children to rear that they may be careful and not fall into danger through failure to punish their children; just as happened to Eli, one of the greatest priests of olden times, as is related in the Bible.[2] Eli was good and led a saintly life, and because he did not punish his sons as he should have, and they were wicked, Our Lord God demonstrated his vengeance against them for their evil works and against their father as well because he had not punished his sons. They were slain in battle, and when the father learned of it, he fell from a high seat, broke his neck, and died. And although the emperor rightly should have sentenced that squire for the crimes he had committed, he failed to do so through the compassion that all judges must have. They should always have mercy on those who acknowledge their crimes and repent of the evil they have committed. Because this squire acknowledged his sins and repented, and the plaintiffs asked the emperor's mercy for him, the emperor through his mercy pardoned him. It is said that justice which is not tempered with mercy is not justice, but cruelty. Therefore all men who have sons ought to be merciless and not compassionate when punishing them. If they rear them properly they will be a pleasure, and if badly, they will always be a problem. The fathers will always be fearful that because of the evil that the sons commit, they may be punished, and perhaps the punishment may fall on the fathers who reared them improperly, just as happened to the lady of whom we just spoke. Certainly youths can be easily trained, for they are like wax, and just as wax is soft and one can knead and shape it in whatever form he wishes, so the one who wants to rear a youth to conform to the customs he approves of, must do so with a rod in his hand and have no compassion."

136. Of how the king of Mentón showed his sons all the things that pertain to being gentlemen

"Thus, my sons, you ought always to accompany and associate with the best men of intelligence and wisdom, because from these men you will learn only good, and you should be friends with both the great and the small. Above all you should honor ladies and maidens, and when you speak with them you must avoid obscene or stupid words, for then they will reprimand you, for they are very perceptive in noticing what is said to them and in the use of scornful speech. And when they speak, they say few but graceful words with great wisdom, and at times with the intention of being scornful and reproachful. And no wonder, because they study nothing else! And you should be well versed in the use of the lance, jousting, hunting, playing backgammon

2. 1 Samuel 2:12 and 4:18.

and chess, and running and fighting, for you never know where it may be necessary to aid yourself with your feet or your hands. You must learn fencing, for it is proper for a knight to be expert in fencing, and you should be moderate in eating and drinking. In Latin they say 'abstinence,' which stands for moderation in eating, drinking, and conversation. Moderation is one of the seven virtues; and therefore you will be moderate in conversation, for it is a mistake to talk too much, and a man is shamed by falling into the error of tending to speak too much, especially if he speaks ill of another and is not careful of his language.

"For man's wisdom lies in his language. And therefore it does no good to be silent to one who speaks wisely, and it does no good to converse with the one who talks stupidly. It is said that God listens to hear what each tongue says. Therefore the man is very fortunate who is more liberal with his possessions than with his speech. And of all the things in the world, it is good for a man to have a great bounty, but not of words, because too many of them are a problem. And therefore it is better for a man to be mute than to speak evil, for there is no advantage, but rather harm to body and soul, in malicious gossip. Wherefore the Scripture says: 'Who is not careful with his language is careless with his soul.' And if a man speaks about something unnecessarily and at an improper time and place, it is a shameful thing. And therefore, a man ought to be careful that what he says is true, for lying shames a man. A man cannot have a worse sickness than to have a reputation as a malicious gossip. And occasionally great sins are inspired by a wicked heart and great evils happen because of the tongue. Frequently worse wounds are committed by the tongue than by knife blows. And therefore a man should use his tongue in the cause of truth, for the tongue is inclined to follow its habitual use. And know that one of a man's worst habits is to have his tongue ready to support evil.

"Moreover a person is very fortunate when God finds it fitting to endow him with patience and tolerance.

"Because patience is a virtue, a man should endure wrongs that are done to him. He should not return evil for evil either in speech or deed, and he should not show anger or ill will nor hold malice in his heart for anything that may be done to him or said against him. And patience is of two types: one is for a man to accept those who are greater than he; the second is for a man to have forbearance with those who are less than he. And for this reason it is said that there can be no argument if one man forbears. Two good men never quarrel with one another, and furthermore one good man never quarrels with a bad man, because it takes two to make a quarrel. However you will find a quarrel between two bad men. When a good man and a bad one, or a nobleman and a commoner, quarrel, all are bad and considered the same. Consequently a man should leave things at peace and be patient.

"And so a man can attain his goals, if he endures some unpleasantnesses. Because, my sons, if a man avoids things that he believes may be harmful, he will acquire things that can be advantageous to him. Therefore it is said that those who patiently endure will overcome. And know that sufferance is of five kinds: the first kind is that a man must bear the worries which result from his just actions; the second, that he endure the things that he wrongfully desires that are harmful to his body and soul; the third, that he suffer worry over the things for which he expects to receive a reward; the fourth, that he endure what worries him over things that might cause him even greater worries; the fifth, that he may bear up by doing good and avoid doing evil. And know that one of the best comforts a wise man can have is tolerance. And therefore they say that the wiser a man is, the more tolerant he is.

"And if a man is tolerant and patient he can not commit a shameful act, for he should avoid shameful behavior. A man ought to value the sense of his own dignity and always hold it before him. Thus he will not fall into sin for fear of shame. And shame is like a fine mirror which does not leave a stain on the face of the observer. Whoever is always conscious of shame cannot fall into sin because of this awareness. And thus whoever tends to avoid sin and shame has the reputation of being wise and prudent."

137. How the king of Mentón instructed his sons to seek knowledge continually and how he showed them the virtues of knowledge

"My sons, you will endeavor to be wise men and to acquire knowledge. Do not be slow to comprehend because if you are dull, you will be lost. Therefore it is said that knowledge is worth more than wealth, for knowledge protects the man but man has to protect wealth. Wherefore they say that knowledge is lord and helper. It is a well-known truth that kings sit in judgment over the land, but they are judged by their wisdom. And knowledge is so vast that no one can acquire it all; so you should choose the best from every thing. The value of each person lies in his knowledge, and the one who loves knowledge has to search for it, just as someone does who has lost his most prized possession. In searching for knowledge he pursues it as diligently as he can, and he asks for it from everyone he meets and looks for it in every way possible and in as many places as he thinks he may find it, for it is certain that everything in this world has greater value according to its scarcity. In the same manner, the larger the quantity the lower the value. Wherefore it is said in Latin, *'Omne rarum preciosum'* for it means, 'The thing that is rarest is most valued,' and to the contrary, knowledge is more valued the more there is of it, and the more a man has of it, the more he is esteemed. And knowledge is like the candle, for no matter how many are illuminated by it, its light is not worth less or diminished thereby. The best knowledge in the world is that which gives advantage to the one who holds it. And know, my sons, that the light of faith is perverted when the wise man shows himself to be heretical and the stupid man shows himself to be of good faith; and he can place the blame on knowledge. Man recognizes the good and grace that God does for him, and recognizing it, he is grateful for it, and being grateful for it, he will deserve it. And the best thing the wise man does is what knowledge commands him to do; therefore a little thing that man does through wisdom is worth more than a great deal that he does through stupidity. And some quest for knowledge but not in God's service and finally knowledge returns them to His service, for knowledge is light, and ignorance is darkness. And therefore, my sons, seek knowledge, for in learning it, you will be serving God. For every man who speaks wisely is the same as one who praises God.

"And know that there are two gluttons who are never satisfied: one is the one who loves wisdom and the other is the one who loves wealth, for with knowledge a man gains paradise, and with wealth a man earns consolation in his loneliness, and with it he will be placed among his equals. And knowledge will be for him weapons with which he may defend himself from his enemies, for with four things the one who has no right to be a lord can become a lord: one is with knowledge; the second is in being well-mannered; the third is in being of good faith; the fourth is in being loyal. And my sons, God raises men with knowledge and transforms them into lords and guardians of the people. And knowledge and wealth raises the lowly and aids the mean-spirited. Knowledge without work is like a tree without fruit, and knowledge is a gift that comes from the throne of God."

138. Of how the king of Mentón showed his sons that they should always practice good and be very courteous

"And therefore it is fitting for a man to work well with what he knows and that he not allow it to be lost, and thus with knowledge a man can be courteous in his speech and his deeds.

"For, my sons, breeding is the sum of all good things, and the substance of good breeding is for a man to have modesty before God and men and himself, for the well-bred man fears God, and the well-bred man does not want to do in secrecy what he would not do in public. A well-mannered man does not do all the things he has the desire to. Nobility means that a man has to work hard in looking for good in men as much as he can. Humility is to consider whatever one has to be abundant, for wealth is the soul of humility and of purity if good use is made of it, and chastity is the life of the soul, and leisure is the soul of patience. Nobility means that a man has to suffer despair or indignity and not be moved to commit a sin on account of it; and therefore they say that there is no good without misery.

"For certainly the greatest blow and the greatest misery that it seems that men are to suffer is when some one does something to them against their will and they do not retaliate for it."

139. Of how the king of Mentón instructed his sons how they should always be humble

"Moreover, my sons, believe that a man can not be a courtly person nor well-mannered nor of good faith, unless he is humble, because humility is the fruit of faith. And therefore the one who is of good faith is of humble heart. And humility is one of the nets with which a man acquires nobility. And therefore the Holy Scripture says, 'Whoever is humble will be exalted, and whoever desires to exalt himself will be humbled.' And the greater power a nobleman has, the more humble he is and the less he is incited to anger by offenses, although they may be serious things for him to endure, just as the great mountain is not moved by a fierce wind. And the person of low estate, with the little power that he may have, takes great pride in himself and his arrogance increases. And the greatest good for a man to do, without hope of reward, is that he endeavor to earn something without malice and to be humble without abasement; for if the noble humbles himself, it is exaltation of himself, and if he takes pride in himself, he is debasing himself. For honor goes not to the one who receives it, but to the one who confers it. Wherefore whoever is humble in spirit, good will seek him out, just as water seeks its own level.

"And therefore, my sons, try to be humble and not full of pride, because through humility you will be loved and prized by God and men, and through pride, you will be scorned, and men will flee from you as from those people who pride themselves more than they should.

"They do not call anyone arrogant except the one who places himself in a higher station than befits him. And for this reason they say no one ever takes pride in himself except the man of low estate, because if the nobleman takes pride in himself, his nobility is diminished, and if he humbles himself, he gains in stature, since it is a weakness of the brain for a man to esteem himself more than he is worth. And the one who does not esteem himself too much is really truly esteemed in body and soul, and the one who prizes himself too much, although he may be of high station, falls into shame when he happens to be among men who know him. It is a great wonder for a man to pride himself for stepping twice in the place where he has urinated. And know that it is not as bad for a man to sin who is humble as it is when he takes great pride in himself but does not sin.

"Therefore, my sons, if you wish to be appreciated and loved by God and man, be receptive to good and not to evil; that is to say, be guided by your reason and not by your emotion. For a man is stupid who does not know that his emotion is the enemy of his reason, for reason and logic stay asleep until a man wakes them and emotion is awake all the time. Therefore, emotion overcomes reason more often. Wherefore the serious danger to reason is for a man to be submissive to his emotion. And know that for a man to be disobedient to his reason and be dominated by his emotion is the stairway by which a man climbs to all kinds of wickedness. And therefore the most advantageous struggle that man can wage is to struggle against his emotion."

140. How the king of Mentón instructed his sons to use their reason more than their emotion

"Well, my sons, if you wish to be good men you must strive to overcome your desires and you must struggle forcefully, and thus you will escape evil which might come to you. And you can well believe that every man who is obedient to his emotion is more a slave than the imprisoned captive, and therefore he who is intelligent does things according to reason and not according to his emotion. For he who is master of himself will rise in station and his wealth will increase, and he who is a servant of his passion will be humbled and his wealth will decrease. And know that reason is a tired friend, and emotion is a wide-awake enemy and a follower of evil more than of good. And therefore a man ought to obey his reason, which is a true friend, and oppose his passion, which is a treacherous enemy.

"Therefore that person to whom God has seen fit to give good native intelligence is very fortunate, because it is worth more for a man to know how to rule himself in this world and to gain the next than to have great erudition. And therefore it is said that one ounce of erudition with good native intelligence is worth more than a hundredweight of learning without common sense; for learning makes a man proud and haughty, and common sense makes him humble and patient. And everyman of common sense can reach high estate by acquiring good manners, especially if they are educated men, because in erudition a man can find out which are the things that he ought to use and which are those that he ought to avoid. And therefore, my sons, strive to learn, for in education you will see and you will understand things better in order to protect and guide your actions in regard to those whom you love. For these two things, common sense and education, maintain the world in justice, truth, and charity."

141. Of how the king of Mentón instructed his sons that they should always fear God if they should become kings and lords over others

"Furthermore, my sons, pay attention to what it is incumbent on you to do, if you are to command lands where you are kings or lords. No one should be king if he is not ennobled with exalted qualities from God. And you must know that the nobility of kings and great lords must be of three types: the first, respecting that of God; the second, respecting that of themselves; the third respecting that of the people whom they are to rule in justice and truth. Therefore the kings should study the nobility of God if they are to find it in themselves. It is divided into three parts: the first, is to fear the power of God; the second, to recognize His truth; the third, to love His will. And these noble qualities ought to be in every king, and he must be tested by faith, and by nature and by examples. Wherefore the first noble quality of the king is the fear of God; for why will the least fear the greatest who does not see fit fear that One who has the power? Certainly he who does not see fit to fear the power of God gives a reason and license to those who ought to fear him, not to do so. And therefore he cannot rightly tell and order his lesser subjects to fear him, for he does not see fit to fear the greater One who has power over him. And you must know that his power is nothing compared to the power of God, which is over all and is never ending. And the king's power is over another and the king is mortal. And since the king derives his power to judge mortals from the power of God, he ought to understand that God is to judge him because God has the power. And it is a sure thing that God in His judgment does not differentiate between the mighty and the powerless because He made every one and is lord of all, and therefore His judgment is equal. Therefore, my sons, may it always be your greatest fear and not your greatest desire for you to want others to fear you. And not only ought you to fear the power of God, but you ought to fear that of the world; for the higher and more honored the estate a man has, the more he must protect himself from falling from it, because the farther he falls, the more serious and dangerous is the fall. And therefore it is fitting that high estate be sustained and maintained by wisdom and good traits, as a high tower with a good foundation is supported, and so is a high arch with strong columns, for the one who is of low estate and near the earth does not have far to fall, and if he falls, he is not hurt as badly as the one who falls from on high."

142. How the king of Mentón instructed his sons to love the truth and always to abide by it

"Furthermore, the second quality of the nobility of kings is to recognize the heavenly truth which comes from God; and men can not recognize it if they do not pay attention to God's works, for much is hidden from the understanding of men, for the works of God have always existed, are, and shall be. Wherefore, my sons, dedicate yourselves to God's truth so that what you do and say may be true, and adhere strongly to it and keep it well, so that it will not change or alter. For the philosopher says that truth is said to be that in which there is no change or variety. And whatever changes from what began as the truth is not the truth; moreover, you ought to know that the truth is praised by the true God and by the kings who recognize the truth of God and follow it, and remain faithful in it, speaking the truth to their people and not lying to them or breaking their promise to them. These are the kings who recognize God's truth, because they love the truth and abhor lying. And the king or lord without the truth is not a king except in name alone; and therefore the lying king does not have nor will have nor can have vassals or faithful friends, because he loses the love of God and of his people and falls into great dangers. This is found in the parables of the ancient histories about those people who were lacking veracity and were accustomed to lies, not fearing God and not desiring to know his truth, through which actions they were killed and destroyed, just as Abenadab, king of Syria, who worshiped idols and deserted the faith of God, was destroyed. He was strangled by the hands of Azael his servant, and likewise Sedchias, king of Judah, who promised and swore allegiance to Nebuchadnezzar, but lied to him as a perjurer and was conquered and taken prisoner in chains and brought to Babylon."

143. Of how the king of Mentón told his sons that the nobility of kings lies in winning the love of God

"Furthermore, the third nobility of kings is the love of the goodness of God, from which all the other good things spring, for He is the source of all good things. Therefore, my sons, if you wish to be nobles, do not let your hearts depart from the goodness of God, loving it and carrying out your works in pursuit of it; for the goodness of God wants and desires that all things be similar to it and that all things be accompanied by all good, according to the power of each one. And, my sons, if you really want to think about where the good that you do comes from, you will find for certain that it comes to you from the goodness of God, just as the evil that you do comes to you from the wickedness of the devil, which is contrary to the commandments of God; for your good works are kept in the goodness of God, just as it is in the power of God to protect it. And know that all things must return to God just as you will on your death. And therefore the holy Gospel says that all the honor and glory forever is through Him, with Him, and in Him; and from Him and in Him are all things that are to come, for the things that are not can be through God's grace, and without the mercy of God, nothing exists or did or can ever be. And do you not see, my sons, that God sheds his light on the good as well as on the wicked, and it rains as much on the sinners as on the just? And how blessed is the kindness of God, for it awaits the sinners who repent and pursues those who flee and even those who are far removed from it! When He sees them return, He watches over them with kind eyes and He welcomes them and wants them to stand near His goodness. Then who is that one whom God's goodness does not love or follow in all his deeds? Truly, one must go with everyone in pursuit of it and seek it. Wherefore, my sons, you must understand and know and believe that all men ought to love the grace of God and show it through their works, especially kings and those who receive favors most liberally from the mercy of God. Among those men, those who are good and love truth and make use of it always progress from good to better and are healthy, happy, and strong. And through their good faith in His goodness they are chosen to be honored and to have an abundance of all the noble qualities of this world and the glory of the next. And my sons, what is it that kings and other men must render to God for the benefits that He has done them? Certainly, I do not know anything else except for them to take advantage of the kindnesses of God in order to serve the goodness of God; and so they may be loved and exalted by God in honor and be sustained in it because of the goodness and honor and other advantages that spring from God's power just as David was, because he feared God's power and recognized the truth of God and worshiped his goodness. Therefore God said of David, 'I have found a good strong man near to my heart.'"

144. Of the nobility that kings and other great lords ought to have in themselves

"And furthermore, having observed the nobility of kings and great lords, I find there are three kinds: the first is to protect the heart; the second is to be careful what you say; the third is to be successful in what you begin. The protection of the heart means to avoid ambition for honors and for riches and pleasures; for since the king is the most honored in his kingdom, he must be more moderate in his desire for honors, because he who is extremely ambitious does things that he ought not to do, for by them he wishes to exalt himself over others. Furthermore he ought to protect his heart from greediness for wealth, for who has great greed for it cannot help but take some one else's without cause. And therefore primarily the fire of greed in his heart must be dampened, so that the smoke of mischief and theft may not make the people cry who might be harmed, and so their voice may rise up to God. Furthermore they must protect their hearts and suppress in them the pleasures of the flesh, in such a manner that their greed may not appear in their work; moreover, a king ought to sever the roots of greed that he holds in his heart, just as Cicero, a sage, said: 'The king must restrain lust primarily in himself, and suppress avarice, and humble his pride, and erase from his heart all other stains, and then by doing good works, he is fit to command others, and such a king or such an emperor is to be praised.' And certainly all evil things and all good things come from the heart and in the heart lies life and death. Wherefore if the roots of greed in the heart were cut away, the branches from it would all wither away, just as when the spring is empty, the rivers that come from it cease to flow. And because Abraham and Isaac and Jacob and Moses and David and Solomon, the prophets, protected their hearts from these things, they were made holy."

145. Of the guard that kings and other great lords must place on their tongues and the other five senses

"And furthermore, the restraint on the king's tongue must be in three ways: the first, that he may not say more than what he ought to; the second, that he not be cowardly in what he says; the third, that he may not be changeable in what he might say, for then he says more than he ought to and says deceitful things needlessly. And he is deficient in what he ought to say when he ceases to speak the truth. He is contentious in what he says when he lies. And then he is forgetful of what he says when he abuses or praises someone. In praising one time and denouncing the next, he speaks ill of God and of his neighbor, placing the blame on them when he ought not, and speaks many blasphemies against God and many lies and deceitful things about his neighbor while at times praising himself and flattering another. Therefore the king or a lord must avoid these things very carefully and not have anything superfluous, contentious, or disagreeable in his speech, because life or death for the people depends on the speech of the king, and the word of the Holy Scripture says: 'The king said, "Strike," they struck, "kill," they killed; he said "forgive," they forgave.' And on this matter Solomon said, 'I wait and I watch the king's tongue, because his commands are like the word of God.' Whatever he wants to do, he does, because his word is powerful, and without this control over his tongue whoever he denounces is denounced and whoever he praises is praised. And therefore the king's mouth must be closely sealed and careful in what he might have to say. For the philosopher said: 'It is fitting for the king to be reticent, not a repeater of gossip, or prejudiced, not a censurer or an inquirer into the secret wickedness of men, not to want to know too much about them, nor to speak of the gifts that he may have given, and not to be mendacious; because discord is born from lying, and displeasure from discord, and insult from displeasure, and from insult, the dissolution of love, and hatred from the dissolution of love, and war from hatred, and enmity from war, and battle from enmity, and cruelty from battle, which destroys all the unions and companionships of men; and cruelty is the destruction of all man's nature, and the destruction of man's nature is harm to all men in the world. Moreover, the king ought always to speak the truth; because the truth is the root of all praiseworthy things; because from the truth the fear of God is born, and justice is born from the fear of God, and from justice, companionship, and from companionship, generosity, and from generosity, consolation, and from consolation, love, and from love, the support and protection of a loved one.' And thus through all these things, the duties between the people and the law are affirmed, and the population increases, and certainly this is fitting to man's nature.

"And therefore it is fitting that the king be slow to speak, and not speak except when it is necessary, because if men hear him many times, they will value him little; because contempt is born from great familiarity. And the king must be careful to abide by and not contravene his own law, for otherwise the law that he made will be scorned, and the foundation of the law also. And he must keep from swearing, except in some matter in which he ought to, and if he swears, not through fear of death or for any other reason, he ought to cease to do so. And my sons, use your tongue in deeds as it fits man's nature, speaking the truth, because the one who lies goes against nature. And know that the tongue is the servant of the heart, and it is such as the bucket that draws water from the well, but the tongue that lies scoops up what it does not find in the heart, and it says what is not there or what it does not find, and it is not suitable to be compared to the bucket, for the bucket does not yield anything except what it finds in the well. And surely it would be a strange thing to try to pick figs from the grapevine and grapes from thorns, for fire does not chill, and he who has nothing does not give. And furthermore, my sons, know that he who speaks blasphemies does so against himself; because when he blames his birth, he speaks against that One who created him, and he is like the branch which fights against the roots that feed it, and the river against the spring, and the inspired against the inspirer, and the work against the maker, and the axe against the one who chops with it. And whoever speaks blasphemies destroys his truth and that of others, and dishonors all who are present, and abuses the goodness of things when he muddies the spring where they originate. And someone such as this enrages everything against himself, and will therefore come to a bad end; because the Scripture says, that all the reaches of the earth will make war for God against the senseless fool who blasphemes."

146. Of how the king of Mentón instructed his sons not to be slanderers

"Furthermore, my sons, know that the slanderer will not go without punishment, for the slanderer endeavors to eat and to gnaw away the life of men with six teeth of evil, and they are these: one tooth is when he denies the good that he knows; and the second is when he remains silent when others praise and speak well; and the third is when he denounces virtue; and the fourth is when he reveals a secret; and the fifth is when he prizes evil and speaks it; and the sixth is when he casts blame on another through slander. And therefore, my sons, you must avoid speaking ill of anyone. And do not give the people any reason whereby they may speak ill of you, because the people, when they speak, can also rise against you. And when some one speaks ill of God, God answers him through His prophets in His judgments, and whenever He speaks, He acts. And therefore, avoid the forementioned and you will escape retribution. And pay attention to the ancient parables: for Rehoboam, son of Solomon, said to his people, 'My father hath lashed you with whips but I will chastise you with scorpions.' The people learned of this speech that he made, and as a consequence he lost the kingdom that his father had left him, for he spoke evil and they rose against him, just as the ancient proverb says: 'Then I lost my honor when I spoke evil and the consequences were bad for me.' And when Pharaoh spoke blasphemy: 'The river is mine, and I created it myself,' he was overthrown, cast out of the kingdom, and died in exile. And Nebuchadnezzar, king of Babylon, because he spoke ill of his people and blasphemed against God, was cast out from among men and he lived with the wild beasts of the field. He ate grass just like an ox, and his body was bent with the dew[1] from heaven until his hair grew similar to the feathers of eagles, and his nails like the claws of birds, and his kingdom was given to another."

147. Of how the king of Mentón told his sons that kings ought to be just

"Furthermore, the nobility of kings watching over the affairs of the people is of two types: the first is to punish men rightfully and without anger; the second is to know how to abide with them with compassion, for punishment rightfully and with law comes from justice, and forbearance with compassion comes from mercy. Wherefore the philosopher says that there are two things that maintain the world and populate it, and without them the world can neither be well populated nor well maintained, and these are justice and truth. Whereby justice does not mean anything else except to protect and defend each in his right, those of low estate as well as the great. For with justice being championed, the cities grow and the king and all his subjects become wealthy, for a rich people is the treasure of kings, and therefore justice must be guarded and maintained in all the business and edicts from the house of the kings.

"The good or the evil of the earth comes directly from the throne of the king just as rivers of sweet or bitter waters are born from springs, and whatever the nature of the springs is, such will be the waters which originate in them; and whatever is the nature of the governors and counselors of the king, such will be the nature of the works which they espouse. Therefore the king is very fortunate who sees that justice is observed in all his orders and

---

1. The dew did not weigh down Nebuchadnezzar—he had to bend over to lick the dew from the grass.

who does not use his power except to promulgate good laws, and may these laws survive as a rule for justice and truth. May the king always have beside him advisers who are not selfish, for surely one of the most beneficial things in the world is justice, for through justice the world is populated, and through justice the world is sustained. Kings reign through justice, and through justice the people obey them, and through justice the hearts of the fearful are reassured, and through justice men forsake anger, envy, and evildoing. And therefore the wise men said that justice is more beneficial in the land than an abundance of meats, and the just king is more beneficial than the rain. And what does it profit men to have an abundance of meats and riches and not be in control of this abundance and to always live in fear and suspicion on account of a lack of justice? Surely it is better to live poor in the land of a just king and be master of what one owns than to live rich in the land of an unjust king and not be master of one's own wealth and have to flee with it, hide it, and not be able to make use of it. In the land lacking justice, all live in fear and suspicion except men of wicked ways, for they do not want justice to be administered to them nor to others, and they want to go on doing evil as they please.

"Moreover, the king and justice are two things that cannot endure one without the other. Without the king to maintain justice, its power cannot be used, nor can the king without justice do what he ought to do, for justice is such as the king says it is and what he does, for the good king does justice primarily to himself and to his own people where he knows it is right, and afterward he metes justice to others as a matter of fact. For how can one who does not wish to do justice to himself judge another, and how can he judge another well if he can not do justice to himself or his own people? Certainly the one who cannot correct himself cannot correct another unless he himself is without blame, for this one is similar to the one who says that he sees the beam in another's eye and refuses to see the mote in his own. Therefore it is a very shameful thing, and even more shameful to a king or a prince, to reprimand another for an error of which he is also guilty. And therefore it says in the Holy Scripture that one who is placed in this world to correct the transgressions of others ought not to be ashamed of correcting his own, because it would be arrogance to persevere in his own harmful ways against another and say, 'I want whatever I order to be constant and lasting, whether it be good or bad,' and so he would not have the name of being a just king; for through love or hatred, or through anything that they may promise him, or through any partisan thing, he must do nothing else except justice and right, and he must protect the authority that God gave him over men, for if he uses it for good, it will be enduring for him, and if he does not use it well, he may lose it. For God does not leave his gifts for long with that person who does not merit them or use them well, and if that person who has the power to administer justice to others does not do it, perhaps

God will subject him to judgment. God is a stern enforcer of the law, although He administers it with great compassion when He realizes that
compassion is needed."

148. Of how the king of Mentón told his sons they should always temper justice with mercy

"And so the king in meting out justice ought to have compassion where it is
fitting to have compassion, such as to those who err by accident and not
knowingly. It says in the Scripture that a king who does not have compassion
can not long endure. And when kings follow a course of law and order, then
violence, wrongs, and crime flee the kingdom, and if they are ignored a short
while, then this evil prospers and harms justice, just as weeds do that grow in
wheat and damage it if they are not rooted out. And therefore, kings ought
never to allow evils to endure for long, but knowing the truth, they should
subject them to justice, for it is a sure thing that justice is born from truth,
for justice can not be administered fairly if the truth is not first known. Thus
every king or prince ought to be truthful in whatever he does or says, because
men are always more observant of the king than of anyone else, for the small
mistake on the part of the lord is very dangerous and more damaging than a
great error of the people, for if the people err, the king ought to correct
it, and if the king errs, there is no one to correct it except God. Therefore the
lord should always want men to find him truthful, for the truth should
always be public and not hidden away, for truth is the source of all praiseworthy things. From truth is born the fear of God; and from the fear of God,
justice is born; and from justice, fellowship; and from fellowship, generosity;
and from generosity, consolation; and from consolation, love; and from love,
protectiveness, just as from falseness, which is the opposite of truth, is born
displeasure; and from displeasure, discord; and from discord, offense; and
from offense, enmity; and from enmity, battle; and from battle, cruelty; and
from cruelty, destruction; and from destruction, harm to everything in the
world.

"And so all the kings and princes in the world ought to love justice and
truth above all other ideals, and those who do so are honored and powerful
and rich and loved by God and by men. They live a satisfying life, because
all their subjects have trust in the fair and truthful king, and they know they
will not receive wrong from him nor from anyone else.

"They are certain that justice and truth are to be found in him, especially when justice is tempered with compassion where it should be, for
the king must be similar to God; for God in punishing sinners, gives them a
place where they may repent, postponing punishment, and He says, 'I do not
wish death for sinners, but only that they be converted and live.' The king
is not only lord of the people, but a father to them. He not only gives punish-

ment to those who deserve it, but provides for and loves his people. As he is king, he ought not to be a tyrant, for the king should love his subjects as his sons, and he ought to rule them and lead them with compassion, and he should be temperate in heart in order to amend errors. And my sons, do you not see that God saw fit not to give the king of the bees any weapons? Know that nature did not want to make him cruel, for it took away his stinger and left his anger helpless. Surely this is a great and good example for kings, so that they will not levy harsh justice, but compassion, on those whom they want to punish and correct. Those who persist in their wickedness and do not wish to mend their ways do not deserve mercy, for just as a great wound of the body can not be cured except with great and strong medicines, so the wickedness of those who persist in sin can not be purged except by harsh judgments without mercy, such as by iron and flames."

149. Of how the king of Mentón told his sons that all kings sought to hold counsel with the prelates of the Holy Mother Church

"And in all these things that have been said about the noble qualities of kings and in all other matters to which kings must attend, they should take counsel with the priests of the faith. They should take some priests as advisers in their government, for without them they cannot do good, just as is shown by natural science, because man was created with both a spiritual and temporal nature, and therefore justice was necessary in order to impose peace among men. Justice must be sustained by the king and by the priest of the faith. And the king must punish public and manifest sins, and the priest, the hidden sins. And in order to punish, the king must have the material sword and knife, and the priest, the spiritual sword or knife. The king is said to be king of the body, and the priest, of the soul, for the job can not be fully completed one without the other, nor can one person alone hold both duties, whether he is king of the body or king of the soul. And therefore the natural philosophers ordained that there should be two doctors, one for the body and the other for the soul, and it is fitting that both be of one faith, just like two knives in a sheath. Being of one faith and in agreement on law and justice tempered with compassion, they can procure benefits for themselves and for the people, for the body and for the soul, because if they and the people were not of one faith, discord would develop among them.

"The difference of opinions among men causes discord to arise among them, and when all men are of one belief, the hearts of men come together in love and this eliminates many evils. Therefore the king, the priest, and the people ought to conform to one faith in whatever they have to do and to believe. The king ought to ask counsel of the priest, for he is the light and principle in these things, and it is fitting for the king to pay honor to the priest just as to a father, and to respect him the same as his doctor and the people's doctor, and to love him as a guardian of the faith. And know, my sons, that it is never found in the Scripture that the king should be without a priest, not even in the era of the gentiles. And every Christian king ought to have with him some good man of the Holy Church and to request advice from him for the body and for the soul."

150. Of how the king of Mentón told his sons how they must keep the truce, the pledge, and the homage that might be agreed among them

"Furthermore, my sons, know that the ancient philosophers, in order to have harmony among men, found that delay in arguments tended to bring agreement. And they agreed on these four things: the first is the oath; the next is the stated conditions; the next is the guarantor; the fourth is the truce or homage, for the breaking of the truce is not as serious as the breaking of the pledge of homage, for the truce has its separate conditions and homage has its own. According to the laws of the Chaldeans, when noblemen pledged an oath of homage, if the one who takes the pledge of homage breaks it, he is a traitor, just as is the one who holds a castle in fief and kills his own lord. Moreover the one who breaks the truce is considered a traitor if he cannot prove his innocence as provided under the law. And the oath, the obligations, and the guarantor are like this: the one who breaks the oath, breaks the faith for he does not keep it; and the one who does not come in time to make good on the obligation that he gave, loses it; and the one who gives his pledge for security, if he does not pay on time, the guarantor must pay whatever the one who accepted him as a guarantor demands; and if the guarantor demands of him what he entrusted, the one who had him as a guarantor is required to pay double what he paid him. Since he swore the oath, he is perjured by the oath as he tries to get out of the guarantee without harm to himself. And according to the ancient laws, the perjurer cannot collect from another what they owe him, and they can collect from him. He cannot be a witness, nor can he have the duty of judging, nor should he be buried in consecrated ground when he dies, because the perjurer neither believes in nor fears God, and he endangers himself and others. And certainly to swear and give collateral or guarantees is more fitting to the lower class of people and does not concern noblemen, in whom dignity must repose, because between noblemen there exist truce and homage, because they believe each other and they strengthen each other in the faith they promise each other. And the truce is agreed to among enemies, for it is given and accepted after hostilities are over. Homage is given and is received among enemies as among friends, and before enmity exists. And so the one who breaks the truce or homage destroys himself, and he destroys the faith that must be kept between men and smashes the great columns and strong foundation of their faith, removes the true love that is placed among them and takes away harmony and good friendships, shatters the councils and breaks the peace ordinances, sets some against others, sets the young against the old, makes lords do wrong against their vassals, and the bonds of friendship and loyalty, which are well tied, he divides and shatters to pieces. And such as he loses everything as soon as he falls into this error, and neither kings nor men forgive him nor do they permit him to dwell among them. And for these four aforesaid things, delays of time are granted in order to have counsel to reconcile friendships which were disrupted, and so that love may endure where it does exist, and in order to keep the law secure so that none may act or speak against it."

151. Of how the king of Mentón told his sons how they ought to keep the faith

"The day that a man is accepted as king and lord, he takes upon himself a great task to do what is fitting for him without censure truly keeping the law.

"For you must know that the law is the foundation of the world and the king is the protector of this foundation, since any work that has no foundation is disposed to fall, and any foundation that has no guardian, consequently falls more rapidly. Therefore the law and the king are two things that are closely related to one another, and the king must support the law and the law must support the power and strength of the king, because the kingdom is maintained by three things: the first is law; another is the king; the other is justice, since law is the protector of the king, and the king is guardian of the law, and justice is the guardian of all.

"Wherefore the king must utilize the law more than his power, for if he desires to utilize his power more than the law, he will commit many wrongs by choosing unwisely. And therefore the king ought to hold the book of the law in his right hand by which men must be judged and in his left hand, a sword, which signifies his power to see that his commands are carried out in support of the law, for just as the right hand is used more and is more obedient than the left, so the king must make more use of the laws and select the best ones in his power.

"Because the impartial king is protector of the law, the honor of the people, and the leadership of the kingdom, he is like the tree of God, which provides great shade and shelter under it for all the tired, the weak, and the unfortunate. Since the law, the king, and the people are three things which cannot function one without the other as they should, they are like a tent. The tent is made of three things: it is made of cloth, gauze, and cords, and all these three when brought together create a great shade and accomplish much, which they would not do if they were separate. And know that when the king adheres to justice and truth, violence, wrongs, and crimes flee his kingdom;

and if they are ignored a short while, they prosper and harm the country, just as the weeds do which grow in wheat and are not picked out. And therefore the governing of the kingdom is a great burden to bear, but God gives a great dominion and power to whom He loves well. And a wise man said in this regard, 'There is no date without a stone nor any good thing without some misfortune.'

"Wherefore, my sons, if God should give you this honor that I have told you about, endeavor to be fair first to yourselves, rectifying your mistakes especially if you have made them in judgment, for it would be a sin to persist in your error made against another. And no one should consider that it is a weakness in men to correct their mistake, for Seneca says that it is not a weakness for a man to recant of a manifest and obvious error, but he ought to confess and say: 'I was mistaken because I misunderstood.'

"It is madness and arrogance for a man to persevere in his mistake and to say what a king once said, 'Whatever it is, I want it to remain firm and unchangeable.' Surely it is not wrong for a man to change his advice to better if it makes sense. So if some one should ask you if you stand by what you proposed, tell him you do unless something better should happen to make you change. And thus none will say to you that you err if you change your purpose to a better one. And you will not cease to be just no matter what may be given to you or promised you, and neither for love or hate, nor for any favor whatsoever.

"And therefore when the king treats his people fairly, he will enjoy a fine reward from God and the gratitude of his people, for the king who does not deal out justice fairly, does not deserve the kingdom. And know that the best age in the world is the age of the just king: because the bad year that may come during the reign of the just king is better than the good year that comes in the reign of the unjust king, because the just king does not deal with force or arrogance. And the most valuable thing in the kingdom is the king who is head of it, if he rules well. The traits that are of most value to the king are fairness and compassion. Besides, it is better for the people to live under the dominion of the just king than to live without him in war and in fear under another. The king who makes his vassals suffer through his own guilt is an unfortunate king. And God said that whoever turns away from good, He will turn away from him, and those who dispense justice fairly will long endure. And know that with justice, the good endure, and with wrong and violence, they are lost. And therefore the good king, in order to set a good example, must be fair to himself and to those of his own town, and when the king dispenses justice fairly, his people will obey him loyally and willingly, but the people will conspire to disobey the one who is not fair; for the justice of the king touches the men in his service and injustice crushes them. And the man who holds the highest place before God and men is the king who is just. And the king is the man who must fear God more and the one who must love truth the most and be merciful and tolerant, for God was merciful to him and gave him the kingdom to maintain and placed in his power the bodies and possessions of his subjects.

"And therefore, my sons, every lord of territory and people must act in such a manner that they may love and welcome him.

"The king and his kingdom are two people, and just as a thing fused together, are two in one. And just as the body and the soul are not one thing after they are separated, so the king and his people cannot complete any good if they are in disagreement. And therefore the thing that the king must strive for most is to have the true love of his people. And know that in this world there is no greater dedication than to govern a people whom the lord wants to govern and guide with truth and loyalty. And therefore a wise man said that the lord of an unhappy people striving to do well is the most unfortunate of them. And the best trait the king can have is strength with tolerance, and gentleness with generosity. It is not fitting for the king to act hastily but he should dispense justice slowly, for it would be better not to act at all than to undo what he has done; and still he ought to show mercy to sinners when they fall into sin accidentally and not knowingly. For the king must be severe with evil men and very fair to the good and he must be true in his speech and in what he might promise, and he should not tolerate anyone daring to undo what he has done for him, especially since he has granted mercy and favors. For a great sin it is to take away the grace and mercy that a lord has done for his servant, for such as this denies God, his lord, and that one for whom the favor was done.

"And the king should as a rule love good men and those who find the truth in him. And the king must observe three things: the first, he must allow his anger to subside before he gives his decision on things that he is to judge; the second is that he may not delay the reward to the one to whom he has to give it, provided that person has done something to merit it; the third is that he may examine matters closely before he takes action. Moreover he must be careful to know the truth of a matter before he judges, because the judgment should be given positively and not through conjecture. Furthermore, the king should know that the sentence of death that he orders carried out on the one who deserves it means life and security for the people.

"And the worst traits that the king can have are these: to be strong toward the weak and weak toward the strong, and to be miserly toward those to whom he should not. And for this reason they say that there are four things bad in four people: one is to be a stingy king to those who serve him; the second is to be an unfair judge; the third, to be an incompetent physician and not know how to give a diagnosis; the fourth, to be a king before whom innocent men do not dare to appear. Certainly great things are corrected in the people more quickly than a small matter in the king, for when the people are to be bettered, the king will better them, and if the king is to be improved, there is none who can improve him except God. And therefore arrogance ought not to be found in anyone awaiting justice and law, for that person against whom the king is enraged stands in great danger, for when he is expecting life, his sentence is death. This person is like one who is very thirsty and, preparing to drink water, is drowned in it.

"Therefore, my sons, you will be just with compassion where men have sinned on occasion and so you will be considered benign; and the man is benign who is faithful to God and compassionate to his deserving relatives. He should not do evil to his inferiors and he should be a friend to his equals and have respect for his betters and live in harmony with his neighbors and have mercy on the miserable and give good and sane advice when it is requested of him."

152. Of how the king of Mentón instructed his sons always to give good counsel to those who ask for it

"And, my sons, whenever they ask you for counsel, first come to agreement with yourselves and with those in whom you trust, so that you may be able to give good and well-chosen counsel. And do not be hasty in giving it, because you might make a mistake and men would not hold you in so much esteem. And know that a man must examine three things in his counsel when they ask him for it: the first, if what they ask is an honest thing and not for gain; the second, whether it is gainful and not honest; the third, whether it is gainful and honest. And if it were honest and not gainful, you should advise them to do that, because honesty is so noble, so virtuous, and so holy a thing that with its virtue it draws us to itself, luring us with its great power of goodness. And if the thing should be gainful and not honest or good, you should advise them not to do that, no matter what advantage or gain there is in it, because this comes only from greed, which is the root of all evil. And if the thing that they ask for is honest and gainful, this is better, and you should advise them to do it. And notwithstanding that, alas! greedy men will choose rather to do what they believe they can do to their advantage and not what is good and honest. . . .[1] and not the gainful and the harmful to the soul and to the reputation, and although they may not select what you advise them. However, they will consider you to be of great wisdom and will esteem you more because you wanted to do good and avoid evil, and none will be able to say rightly that you advised evil. And furthermore, my sons, everything that you are to do, do with good counsel and sense, for the saying of Solomon is thus: 'What you do, do it with good counsel and you will not regret it.' And when you may wish advice from others, first you ought to consider from whom you ask it, because all men are not able to give good counsel; and therefore, first you will ask advice and aid of God for what you

1. Immediately after the word *honest* a complete sentence is missing in the manuscript.

may wish to do, for whoever needs to be sure of some matter and to be wise, first should ask it of God, for all wisdom and truth of everything is in Him, and frequently He can give it. Wherefore Saint James says, 'All good and complete things above descend from God the Father who is the Light of all, who is ever unchanging.' And when you ask advice of God, request it of Him very humbly and be careful that your request is good and pure. And if you do it thus, be certain that you will not be denied what you request, and if you make an improper request of God, evil will befall you and you will not know from whence it came, for the judgments of God are hidden from the people of this world. Wherefore if such a law is established rightly in the world, we should not request or ask ugly or wicked things of our friends, nor should we do such things for them. Hence all the more ought we to avoid asking them of God, who is the true Friend and knows what lies in our hearts, and from whom nothing can be hidden. And therefore whatever you begin, may it be in the name of God.

"And after you have asked the counsel and help of God in your affairs, you will ask it of yourselves, and you will examine your hearts, and you will choose what you see that will be best. And do it as wise prudent men putting away from yourselves and those who have advised you three things that are always obstacles to good advising: the first is anger, because the heart of man is disturbed by anger and he loses his discernment and does not know how to choose the best; the second is greed, which makes a man err and fall at times into shame and danger, paying more attention to the gain he plans to get than to honor and reputation for himself. Wherefore they say that '*codicia mala, mancilla para*,' 'greed brings dishonor.' And the third is haste, for certainly there are very few who can do things well and hastily, and therefore they say that haste makes waste.

"Wherefore it is better to carry out plans leisurely and slowly than precipitously. Before the start of plans, a man should meditate about what he plans and what are the chances for success, and he should plan and look ahead, and if the matter is of benefit, he should pursue and complete it. And they say do it well or not at all. Leisure is a help to the intelligent, for at times a man thinks to further his affairs by haste and things go in reverse, and at times he has to delay and plans go forward. Hence you will be able to do what you have to do quicker and better by not hurrying, because whoever hurries, although he obtain something thereby, errs, for it is done recklessly, and risks may still come. Foresight means to pay attention to something before it is undertaken, but delay causes a man to become reckless in order to accomplish what he wants to do. And the fruit of haste is repentance after the deed. And when a man is advised in what he should do, he understands it better, and after good counsel is verified, then the matter can begin, because what a man does with counsel always winds up happily, and what is done without counsel and hurriedly ends in regret."

153. Of how the king of Mentón told his sons to primarily be careful in revealing their secrets to anyone

"Unless you understand that through the advice of others you may be able to improve your estate, in no way should you tell your secret to a friend, either male or female, or reveal the sin or error in which you have fallen, because many of them will listen to you willingly, and will observe you, and, pretending a defense of you and your mistake, will mock you and endeavor to carry out evil against you. And therefore what you wish to be secret, do not tell to anyone, for after it has been told, it will be out of your control. What one knows is hardly a secret when many know of it, and so whoever keeps his secret, retains his power. Wherefore, it is a far safer thing for a man to be silent about his secret than to tell it to another and ask him to be quiet about it, for how can the one who cannot discipline himself or have control over himself, have control over another to whom he has revealed his secret? Certainly, he who has no power of reason over himself, cannot have it over another. But if by chance you see that you will be able to improve your estate through the advice of another, then come to an agreement with those from whom you will take counsel and reveal your secret to them. And although you should ask advice of some, you ought primarily to ask it of that person who has proved himself to be a true friend, because at times an enemy pretends he is a friend while he plans harm under the pretense of friendship.

"Furthermore, you will not reveal your choices on the advice you ask of your counselors, nor may you reveal to them what you think thereof; perhaps in order to please you and to flatter you, they will say that what you say is good advice, although they believe the advice they planned to give you is better. But listen to them all well, and examine what each one says, and so you will know how to choose the best. And the reason why you ought to do so is this: great and powerful lords, if they do not know how to choose by themselves, will never be able to have good advice from others either now or ever if their counselors first learn of their decision. This is especially true for those who seek nothing else except to follow their lord's will with flattery, thinking they will gain advantage for themselves. They never care if they bring harm upon their lord whom they ought to serve, guard and advise well in all circumstances. Wherefore always try to get advice from good and proven friends, and not from such false friends or from enemies, for just as the heart is delighted with good works, so the soul delights in the counsels of a good friend. And it is true that there is nothing in the world so delightful for a man as to have a man as a good friend to whom he may tell his secrets and reveal his heart with safety. Wherefore Solomon says: "There's nothing to compare with a true and faithful friend," because there is neither gold nor silver with which the true and faithful friend can be purchased, because the true and good friend is for a man like a strong castle in which a man can be sheltered and defended in many ways. Surely whoever has a good friend, I believe has a good treasure with which he can be aided and get help whenever he wishes. And therefore every man should endeavor as much as he can to acquire friends, because the best treasure and the best power that a man can acquire to his advantage are friends. For what advantage does a man have in being rich and not having friends with whom he may share his thoughts? Although he may have many other people about him, the man without friends lives alone, and they are accustomed to saying that a man without friends is like the body without a soul.

"Furthermore, you will ask advice of those whom you know to be understanding and wise; because the wise thought comes from the wise man, and good advice is a greater defense than weapons. And furthermore if some wish to give you advice secretly and not publicly, pay close attention, for you should be suspicious of their counsel. Wherefore a wise man says that the one who says one thing privately and demonstrates something else in public wants to hurt you more than to aid you. Such as this is not a true friend but is an enemy who wishes to deceive you. You ought not to trust in those who once were your enemies although they come before you very humbly and bowing, for they will not protect you through any true love they hold for you, but in order to obtain some advantage from you. Such as these will cry before you, and if they should see the opportunity, they would not be satisfied with your blood, for the enemy, although you may forgive him, does not lose from his heart the old pain that he held for the hurt that he received. And therefore they say that the wolf loses his teeth but not his intentions. Furthermore, you should not trust in that person when you see how he counsels you with fear and flattery, rather than with love, for true love is not shown with fear or flattery. From among all men, you will choose wise and old men and not young counselors. Young men are pleased with amusements and entertainments and tend to feast in the morning, because they do not have maturity as they ought to have. Wherefore the Holy Scripture says that where the king is a youth and his advisers and his privy counselors feast in the morning, the kingdom does not fare well. But there are some youths in whom God saw fit to place His grace, and He takes from them the recklessness of youth and gives them the wisdom of the old in order to recognize and see things with good common sense, although there are few to whom this grace and this beneficent gift is granted."

154. Of how men ought to protect themselves against those who have erred against them once

"And furthermore, my sons, while you are youthful and do not have your full wisdom, men who do not wish you well will endeavor to act to their advantage against you, and will try only to do well for themselves and to seize power over you, to seek your undoing, and to take away your power. When you are older and have your full wisdom, you may not be able easily to undo them, although they may give a reason for doing so. Nor will you be able to execute justice against those who deserve it, for they will stand together to defend them, like those who do not wish that justice be carried out against them or against any others. And certainly while you are young, they will not work at anything else except to enrich themselves and to bring you into poverty, praising you and advising you to pursue youthful ways, eating and drinking, and in all other things that please youths, and inciting you against those who wish to be at your service and to do you honor. And they will search for excuses for you, discrediting men to you so that you do evil to yourself, and so they will be separated from you and unable to counsel you suitably, and those against you may be able to fulfill their plans and do what they wish to. Wherefore it is necessary for you to be on guard about such things as these, and do not attempt to open your heart to young men who lack wisdom. Instead, gather around you old men of wisdom and those who have served you and yours loyally, and not those who failed in their duties. Men who eat green grapes are left with a bitter taste in their mouths, and those who have done a disservice unjustly to their lord will always remain with ill will and misgivings of what they have done to their lord, for they wanted to be lords over him and not he over them. Therefore you should guard against men such as these and not entrust your person or your affairs to them, although you should retain them and do favors for them, because with all your subjects, the good and the bad, whenever the occasion arises, you will take notice of their deeds. Kindness, loyalty, and good counsel are more to be valued and prized than wickedness, disloyalty, and bad counsel, for good, loyal, and wise counselors will protect you from shame and error and always endeavor to enhance your honor and welfare. The wicked, disloyal men of evil counsel will be pleased when you fall into error and shame and will conspire to diminish your power—for these men live insecurely because of the evil they do, and want to decrease your authority—so that you will be unable to do them harm."

155. Of how kings should guard themselves against placing their affairs in the control of Jews or anyone else outside the faith

"Furthermore, my sons, be careful not to place yourselves in the power of the Pharisees, who are very artful in all evil and are the enemies of the faith, nor entrust your affairs to them in any way. For it is the natural wickedness of the Jews always to wish ill to the servants of God, because of the error and sin into which they fell at His death, for so they are and must be servants of the Christians, and if they could, they would gladly place the

Christians into servitude. And therefore when they hold power in your house, they will endeavor to flatter you with those things that they believe will please you, and under some pretext they will show you that it is in your service and that you can gain more, they will plot how your villages can be destroyed, and they will become rich. And when you do not have the towns that serve you, you will have nothing to give to your noblemen, and they will have to search for other lords and will abandon you and rise against you. And when those who advised you see you standing alone, they will go to the others and will support them against you. Certainly it is no wonder that the enemy of Jesus Christ looks for ways of evil against His servants, because this hatred comes to them through their nature. Therefore all Christian lords ought primarily to incite indignation against the enemies of the faith, so that no power whatsoever remains to them with which they can harm anyone else. You ought not to place them in your councils, for it is apparent that there is no good counsel in them, nor in those of their faith. And those people in their wickedness, especially the Jews, endeavor to subvert the good counsels of princes, making them believe that they may get more out of their lands, and the princes full of greed believe them, alas! and often fall into great dangers because of this.

"Know that the story found in the Holy Scripture tells that in Judea in ancient times, there was great hatred among the Jews, and they divided themselves into three sects, desiring to deceive each other with trickery or evil doings, for they are of such a nature, being full of deceit, that they cannot live without agitation. And one of these sects was called Pharisees, another, Sadducees, and the third, Essenes. The Pharisees took the name of Pharaoh, who was not of the Jewish faith, and so the Pharisees were outside the faith, and they wore parts of letters on their foreheads and on their right arms, and they wore thorns on the hems of their skirts so that they might remember God's commandments when the thorns pierced their legs. And they were doing this in order to deceive the people so that they might not realize that they were not members of the faith, for the one who is a true believer has thorns in his heart to remind him of his faith and the commandments of God.

"Furthermore, the Sadducees were heretics, and they said that the dead were not to be resurrected and the soul then must die in the body, and they said that they did not believe there were angels in Heaven, and they called themselves just, taking the name of Sedin, which is the name of God, which means the All-powerful. And furthermore, the Essenes were deserters from the faith, and were called Essenes because they were in complete disagreement with the belief of the others and did not agree with any of them on anything. They wore white vestments and never married. They avoided married people, and they did not want to have a definite place in which to dwell, but stopped wherever they happened to be, and they did not worship anything except the rising sun. And for sure there are still many evil divisions among them, plots to deceive one another, but however much they wish to keep themselves concealed, they cannot, for their evil deeds reveal them. The wise man says there is nothing so hidden that will not be found out, especially wickedness, which cannot be hidden. For the Scripture says that an evil reputation is known sooner than the good one is praised. And the proverb says in another way: 'Evil reputation is revealed before a good one is known.' Besides, if there is no true love among them and they try to deceive one another, the more we should believe that they are striving to deceive the servants of Jesus Christ, for they deserve the punishment of death for the evil and treachery that their grandfathers committed in His death, for their grandfathers ate of the unripe grapes, and the bitter taste of envy remained in them against the followers of Jesus Christ. May God confound them with such envy; for it is in their nature to be turned against the Christians, and never will they lose it; so it is rooted in all those who are descended from them, despising Jesus Christ and all of His followers. For as soon as they learned that Jesus Christ was born, they revealed that they wished him harm, and they made it understood through speech and deed, as you will now hear.

"The story says that in the time of Caesar Augustus, emperor of Rome, he ordered everyone listed in order that each should give him the tribute that they owed to him. The Jews, who were subjects of the emperor, full of hatred and thinking to deceive the emperor, praised him to his face, saying that he was very just and that it was only right to pay him the tribute. Openly they supported him, but secretly they raised a hue and cry among the people, saying that those who were giving the tithes and the first fruits of their crops to God of what they earned were not subjects of the emperor nor were they to give him any tribute whatsoever. And when the emperor investigated this agitation which they had instigated, he gave Herod to them as their king, and he ordered that they should pay tribute to him. And from then on it was established that wherever they should travel they would be identified by a vile badge so that they might be recognized among all the people of the world. This rule is adhered to throughout the world except in lands where they were not expelled and where they hold power. And when King Herod sent his knights to find out the birthplace of Jesus Christ, after he learned of his birth, the Pharisees, who consider themselves clever tricksters, sent their messengers, well instructed in what they should say and do to the knights, and they spoke flatteringly to the knights of King Herod, mocking them, and said they had learned as a certainty that King Herod was the Messiah they were seeking, and that they believed it. This has never been found in any scripture.

"And when they found Jesus, the Pharisees questioned him and said to him in the presence of Herod's knights: 'Master, we know completely that you are truthful, and that you demonstrate and teach truly the way to God, and you do not think of any other thing but to tell the truth, for you do not create any trouble among men. Tell us in the presence of these knights of the king if it is fitting or not for us to give tribute to the emperor Caesar which he demands of us.'

"And they asked this question of Jesus, thinking that he would tell them that they did not have to give tribute to him, in order to incite all the populace against the emperor and then the emperor would be set against Jesus and do him harm. And Jesus, seeing and recognizing their wickedness and the deceitful words they were saying to Him, answered them, 'Oh, you hypocrites! Why do you tempt me?' The first quality of the person who is to answer a question asked of him is to recognize the intent of those who make the request. For 'hypocrite' means one who says one thing and holds a different view in his heart. And He said to them, 'Show me the coin of which he demands tribute of you.' And they showed Him a coin on which there was the image of Caesar. And there was an inscription over his name. Jesus examined it and said thus to them: 'Render unto God what is God's and unto Caesar what is Caesar's.' And this means that they should render unto God the tithes, the first fruits of the crops, the offerings, and the sacrifices, and unto Caesar the tribute which was his due.

"And after they saw that they could not get him to do what they wanted, full of deceit and craftiness, they searched for a way in which they could have him killed. And so they did, considering that if he should long endure in the world, they would be unable to succeed with their wiles and deceits on account of the wisdom and good judgment that they discerned in Jesus. Every day they saw so many signs in Him and He performed so many miracles among them that they were afraid of losing their power and the style in which they lived, because they were considered to be very wise and ingenious. And therefore they did not rest until they had Him killed, although He knew he was to suffer death in order to save sinners, for He had power over the others and not the others over Him. Moreover he was determined to be obedient to God the Father, and to fulfill His commandments, and to receive this death in order that souls should not be lost, as they were lost before He went to His death. And therefore, my sons, follow my advice and never place yourselves in the power of the Jews nor believe counsel of them, no matter what gifts they give you nor what loans they make you, for they will not serve you loyally, because it is not in their nature to do so."

156. Of how the king of Mentón showed his sons how they ought always to acquire friends and how they should learn how to keep them forever

"And furthermore, my sons, endeavor to acquire friends and to keep and retain those whom you have acquired; for one can acquire a friend very easily, but it is very difficult to keep him. In order to keep and retain them, you should avoid making them angry in anything, for a friend, when he receives harm or anger from his friend, feels it more deeply. He becomes more angry than if a stranger had done it to him, for the hurt is doubled when he receives harm or dishonor from that person who ought to protect him in all things. Wherefore a wise man says that the hurt is greater when it comes from someone near to you, especially if it comes to you from a person whom you consider a friend and you receive harm and dishonor from him, just as happened to Saint Stephen when they stoned him. He never complained of the large stones with which others hit him, but he complained loudly over a small stone thrown by his friend, and rightly so. The greatest possible evil is when harm and dishonor come to a man from that person from whom he expects to receive benefits and honor; for the more a man trusts his friend, the greater is the wound in his heart if he is deceived by advice or anything else, for he is deceived by that person from whom he ought to be protected or be well advised. And if you wish to really keep your friends, be of good will to them.

"The man of good will is very fortunate, because he makes himself loved, and the one who is of ill will is unfortunate, because he makes himself hated. And the one who is happy and welcomes cheerfully, gains countless friends, because the welcome spirit is the key to love. And those who do not have an abundance of wealth with which they may acquire the love of men, may have an abundance of good will, for these make a good life. It is a sure thing that whoever shares life with a man of ill will, will suffer his anger, however patient he may be. And the man of good will and virtue must have three things in himself: the first, patience with which he may know how to get along with men; the second, chastity, so that he may not sin; the third, good will with which he may acquire friends, and he can acquire men with good will better than he can acquire them with his piety. And know that the best companion a man can have in order to lead a satisfactory life is to be a man of good will. And the man with a bad disposition cannot be loyal or have lasting love. And whoever may be soft-spoken without deceit will be loved by men. But in every other way a man has need of God's grace to be loyal and true to his friends. Without God's grace, he cannot be loyal and true, nor can he have God's grace unless he works to merit it.

"For know that a man earns the manifest love of his friends through three things: the first, that he greet them wherever he meets them; the second, that he always welcome them when they come to him; the third, that he speak well of them publicly when they are not present.

"And he who settles grievances on friendly terms with his friends will gain their love, and he who does not will earn their hatred. Whereby with reconciliation there comes consolation and peace, while hatred and struggling come from disagreement. And he who treats men with fairness gains their love, and he who scorns them is ostracized.

"But it is better for a man to walk alone than with an evil companion, for a man cannot do himself any good in the company of an evil companion; and therefore they say that whoever lies down with dogs gets up with fleas.

"And when one friend agrees with another, love grows between them, for harmony brings love anew, and disagreement kills old love and brings hatred again, and reveals a false love; therefore, agreement gives happiness and love, and discord brings enmity and hatred."

157. Of how the king of Mentón instructed his sons always to be generous with everyone

"Furthermore, my sons, you must be generous with what you possess on those occasions where you understand that it is proper. Generosity is nobility of heart and whoever is generous is master of what he possesses, and the stingy person is its servant. Although you should be generous in sharing what you have, you should be sufficiently foresighted in keeping what you can and not become too poor, for, alas! you will find few friends if you are poor who will come to your aid with what is theirs, unless it is a great advantage to themselves and great harm to you. And when you have a great treasure, you will have something to give, and thus you will have your followers.

"For know that wealth is respectability and poverty is scorn, for it leads the man of weak will to discredit, but with wealth he gains the esteem of this world. And the poor man is denounced for the same thing for which the rich man is praised. If the poor man is brave, they will say that he is crazy; and if he talks sensibly, they will say is garrulous; and if he is calm, they will say he is lazy; and if he is silent, they will say he is stupid. And therefore death is better than poverty with laziness, since there is no greater vileness than poverty combined with laziness. For although the poor man may be in his own land, they treat him as if he were in a foreign land. And when the rich man is in a foreign land, he travels accompanied as if he were in his own land, for all honor the rich man and all treat the poor man miserably. But wealth is harmful to many, because they become full of vanity with it, for with wealth, men of bad quality are disobedient to God, and with poverty, they obey Him. But poverty is more valuable in gaining Heaven than wealth with which a man may lose it. But they say that the good of this world consists of two things: one is kindness and the other is wealth; and the two worst things are poverty and wickedness, since it is an easier thing to endure the burden of controlling wealth than the wretchedness of poverty. The rich man, if he is charitable, will be able to do good for himself and for others; and the poor man, although he may be a good person, will be unable to do good to himself nor to any other, although he may wish to. But very fortunate is he who considers himself satisfied with what he owns and leads his life the best he can when he cannot have more.

"For know that whoever is pleased inwardly with what he possesses, is free, and whoever is greedy for something belonging to another is a slave. That person is fortunate who does not turn his head to covet another's wealth, for greed would destroy his vassals and the desire for rapine would destroy his lands, although it is fitting for kings and great lords to obtain riches, because they are obligated to be charitable and do many things. And therefore the honor of the great lord consists of giving and not of asking, for to ask and be rejected is worse than to ask successfully."

158. Of how the king of Mentón instructed his sons and told them how all men ought to strive to gain wealth and to be prudent

"But, my sons, if you wish to be prudent and to gain wealth, be astute in obtaining what is yours, not doing ill or wrong to anyone, and demand what is rightly yours, and do not be lazy, for laziness is the key to poverty and diligence is the key to wealth; and whoever lies around his house idly will be late in gaining anything to enjoy, for laziness is the enemy of accomplishment and the destruction of wealth. For know that idleness brings poverty and misery, and activity is the road to acquiring wealth. What is not acquired rightly is not wealth; rather it causes deprivation for the body and soul, for the body is defamed and the soul is lost. And therefore, my sons, you will endeavor to be prudent, for I truly believe that if men tried to understand prudence, they would value it greatly and would make great use of it, because prudence is to recognize the things that a man currently possesses and the estate in which he lives, and to foresee what is to come and what can be of advantage to his estate and the good fortune he enjoys; for the duty of prudence is to examine and forecast things that are to come and to surround oneself with good counsel against the dangerous and wretched time whenever it comes. And is is fitting, not for a man to observe the present, but to watch out for what is to come, for the cleverness of man finds a way out of present troubles and knows what is to his advantage. Wherefore Solomon says, 'Look before you leap,' which means: whatever you wish to begin, before you begin it, think of what the advantage can be and thus you will be able to complete it well. And if you are not inclined to look, your beginning will be your fall. And therefore, they say that whoever does not look ahead falls behind. Certainly, the man who wishes to look first at what can happen in the things he is planning, is clever and subtle, and if something should happen, he will know how to protect himself. And he ought not to do anything for which he may say afterward, 'I did not think that it would be thus, for if I had known, I would not have done it.' Anyone who can say that is without foresight. And certainly, without foresight no man can go through life satisfied or safe, except the thoughtless and lazy man who does not wish to observe his own deeds, because he does not know how the times may change. And therefore, all men ought to plan their lives with foresight, men of high estate as well as those of low. And whoever among them makes no attempt to look ahead and is reduced to poverty and misery ought not to blame those who do not want to come to his aid, but place the blame on himself, for he refused to foresee the bad times that come after good fortune and to make use of wealth that he had in the times when he could have provided for the future. And therefore each man ought to be moderate in expending his wealth.

"And everything in the world must have a standard, and whoever exceeds the standard does too much and the one who does not fulfill it, does too little. And certainly moderate wealth is worth more to whoever spends it with prudence than great wealth to whoever is a great wastrel, for wealth will last for the one who spends with moderation, and the one who is a wastrel will lose his wealth completely. And know that the goodness of man is affirmed through three things: the first is that he may be tolerant; the second, that he may be merciful when he is powerful; the third, that he may be indulgent when he is a lord. And my sons, you should be satisfied when you have as much wealth as is necessary for you, for too much wealth is harmful and often a burden to the one who has it, except for kings who have a great need of keeping it for their great plans. And too much wealth is a great evil, just as is too much poverty, and therefore it is said that the best of all things is moderation. Wherefore a wise man says, 'Those of good fortune hold to the middle of the road,' for extremes are not good, except the good deed that has a good beginning and a better ending. And whoever wishes to be sure of not lacking anything should live with moderation and foresight although he may possess little, and he should give for God's sake although he is poor. And know that moderation impoverishes few and immoderation wastes much. And whatever a man expends in the service of God and in doing good is not wasted, although it may be a great amount, and no matter how much it may be, it is not a little. Well then, do not hesitate to spend where you ought to, and do not spend any amount where you should not do so.

"And therefore they say that whoever is prudent is intelligent. And certainly, my sons, there is no greater advantage than intelligence, nor greater wealth, and there is no greater loss or greater poverty than madness and stupidity; for the reckless man, the more his wealth and power increases, the more his pride increases. And certainly madness in a man is a great affliction, and therefore they say that who gets sick with madness is a long time getting well. Wherefore know that the body is like the kingdom, and intelligence is like the king, and manners are like the people; then, if the king is more able than the people, he will guide the kingdom and if the people are more able than the king, the king and the people can be lost. And hearts without intelligence are like land that is barren and uncultivated, whereas hearts with intelligence are like the land that is populated with good workers, for the brains are the laborers of the heart. And know that the brain is the leader of the body in this world and of the soul in the next world, since when God wants to take his grace from someone, the first thing that he does is to take his sense from him. Wherefore, see what the nobility of intelligence is, for he who does not have it cannot purchase it for wealth, and it cannot be stolen from whoever has it, and although a man expends it, it does not diminish. And therefore it is better that a man be complete in intelligence and sparing of tongue than complete of tongue and sparing of intelligence, for intelligence is father of the one who believes, and patience is his sister, and gentleness his guide. There is no better friend than intelligence, nor a worse enemy than ignorance. And nothing that he acquires is of value to the man who does not possess intelligence. And whoever has a full complement of intelligence will never lack for anything. And that person is intelligent who has envy of no one, nor holds malice toward any, nor deceives any, nor mistreats any, not takes what is another's from him without cause. Furthermore, he is intelligent who can master his own will and is very pleased with the little that is done for him and does not meddle in matters which do not concern him."

159. Of how the king of Mentón instructed his sons to give and dispense their favors

"But although, my sons, I advise you to be prudent in what all men should want, if God should give you lands to rule of which you may be lords or kings, I charge you to resolve not to be stingy but rather you should be very liberal, that is to say, generous, for liberality is a virtue always maintained by giving and in rewarding; but with all this that I charge you, be careful that your favor may not exceed your wealth, for you will be unable to fulfill it and you would be shamed and in danger. And furthermore, through resentment you may hold toward that person to whom you have given something, you may not want to embarrass him for it or retract your gift, for the rule is established between the one who gives the gift and the one who receives. Afterward the one who gives it must forget it and not mention ir or praise himself about it at any time, for the good man should never think about what he has given, but about what he ought to give. And the one who receives it, should always remember the gift that he receives and be grateful to the one who gave it to him.

"And if some one does not acknowledge his debt to you when you have need of his aid, and he is against you, do not trouble yourself about it, for ingratitude will bring him down, just as Lucifer, who fell from Heaven to hell for his ingratitude to Our Lord God. And if some one should tell you that you are malicious in what you give and employ toward those who are against you or yours, tell him that person is ungrateful who does not acknowledge a good deed, for you did what you should and what was fitting for you. And a man will waste many gifts by giving them away indiscriminately until he happens on a person on whom they may be well bestowed. And for this reason they say, 'Do good and don't be particular to whom.' For if a man should examine each person to whom he wants to make a gift and who could use it well, he might by chance be able to find or recognize such a man to whom it might be fittingly given, for man's judgment is many times deceived in attempting to know which is good or which is bad, for many appear good who are not, and men think that many who seem bad are not so. And therefore you will give your gifts willingly and quickly, for there is not much to be grateful for when the gift is held a long time in the hands of that person who ought to give it, for on examination it appears he does not wish to give it or he delays and is about to refuse it, and he makes it understood that he is reluctant and that he does not want to give it, since he delays in giving it. And certainly much of the appreciation is taken away that was to be shown for the gift, inasmuch as the giver held back and delayed the gift that he promised to the one who asked for it, for every man who begs something of another certainly does so with embarrassment. And therefore he does not have much to be grateful for, if the donor has been hesitant in giving it. If whoever wants to give the gift, gives it before it has been requested of him, he makes the gift greater than what it is, for it is a great good to give something to one who has need of it before he asks for it.

"My sons, pay attention to what I now will tell you, and it is true, there is nothing that costs so dear as what a man has to ask for over and over again. And certainly they are sad words and a great burden for a man to have to say to another with great embarrassment, 'I beg you to give me something,' and therefore the small gift that is given quickly is more appreciated than the large gift that is given reluctantly.

"Furthermore, my sons, you should avoid refusing a gift in a malicious manner to one who asks it of you, as King Antigonus did to a minstrel who asked him for a gold mark because he sang for him, and the king responded that he would not give it to him because he had asked for more than was suitable for a minstrel; so then the minstrel asked for a denarius, and he said he would not give it to him because he had asked for less than was fitting for a king to give, for it was not a gift worthy of a king. Of course he maliciously refused to give it to him, for he could have given him a gold mark fitting to a king, or a denarius fitting for a minstrel. And this king did not attempt to be like Alexander, who bequeathed a great city to a man of low estate, and the man to whom he gave it said to him:

"'Lord, such a great gift as this is not fitting for a man of so low estate as I.'

"Alexander answered like the magnanimous man he was:

"I do not ask nor did I question if it was suitable for you to receive, but what is fitting for me to give.'

"Truly, Alexander the king did not speak deceitfully, but with nobility of heart."

160. Of how the king of Mentón instructed his sons to be careful not to employ men who serve with malice

"And therefore, my sons, you will not speak with malice nor any kind of deceit with any men in the world although they may be strangers, and especially with your subjects, by whom you are to be served or protected, for they will understand you and may speak to you deceitfully too; for through whatever road you lead them, along such a road will they take you. Wherefore the Scripture says that a man must be judged by the same law by which he judges others. And although they may not understand the deceit and lies which you tell them, when they find out and see what you have done, they will be extremely hurt and will strive to slander you as much as possible, since they have been hurt by the deception of that person who ought to support them. And this is certainly the thing in this world that great lords err in most: in believing that the men they deceive do not understand them. And if they would just think about it, they would realize that there are some people just as clever as they who understand them. And if they don't dare to tell them truth, they should not lie to them, for they look for artful and deceitful ways to answer them. And also, if through fear of the lord's cruelty, they do not dare nor are able to respond, then they may plan to rid themselves of him, just as happened to a king of Ephesus who was very rich and powerful."

161. Of the parable that the king of Mentón told his sons about a king of Ephesus and one of his vassals

"The story relates that this king of Ephesus never spoke with his subjects or even his household, except with malice and arrogance, in a deceptive manner, and he did not know how to protect himself from the artifices of others with whom he spoke. And so great was his cruelty that all his subjects and retainers were afraid in his presence and even when they heard talk about him. Some, in order to serve him, made him aware of these things, and he treated them badly and sent them away, and they lost his favor by doing good. Therefore they say that no good deed goes unpunished. They did not dare to tell him anything, although they saw him say and do unjust things, so that everyone hated him and was angry with him

"So there was a count, the most powerful in the land, against whom the king had committed many dishonorable acts in speech and deed. The king was unaware that the count understood the actions and deceptions he was instigating against him. The count, seeing that all the people of the kingdom were very displeased with the king, looked diligently for a subtle way in which he would be able to revenge himself, not caring if it was a good or bad way. The king was greatly annoyed with him and continued to carry out evil against him with deceptive stratagems, and at times very openly. The count was forced to plot the worst thing he could against the king, and so it is said that even a wronged dog will turn against his owner. Feeling great resentment, the count said to the king as a stratagem that he had decided to burn his only daughter for something she had done and for which she should be burned. He had it proclaimed throughout the kingdom that all should come to see sentence carried out against his daughter. All who heard it were greatly astonished and were startled at such great cruelty the count wanted to commit, for the young girl was the most beautiful and charming in all the kingdom, the most shielded in everything, and the most sought after in marriage by the sons of other great men.

"When the day came on which the count had said she was to be burned, he ordered a large quantity of firewood placed in the middle of a field. And as soon as the king arrived, he asked why the count had not brought his daughter in order to carry out justice against her as he had stated. The king was greatly pleased with the folly that the count had said he wanted to do. The wretch did not realize or think that the count's plan could be something else, and not to kill his daughter. The thing he most loved in this world was that daughter, for he had no other child. And the count said to him, 'Sire, I am waiting until more people arrive.' However, the majority of the subjects had arrived, and with masterful craft, he said:

"'Lord, while the other people are arriving, go aside to speak with these good men of your council, and speak about whatever you consider proper and I will go arrange with the other good men and those townsmen how justice should be carried out.'

"And the king went aside, not perceiving the deception which they were doing to him with crafty words. The king began to mock and malign the count, being pleased because he wanted to kill his own daughter. And the count went out to the people and began to speak with all the townsmen there.

"'Friends and relatives, I have many ties of kinship and love with you, for I have received many pleasures and great honors from you, for which I am obliged to return the favors and to feel your misfortune as my own, for whoever harms his friends and relatives and does not feel for them is not a friend, nor is he a relative. And therefore I want you to know that we all live in great danger from our lord, who has no sympathy or pity for us, for you all well know how he was served by us in everything he wanted, at his whim, and he to his misfortune and ours has always done great wrong to us and no good. He has always spoken with cunning and deception, or openly in order to carry out evil against us and to dishonor and ruin us. He considers us to be nothing, nor does he wish to have counsel on matters affecting the country. If he requested advice from us, he did not bother to abide by what was given him, and he says that a man is not a man who is guided by the advice of another, for he credits us with little wisdom. Certainly this is contrary to the opinions of the wise men who say that a man ought not to undertake anything without good advice, and particularly so in events which occur for the first time. New counsel is needed for a new event, just as new medicine is needed for a new disease, in order that what a man wants to be successful may be successful. And now he has thought of how he can dispossess us illegally of what we own, and he is planning to have those killed who are not willing to consent to what he wants. And I, recognizing this great evil which he wants to do to us and the way he has deceived us and that none of us dares to speak of it although aware of it, dared to take the risk and expose myself to this great danger in order to warn you. I said that I wanted to have my daughter burned. I had it proclaimed throughout the land, so that all of you would gather together and might learn of this great wickedness that the king is conducting against you, and we could take counsel together on it. And friends, I have said what I had to say to you, and from now on, plan to protect yourselves, for I am certain that as soon as he learns of what I have said to you here, he will order my death in a cruel manner.'

"And a member of the count's council arose and said:

"'Friends, let us kill the one who wants to kill us and is our enemy.'

"'Certainly,' said the count, 'it is the truth, and it seems clear, with death staring us in the face, that we are willing to maintain a stubborn loyalty to the one who wants to kill us and allow ourselves to be killed like cowards.'

"And at this, one of the men from the town got up and said, 'Is there anyone here who will cast the first stone at the one who wants to kill us?'

"And he leaned over, took up a stone, and threw it at the king, and all the others came forward and did the same thing; so they battered him with stones and killed him. The wretches paid no heed to how they had committed treason, for it is one of the worst things which a man can do. And truly the king could have avoided this if he had wanted to protect his people and to live with them as was right, by avoiding lying to them and by being disposed to deal lawfully with them.

"Wherefore, my sons, through my advice, you will always be good and loyal and true to your people, and you will not speak to them about anything in deceitful ways; for those who serve well are extremely hurt when their lord leads such a life, speaking to them with deceitful intent. And although he may speak the truth to them, they cannot believe him because of the wicked and deceitful artifices he still uses with them, and they believe he always tends to lie and to deceive. And therefore, my sons, avoid speaking to men with deceit and speaking ill of them in secret or in public, for there are four kinds of men to whom you ought to pay attention if you want to have a tranquil and safe life: one is the man who does not speak evil or do evil to anyone, but has the desire to live in peace and serve loyally the one he has to serve. Such a person as this is like a good dog which neither barks nor bites except when it is necessary to protect his lord's interest with his own self; the second kind is the one who is silent and attacks and is eager to strike mortal blows and is not satisfied unless he draws blood. And this person is like the dog that does not bark and bites without warning and draws blood with the intent to destroy completely the one whom he bites. And may God protect you from such men, for these endure a great deal and do not retaliate, and when they see that the time is ripe, they bite and attack and strike blows without mercy, not caring if they do evil, but determined to carry out their will just as the count did to the king of Ephesus, as you have already heard. The other kind of man is the one who speaks and does not act; and such a person as this cannot do much harm, and through a lot of talk, the person he speaks against is forewarned. Perhaps he talks profusely to inspire fear because of his own great fear. And such a person as this is like the dog that barks a great deal and does not dare to bite because of his own cowardice, but barks in order to frighten. And the other kind of man is the one who speaks and acts in public rightly and with strength. And such a person as this is virtuous and honest, always abiding by reason and the law, which strengthens the heart so that it carries out its actions. And such a person as this is like the good dog that barks and bites courageously when it must, and does not hesitate to attack when its owner orders it to do so.

"Wherefore, my sons, if you will pay heed to these four things and kinds of men, you will know how to protect yourselves and living among them in harmony with honor to yourselves by not speaking to anyone in a deceptive manner, but honoring them and giving grace and mercy to them as each deserves. Do not listen to ill of anyone or praise anyone who speaks it, and do not mockingly forbid him to talk, saying, 'Silence, do not talk like that,' and afterward say to him, 'Tell me again what you said?' as you want to have him tell it, just like those gossips and slanderers who take pleasure in gossip and slander, when they could be hearing and saying other things in which they could take more pleasure and which would be more to their advantage and of greater honor to their souls and bodies."

162. Of how the king of Mentón told his sons how every man must tolerate the ingrate by continuing to do good to him until he recognizes ingratitude in himself

"And furthermore, my sons, avoid having a dispute with anyone over a gift that you have given to him, who does not wish to show gratitude for it, for in quarreling with him you will do harm to him, and in tolerating him you by chance will do good to him, as may happen with a man when he does some evil and is not challenged for it. There is shame when that person thinks that the one to whom he did wrong still may not know, but after being reproached, there is no shame, and after it is over, he pays no attention to it and is the worse for it, for a greater shame is impossible. And, my sons, why reproach the person for whom you have done many favors? Do not do it, for you will make an enemy of a friend. And if you do not find in him what you hoped, realize that there may be something you do not understand, and that if he is ungrateful in one thing, perhaps he will not be in another; and if he is ungrateful in the second thing, then in the third, if you do good for him, he will remember how he failed you and offended you twice, and if he has good sense, he will be greatly ashamed of failing in the third thing. And if he should fail you in the third thing, from that time on you have no reason to do any more. But, my sons, you will not cease to do good, although the recipient does not show gratitude to you for it.

"For doing good is a lasting maxim. And doing good is accomplished in three ways: the first, that a man may do it quickly; the second, that a man may do it in secret; the third, that he may pretend that he did little although he may have done much, for know that by doing good a man avoids many problems, since God shows great mercy on the one who has to endure many problems from men. If he is not inclined to endure them, he stands ready to lose that grace, for God greatly loves the one who does good to men and withdraws His love from the one who can do it and does not. Wherefore whoever does good does not fall, and if he should fall, he will find that many will aid him to get up. And whoever does good is better than the good that he does. And the one who does good does not lose his reward, even if he does not receive one from men, for God rewards him for the good he does. And therefore, it is fitting for a man to do good in as many ways as he can, although the ways may be narrow and the roads harsh. For know that all doing of good is a virtue, and a man ought not to take back the good that he has done, for it is more fitting not to do good than to do it and retract it. Wherefore the Scripture said, 'Do not let your left hand know the good that your right hand does.' And therefore they say, 'Do good and do not concern yourself about to whom.'"

163. Of how the king of Mentón instructed his sons and told them to give their gifts without hestitation, and furthermore to be careful to whom they give them

"Furthermore, I advise you not to look for appreciation from that person to whom you give your gift, for then it would cease to be a gift and would appear to be a loan, and you would rightly lose the thanks and acknowledgment which was due you for it. Moreover, my sons, if you wish to emulate God in His works, give to whoever asks of you and to the ungrateful; for thus does God do. And do you not see that the sun when it rises warms the wicked as well as the good? And certainly God does many good deeds without waiting, so that all may take advantage of them. And therefore, if you want to emulate Him in His works, give while you are able, although many things may be put to wrongful use and the recipient may not be grateful to you for them; for the ungrateful does not do a wrong to you but to himself, because he is lacking in the wisdom that God gave him to know good from evil. For the person of perception is always pleased with the gift that he receives, for he always remembers it. And the ungrateful is delighted with the gift only once, and this is when he receives it, and later he forgets it.

"Furthermore, whatever you promise, by all means give, for if you do not give, people will judge you as mendacious and devious in your statements, believing that you do not hold to what you promise. If you promise a gift to a person who is not worthy or deserving, you must give it to him because you promised it, and not because it is a gift, but to be true to your word. But although you must give to whoever asks you, it is fitting that you may know by whatever ways you can if he is well-mannered, what kind of person he is, what feeling he has toward you, and whether you are able to profit from him. And if this is adhered to in temporal gifts, so much more ought one to observe this in spiritual ones, for they must not be given except to the one who deserves them, and by paying heed to these aforementioned things. But I truly believe that the person in whom some mark of virtue appears ought not to be scorned or denied all the spiritual gifts, although he may be endowed with a degree of wickedness; because that trace of virtue in him can change him into a good man. And if this ought to be done with spiritual gifts, how much more ought it to be done with worldly gifts. Small gifts given often are worth more and are of more advantage to the one who gives them than large gifts that are given occasionally, for that person to whom something is given every day is always careful to serve and protect the one who gives him something, and that person to whom the large gift is given, believing that the gift will last all his life and believing that late or never would he obtain another such, does not look for anything else and abandons everything else and does not look forward to serve or protect that person who gave it to him. He is nothing but a worthless person and lacking in intelligence, for the greater the gift he is given, the more he ought to be ready to serve and do good.

"Wherefore, my sons, be very generous with your gifts, and give to each according to his merit and his deserts, especially to those that you have tested when in need, and to those whom others have tested and you have learned for certain deserve it. And I truly believe that from such as these, who are grateful for the good you do them, you will always receive greater service than your gift, for grateful persons such as these will appear similar to rich fields that bear much fruit so that they give more than they receive. And, my sons, if a man does not care to give his gifts to a person by whom he expects to be served, so much the more ought he to be sure to give to that person from whom he has received great service and loyalty. And certainly a person would be reprehensible who does not pay heed to such advice so as always to do his best. And therefore, my sons, pay heed to what is fitting for you to do in this regard, for the giving or not giving of what is yours is in your own hands."

164. Of how there are two kinds of largesse: one, which is called extravagance; and the other, generosity

"Yet there are two kinds of generous men: some are called extravagant and the others, generous. The extravagant ones are those who squander their wealth in eating and drinking with cheats and men of evil counsel and in lavishing what they have on lovers and wicked men. The generous are those who give their gifts to their servants, to ransom captives, to their friends, for the weddings of their children, or to some other honest cause that is necessary to them. And thus, among the finest virtues of the highborn is generosity.

"For all generosity is in God, and he loves it and appreciates it. And therefore generosity brings the love of God and stinginess brings the dislike of God. And the generous one has as great a desire to give as the miserly has to take. And he who has the power to do good and does not do it is diminished and displeases God. And whoever squanders his wealth in doing good is the same as the one who goes to seize the wealth of his enemies and keeps it for himself. And whoever has an abundance of wealth and is stingy is only the keeper and it does not matter whose wealth it is. And whoever is generous and noble of heart is beloved by all, for generosity leads to kindness and the acquisition of friends. Know that when the generous are poor and the stingy are rich, then good people are in trouble, for it is a well-known fact that when the doers of good are absent the poor are deprived. Since whoever values his wealth depreciates himself, and whoever esteems himself does not trouble himself about his wealth. Whereby the foundation of generosity is not to covet someone else's wealth, for God will always give wealth to the generous and will always cause losses to the stingy.

"And therefore the one who does not want to distribute his wealth in such a way that the recipients show gratitude for it will have to leave it to men who will not show gratitude. Wherefore the greatest thing a man can do in his life is this: that he may do well for his soul and honor his body through his wealth."

165. Of how the king of Mentón told his sons that every man ought to acknowledge a good deed

"Furthermore, my sons, if some great lord should benefit you, or if your vassal has rendered you a good service, strive to show your gratitude for it by service to the lord and by giving aid to his vassals. In regard to gratitude, the first thing that a man ought to remember is this: that he not forget the benefit he received or the service done for him, for each action is considered a good deed. because the one who serves well is also doing a good deed. And therefore, a man should not forget the good deed when he receives it, for God and men despise the ungrateful man, and God and men consider that the ungrateful man does wrong in not showing gratitude to those who did good to him. And you must know that the one who denies that he has received the gift is an ingrate, and the one who pretends that he does not remember what he received is more ungrateful, knowing full well that he did receive it, and much more ungrateful is the one who forgets everything completely and looks for more gifts rather than remembering the one who gave the gift and did him the favor. Surely that person who completely forgets the gift that he received can only be an ingrate, for truly it seems that he never planned to acknowledge it since he forgot it completely. The person who casts far from his thoughts the gift that he received and cannot remember it or see it never did intend to acknowledge gratitude to the giver, for man's memory never loses or forgets anything except what many times it does not want to remember. And therefore I say to you, my sons, that you should not forget a benefit received, because, alas! few hearts remember things of the past, for many do not want to acknowledge the benefit, as if they had not received it, or as if it was received and later lost. But, my sons, you will give thanks and express gratitude publicly and openly for the good that you receive, and not in secret; for he who wants to give thanks for what he received does not want to appear ungrateful, and also that those who do not know about it can understand whether he is doing good or evil.'

166. Of how the king of Mentón showed and told his sons how every man ought to be forewarned against his enemies and those who wish him ill

"Furthermore, my sons, pay close attention to what is fitting for you to do if you have war with any of your neighbors as powerful or more powerful than yourselves, and be well prepared.

"For the person who places himself in a known danger is not said to be valiant. And know that there is no better counsel than preparation, because many are lost through poor preparation and not being alert, for a man is long in recovering from the blow which comes through lack of watchfulness. Wherefore alertness is the foundation of the art of a man's protecting himself. And whoever places himself in danger does not have a castle in which he can defend himself, and whoever is too reckless is lost, and the prepared person, never, for he regulates his conduct based on the worst contingency and protects himself, and whoever does not do things with wise counsel, places himself in danger. And therefore a man should yet be alert because if something should suddenly happen to him by surprise, it will find him prepared, because from alertness is born security, and repentance is born from recklessness. And when a man risks danger, although he may escape, he does not escape unhurt, because there is no profit in being caught offguard. Whoever is mounted and on the alert escapes unhurt and saves himself and those who are led by him.

"Well, my sons, always be prepared and keep your mind alert, for if things come about as you wish, men will realize that you succeeded through intelligence and preparation; and if events should be contrary to your will, men will know that it was not your fault, and you will be blameless. It is more worthwhile for you to delay and wait in a place where you are safe than to be reckless and place yourselves in danger, and it is more worthwhile for you to forbear in order to remain safe than to dare recklessly and place yourselves in danger.

"And know that it is a great safeguard for a man, before he begins matters, to look ahead until he knows what will thereby be born of them or what help he can expect; for he who risks his life in things in which he can be mistaken is like the blind man who sets out to walk in places where there are holes or wells into which he may fall. Surely carelessness is like a net into which those who are careless will fall. And furthermore, he who goes forward too fast, errs, and the one who holds back does not succeed. Certainly, you ought to have a greater feeling of gratitude toward the one who cautions you until you reach safety than toward the one who urges you on into a place of danger, for fear is close to safety and safety is close to fear.

"And they say that at times artfulness is worth more than bravery. Laziness and a lack of alertness lead a man to death's door. And know that whoever asks for a thing beforehand can have it on time; and if he asks for it exactly when it is needed, it is doubtful that he will get it. And therefore, when opportunity comes to a man and he loses it through laziness, he is to blame. Furthermore, whoever ceases to do what he ought to do will have to do what he ought not. And the perceptive person always strives to do good every way he can and does not meddle into what he ought not. Therefore a little done with intelligence is worth more than much done with courage and without intelligence. When you are forewarned and you lose, don't be angry at yourself, and when you venture recklessly and win, do not take pride in yourself. And know that whoever sets his mind to work will understand where he erred. Therefore put your mind to work when you have leisure as you do when you are in trouble, for when something happens unexpectedly, you should be prepared to protect yourself.

"And therefore, my sons, do not attempt things except when the time is right. For an opportunity seldom returns if not seized upon at the proper time, and when a man hesitates, he is lost. And therefore, do not fail to advance when you see the time and place is ripe to do it. Furthermore, be careful not to place yourself in danger. For they say that seldom does the lazy man accomplish a good deed, since idleness is laziness, and to stir up excitement is a nuisance and commitment is a virtue. Wherefore a wise man says, 'Cowardice is when the lazy man asks for counsel in matters of urgency.' For it is a virtue when a man does a work alone that he has meditated long about doing. And laziness is of two kinds: one, is when a man is dilatory in asking for something at the proper time to obtain it; and the other is when he hurries his request after it is already out of his hands. Then discretion means that a man should set himself to matters before they get out of hand. Of course, my sons, commit yourself to what you have to do when the time is right and plan carefully in advance what you intend to do. Get advice on what you plan to do before you do it, and be prepared to do it when you have considered everything, and then work hard to complete it.

"And especially in the matter of wars, provide yourselves fully with all the things you might need before you march into war, for weapons are worth little in the struggle if you enter it before there is a firm resolution and you are not prepared in the use of weapons. And every man who wants to attack another in war ought not to do it with the intention of doing wrong to another, but in order to be able to live in peace defending what is his own, for such a person as this is aided by God because he does it with good intent. Wherefore the Scripture says, 'We go to war in order that we may have peace.' But first one ought to prepare carefully and ought not to be vexed or hasty because the preparation lasts a long time, for a long and good preparation leads a man to conquer his enemy more easily. And therefore they say, 'Delay is good which makes the way safe, for he who is prepared is successful.' And, my sons, know that the right preparation to make war and to enter the struggle has need of five things: the first is to be a man of good natural intelligence in order to know how to choose the best thing; the second is to be of strong fiber in order to attack tenaciously, and not weakly, the course that you begin; the third is to be rich in order to spend and to give freely; the fourth is to be generous of heart and not to be troubled about a thing that you give, for stingy persons have few comrades nor are they well served; the fifth, to be a lord over good people who may love you truly, for if they do not truly love you, you cannot be served well by them.

But every wise man ought first to know how to make use of things, especially in deeds of war, before he sets himself to their use, for it is not good sense for a man to do or undertake something that he does not know. And my sons, it is better for you to observe everything well beforehand and seek good advice about them than to start out and not be successful, for your enemies will revenge themselves on you and you will suffer. And you ought not to postpone things that you have to do with force, for long delay impedes the powerful lord in vast undertakings, for the king who postpones things too much suffers in his attempts. And for this reason they say, 'You who postpone until tomorrow what you should do today will probably be unsuccessful.'

"And kings ought not to ignore matters that suddenly arise, or consider them as nothing although they may be small, because the greatest matters that have occurred in kingdoms began as small things and grew in size. And this was because they thought little of them and ignored them, and so they increased in size, for a small dispute or a small wrong can grow so much that it can cause great damage, just as the fire that originates from a spark which, if not extinguished, does very great harm."

167. Of how the king of Mentón instructed his sons and told them how all men ought to be constant in all their actions

"Furthermore, my sons, you ought to be constant in all your actions, which means to be firm and strong. For constancy is a virtue which means to be firm, persevering in what you begin and not changing on account of what may come to you, but be calm and persistent in your actions, showing as good a face to the good fortune that may happen to you as to the evil fortune that occurs. Wherefore a wise man says, 'If I had pain, I did not show it, nor did I want the pain in my heart to be shown in my countenance, but I forced myself to hide it in order to cover my feeling.' Wherefore, my sons, you should not change for anything that may happen to you, whether it be good fortune or bad, but you should be strong and confront any fortune that may come to you without any change whatsoever so that men will know you, for a changeable and fickle nature belongs to weak and evil men. However, many times, the wicked are constant and strong in their wicked deeds. But this is not a virtue. It is primarily foolish and shows a lack of wisdom to be persistent in evil and hesitant in good. And certainly this is contrary to the rule of constancy, which signifies firmness and which commands us not to commit wrong in any manner, or to be slow in doing good, or to cease to do so through vexation or anger.

"When adversities happen to you, show yourselves to be men of courage and strong, and thus you will inspire courage in your men and make your enemies afraid. For it is true that fear makes a man faint of heart in times of great danger, and makes him dread the misfortune which is to come, and it makes him cease what he began and cower in fear and anticipation, making him become fearful and alarmed at dangers he cannot see just as though they were right before his eyes. It is very likely that those dangers which frighten him will never materialize. Surely a man is strong and courageous not to be disturbed when adversity fall his lot and he is already involved with it, for if he showed little prudence in not anticipating that it would be detrimental to him, it still behooves him to take great care to extricate himself with honor, since he is already in trouble. He is considered courageous who is prepared to suffer frightful and terrifying things and who does not fear that anyone can remove him from the position he holds, unless it is right that he should be removed. Rather he should firmly exercise his position as a man of courage and not flee from things that happen rightfully, for there are more things that alarm and frighten us than those that can actually harm us. Sometimes a man worries more thinking about what he wants than in trying to achieve it. Therefore, my sons, you should not despair of what you undertake once you are engaged in it, although you see your people weak and unable to bear up, for God helps to support those who are about to fall and in particular sustains them firmly and rightly. It is a great disgrace for a man to cease what he has begun through cowardice. Therefore, strive to complete the things you begin and try to carry them through to success.

"For the valiant inspires fear in his enemies and he honors and defends himself and those who are with him, and the coward abandons father and sons and brothers and friends and aids their enemies. And the two worst traits a man can have are to be miserly and cowardly. And let not the coward think that through his cowardice he can avoid death if it comes for him; it is a well-known fact that cowards always fall in battle and the valiant escape. And certainly it is better to face death and die as a brave person than to act in another manner and die as a coward. The first thing that a man gains from courage is assurance and a lack of fear of his enemies. And know that faintheartedness is born from lack of courage and is the cause of death in battles, and it is a certain thing that more of those who flee die in battle than those who stand and defend themselves.

"Patience in misfortune is a great aid, and the person who is courageous knows how to fight mightily as if he were in a castle. And you should know that through valor a man acquires honor, and he is feared and dreaded and he defends himself bravely and fiercely. You will always find generosity and valor in the religious man, and he who trusts in God is always under His protection in battle.

"Therefore whatever you do, do calmly and thoughtfully; for calmness springs from good sense, and recklessness from madness. Wherefore whoever undertakes a great task with calmness and thoughtfulness can carry it out, and the smallest task in the world cannot be carried out with recklessness, for recklessness is the maddest trait a man can have. And certainly madness and recklessness prompt a man to attack those with more power than he.

Few can take shelter from the blow struck by the intelligent, and the shrewd person will succeed with intelligence and skill in what he wishes, although he may have little power. However, the reckless foolish man will not succeed although he may be extremely strong. And therefore calmness is a thing that nothing else resembles, nor can anything accomplish as much as it can. With calmness a man can break the cleverness of his enemy, and he who knows how to get along with his men in tranquillity can give less than he should and take more than he ought and yet be praised for it. Tranquillity, then, is the key to all fortune. And therefore when a man begins things with intelligence and asks for them rightfully and calmly, God will aid him to acquire them.

"Moreover, my sons, do not let your adversaries deceive you by fine gifts they may give you, believing that you are greedy, for greed brings great dangers and dishonor to a man. And you should know that gold and silver always causes problems among enemies, injuring first one and then the other. And you should know that just as the lightning bolt from heaven shatters the mountaintops by force, so does giving shatter and overcome the most stubborn hearts of men, especially those of the greedy. And fine gifts subvert the hearts of the greedy and of the most powerful and cruel chieftains, and they turn one against another.

"And therefore, hold strongly to your purpose and keep an eye on goodness and honor, for shame is more to be feared than death, and death is better for a man than life or any other advantage that he thinks to gain. After you march into battle always guide your people astutely, telling them that they are doing well, and frequently praising the men and strengthening them and inspiring them with good words, and aid those to stay on the road whom you see are inclined to fall, and those who fall, aid them to get up, for you will be aiding yourselves, for when armed men fall they cannot easily arise if others do not help them. And so order it done to all of your people by each other."

168. Of how the king of Mentón instructed his sons and told them how all men in the world ought to share their profits

"Furthermore, my sons, if God should grant you victory, order all the booty you have won placed in a common account, and allot fairly to each one according to his value and how much he deserves it. Even share your own part and make it a portion for those whom you see have done well, because then you will have their support more easily for other deeds when the occasion arises. If you shrink from sharing, you will find them resistant to serve you."

169. Of how the king of Mentón instructed his sons and told them how they ought to keep the agreements that men make although they may make them with their enemies

"Furthermore, if you have some agreements with your enemies in which you promise to maintain friendship or any other matters with them, keep them completely. Do not break the truce with them if they have one with you, for a man is deeply obligated to keep what he promises to his enemy as well as to his friend. And do not believe those who tell you that you should not keep these agreements with the enemy but should strive to conquer him in any way you can through deception or any other ruse. And certainly you ought not to do thus, for he would speak evil of you for it because you had not upheld what you had promised as you should. And this is shown as it should be by a king of Rome who was taken prisoner at Athens in a battle.

"The story relates that an agreement was made with this king to exchange the captives taken by the troops of Athens for those taken by the troops of Rome, and this king was sent to Rome with this agreement, and he swore that if the people of Rome did not desire to do this, he would return himself to captivity. And when he was in Rome, he told them of the agreement with which he came, and through their greed, and thinking to obtain great ransom for their prisoners, they refused to exchange them. Having no pity on the prisoners that the troops of Athens were holding, nor paying heed to how it would be bad for the king if he did not fulfill the pledge and the oath that he had made, they tried to detain him.

"And when the king saw that the people of Rome had this intent, he left secretly one night and proceeded to place himself in the power of the Athenians in order to comply with what he had promised. He refused to fail them or to lie to them. And he did what he had to do and preserved his reputation and his soul. For it is a mortal sin to lie, just as the Scriptures say: 'The mouth that lies kills the soul.' And therefore all men in the world ought to keep and hold to what they promise; thus they will be more loved and more respected by God and by men, and men will trust them in everything without any doubt whatsoever."

170. Of how the king of Mentón told his sons how lords must protect all their lands and all the places of discontent

"Furthermore, my sons, you must be just in the lands that you are to rule, and do not cease to do justice for the sake of greed or for love, or hate, or a debt that you may owe someone, just as it says in the chapter on justice,[1] and thus you will be loved by God and by men, and all those of your

1. Note here that the king speaks to his sons and refers to what he is teaching them as though they are reading a book ("just as it says in the chapter on justice, . . .").

dominion will be protected, each one in his own estate. And do not encroach upon the rights of anyone of your country nor impose more taxes on them than they ought to pay according to your law, except when your enemies try to invade your land to lay waste and to conquer it, for then all must aid you with their bodies and what they own, for you have to form a conscripted army. And you must know that there are two kinds of armies: one kind is conscripted when enemies invade the land, and all must aid their army because they are aiding and defending themselves; the other kind of army is the volunteer army which is created willingly, as when a king wants to seize land from his enemies. The citizens do not have to join this army or pay tribute other than their legal taxes, except those who hold the land in fief or those whom you pay to serve you or to whom you give generous payments in order for them to enlist in the army.

"However, counts and dukes and other great nobles often strive to stir up trouble in the land and to make war against their neighbors in order that the king may have to create a conscript army and levy taxes on the land and divide it among them. For that reason you must protect yourselves as much as you can from the counsels of such as these, for they would easily make you lose the support of the people and the people would tell you not to ask them for anything. And when the people deny their lord what he needs, out of mistrust inspired by those counts or lords who have no confidence in him, they often set themselves to do harm, not considering whether it is good or bad for them. And afterwards it will be very difficult to return them to your service, and it could happen as happened to a very powerful and wise emperor of Armenia, as he appeared to all men, and it happened to him in this fashion.

"The story relates that through the advice and scheming of evil counselors, who thought they would have a great share in what the emperor would exact from his land, they advised him to burden his people with taxes, although it was against his own laws. They advised him to order money of base value made that could be used in purchases and sales, and other coins of great value that his taxpayers, the privileged as well as the nonprivileged, could pay him and in this way he would acquire all the wealth of the land and would be able to give and to spend as extravagantly as he wanted; and so he did. And when the people of the land realized it and understood this great oppression that came to them from all these things, they rose against the emperor and refused to welcome him in any of his towns. And what was worse, those who advised this, sided with the people against the emperor, so that he died fallen from favor and sorely afflicted. For that reason, my sons, it is necessary that you pay attention to such things as these and not let yourselves be deceived by evil counselors or by greed, for you will be wrong and fall into great trouble, for it is not good to close the doors to the enemy at one point and open them at another. Thus if you want to make war against your enemies while at the same time taxing and corrupting your own domain, you will close the doors at one point where the other army is, and open them for it at the point where your subjects were taxed exorbitantly and oppressed. As they consider themselves deprived of their rights and preyed upon with no hope of recovery, these people will open the gates for the enemy. And surely you must protect your subjects, for they are the source of treasure for kings when the time comes for great events."

171. Of how lords ought not to place too many officials in posts or too many guards over their wealth

"Furthermore, my sons, you should not plan to place many officials in your offices, nor should you plan to place many guards on watch over your treasure, for many can do more harm than one. In your chancellery, place only one in whom you trust. And all the harm, benefit, and security of your dominion from here on will come from this. Your kingdom can be great if those whom you employ are not evil and greedy, for through greed they will not look out for your welfare. They will not safeguard your dominion and they will grant favor after favor and will undo the favors and services you and the other kings granted who preceded you. Do not sell your chancellery, for the buyers do not care for anything else except to plunder in every way they can, neither supporting and honoring the great nor having compassion on the poor. And surely the chancellery which is poorly guarded and poorly commanded will be the conflagration and destruction of the kingdom. And if a faithful and true man holds the chancellery in trust and employs an overseer or guards who are incapable of wickedness, the kingdom is protected and secure and the lord is served well. A man such as this guards the welfare of his lord, honors the good men of the domain, and has compassion on the poor. Furthermore I tell you and I advise you not to place an overseer or any guard whatsoever over that person, for then what happened to a Moorish king may happen to you, in this fashion:

"The Scriptures say that this Moorish king had a vast treasure. He made one of his servants whom he trusted the guard of it, and he ordered him to take one gold coin a day for his services and his expenses. The servant did not comply with these conditions and took two gold coins each day, so that he became rich, and what remained after his expenses, he guarded. And some greedy people said to the king:

"'Sire, you know well that your steward who guards your treasure was very poor when you placed him there, and now he is so rich that he does not know how much he owns, and you would do well to place some other one there to guard it with him.'

"And the king did so, and he ordered him to take a gold coin each day as the other did. And this second guard found out how the other had taken two gold coins each day, and he agreed with him to take just as many, so that he became rich with what he took each day besides his pay, just as the other had.

"And others came about this matter and they told the king to pay close attention to his treasure, for these men were very rich and he should put more guards there. And the king believed them and did so, and he placed ten guards there, thinking they would guard it better. And they all agreed as one, and each one of them took two gold coins every day, so that one day the king went to check his treasure and found it much smaller. He reprimanded the guards and each one excused himself saying he did not know how the shortage came about. Afterward, the king drew aside that person he had placed on guard first and told him under the threat of the king's wrath to tell him how such great damage and loss to his treasure had occurred. And he, as a wise man, fearing to deny him the truth, answered him as follows."

172. Of the parable that the treasurer told the Moorish king about the wolf and the leeches

"'Sire, I say to you that it happened to you just as happened to a wolf who, wandering through a field, met some sheep dogs. And the dogs pursued him, and the wolf, because he did not see a place where he might hide or flee, jumped into a large lake in the field and swam to the other side. And in that lake were many leeches and many of them stuck to the wolf, so that all his body was covered and they were full of the blood they had drawn from him. And he began to tear them from him with his teeth and cast them off, while the dogs circled the lake after him. And he, after he had taken all the leeches off himself, saw the dogs were near and again jumped into the lake and swam to the other side. He found himself again covered with leeches full of blood, and he began to tear them loose; however, he was weak on account of the great quantity of blood they had sucked from him.

"'And while he was worrying about this predicament he was in, another wolf happened along and asked him what he was doing. He told him he was pulling those leeches from himself, for he was very weak because of the blood they had drawn from him, and he was afraid because of weakness that he would be unable to cross the lake if the dogs should come circling around the lake again.

"'Friend,' said the other wolf, 'since the dogs are coming, I do not want to delay, but I will give you advice. If you cross the lake again, do not pull the leeches from you that are sticking to you and are full, for these should not be pulled off, since they are surfeited. If you pull them off and have to cross the lake again, other hungry ones will stick to you which want to bloat themselves on your blood, just as those others do, so you will lose your strength and be unable to walk. If you had allowed the first ones that stuck to you to remain, since they were full, you would have done better, for there was no place for the other famished ones to cling, and so you would not have lost so much blood from your body.'

"'Therefore, sire,' said the steward, 'since I was already rich, if you had left me alone on guard over the treasure and had not placed more poor and hungry security guards there who were greedy to enrich themselves, you would not be missing so much of your treasure. Each one of those that you stationed there carried off as much each day as I until they became rich, as you see, and the great deficit in your treasure results from this. And even if you leave them here, they will not quit digging into your treasure, because of greed to carry off as much as they can; for the heart of the greedy person does not believe that what he has is enough, although he may be very wealthy. And you cannot trust any assurance the greedy gives you. No matter how much he owns, he may say that he will not steal from you and it will not be true, just as a cardinal, a good and virtuous man, said in giving advice to a pope who was in power in his day.'"

173. Concerning the advice that a cardinal gave to a pope in Rome

"'The story is told in this way: This pope was a good man and a good Christian, and he was pleased with good and displeased with evil. Because he saw that the cardinals were prolonging the lawsuits of those who were coming to court and were taking all the money they had, the Pope told them he wanted the suits settled rapidly.

"'He did not want them to take anything from those who came to court, and said he would give each of them every year a certain share of his own stores, which they could share. The cardinals answered that they would gladly do it, except for this one good man who did not respond at all. And the Pope told him to tell him what he thought and what he would advise. And he responded and said:

"'Holy Father, I advise you not to throw away your wealth, for the more you give, the more you will lose, for we cannot in a short time break the habits we have long been accustomed to, and I will tell you why. May you know that we have the traits of the rooster, for no matter how much wheat you place before him to satisfy him, he does not cease to scratch according to his nature, although he may be satisfied. And you, sir, may trust that by giving what you can to us of what is yours, we shall not cease to take what you give us but still scratch and strive for as much as we can, no matter what you may give.'

"Wherefore, my sons, avoid as much as you can placing too many guards over your possessions, and especially over your treasure, for it is a thing that inspires greed. Those who truly protect your money are few, and it is better for you to select one whom you trust and make him guard over it, and not appoint many. Although he may carry something away, one cannot carry off so much or do so much damage as many can."

174. Of how the king of Mentón instructed his sons and told them of the harm that came to the land through putting the duties of the king and lords on sale

"And furthermore do not plan to sell the offices of the law, for the law will never be enforced nor will justice be done through the greed for plunder, just as happened in the kingdom of Orbín.

"The story relates that there was a greedy king there who sold the office of justice for a quantity of wealth given him, so that when those who were sentenced to die were turned over to the official to be executed according to their sentence, he released them for the payment they gave him and thus justice was not satisfied, and for this reason the wicked dared to do more evil. And when the public complained to the king that justice was not being carried out in the land, he indicated that he considered it wrong, but he did not correct it.

"And after a few days he became ill. While he was delirious, it seemed to him that all those on whom sentence had not been carried out had come to him in order to kill him and that they were holding him with his hands tied, saying, 'Since you refused to carry out sentence on us, we are going to carry it out on you, for thus God considers it right.' And he began to cry out, asking for help. And the people who were guarding him came in response to his shouts, saying: 'Sire, what is the matter?'

"And he came to his senses and told how a large number of those who had not been executed had come to kill him and had tied his hands, and that they would find his hands tied. All were greatly astonished by this, and not without reason, for surely it was a miracle of God.

"And then he sent for the official who was supposed to mete out justice and asked him why he had not carried out sentence on those who had been turned over to him to be executed. And he said it was true that he had not executed any of those, on account of the payment they gave him. He realized that he had rented the office from him for a large sum of money, and knew that he would not receive enough money for the bodies of the dead to pay the rent. Therefore he had not executed them, but had taken payment from them so that he could pay his rent; but if he had known that the king would have accepted the bodies of the dead in exchange for his payment, he would have killed them and saved the bodies for him.

"When the king heard this, he considered he was to blame, for he had rented and sold the justice that he should have administered according to law, and he distributed great wealth to the complainants so that they would forgive him. He fasted a great deal and went on pilgrimages, making amends to God for that sin he had committed through greed. And he made a vow, which he swore at once upon the Holy Gospels that neither he nor those who should come after him would ever break, that no office in which justice was to be administered, to the nobility as well as to the public, would ever be rented, but that it would be entrusted to the best and most honest man to be found in the kingdom and to no one else, and that there would be no more than one officeholder in that office where the duty was to be discharged, and this person would have a reward for the good he did or punishment if he deserved it. And he carried out sentence on those who had advised him to rent the office, in order that none should dare to advise their lord wrongly. And this vow was always kept in that kingdom so that each man was master of what he owned and was protected and defended in his rights.

"And, my sons, know that I heard your mother the queen relate this parable, for she learned it when she was there. And surely where justice does not exist, all evil does. For in all the duties in the palace of the king and in all good places, justice and law must be upheld so that men may do no more nor less than ought to be done according to fairness and proper rules. And so, in being careful and prudent in all these things I have told you, you will be honored, respected, and loved by your people and by all strangers who have wisdom. You will be wealthy and fortunate among all your neighbors, and your good reputation will always precede you. Your land will increase in population, your people will be richer, and you will be served well and aided by them in all matters, for people who come to the aid of kings are a treasure. And thus you will be loved and honored by God, whose love is over all good things, and may He permit you to live and die in that love."

"'Amen,' they said."

175. Of how Garfín and Roboán were grateful to their father for the instruction he had given them

After the instruction the king had given them, they both knelt at his feet and kissed them while shedding many tears of happiness and showing gratitude to him for the great favor he did for them. And Garfín said:

"Sire, now we see and understand that the advice and counsel you gave us in the past were not in vain. And certainly it is true that once when you advised us and we were grateful for the favors you did for us, you said, 'Sons, a time may still come in which I may be able to render services for you like a good father to his good sons!' and we were doubtful then, and we said to each other that this could be true, for you showed a love to us greater than to anyone else from another country, and as we debated, we said, 'Could this really be our father?' because we were so small when you lost us that we could not recall over so long a time. But blessed be the name of God for the great mercy he deigned to show us for having you recognize us as your sons and for having us come into your favor! And I trust in His mercy that these two students whom you instructed and advised have learned your teaching well, so that whatever happens to them, they will work in the service of you and of God."

"May God wish it so," said the king, "through his mercy."

"Amen," they responded.

BOOK FOUR

The Adventures of Roboán

176. How Prince Roboán asked his father, the king of Mentón, to grant him permission to leave, and he let him go

"Surely He so wishes it," said Roboán. "What God inspires us to begin, we ought to consider as successful, for He has never begun anything which was not completed in the manner in which He planned to complete it. Just as you see that God began by favoring us, there is no reason why we should doubt that He will continue to give success in everything. And I ask you for the love of God to find it in your heart to forgive me and to send me away and not detain me, for my heart tells me that you soon will hear news of me which will please you."

"Of course, my son, I will not detain you," replied the king, "but it would be well for your mother to know, but I am certain that it will worry her very much."

"Sire," said Roboán, "comfort her with your gentle talk, just as I know you can, and reassure her and make her happy."

"Of course I will do whatever I can," said the king, "for I want you to do what your heart desires. I believe that your request is an honorable one and am sure if you strive diligently and control your passions, with God's grace you will be successful. Every man who plans to achieve some task can achieve it honorably as in anything he can do if he has the wherewithal to pursue it, and, if he is not impatient, he will surely be successful. Therefore, my son, take strength from God, and He will guide you, for He does not guide any except those who call on Him and wish to be guided by Him. And therefore they say that God guides whom He wants to guide."

177. How the king told the queen of Roboán's departure

Then the king sent for the queen to come to them, and when she arrived and seated herself on a throne equal to the king's, he said:

"My queen, I have been with your sons like a good teacher who has the desire to instruct and advise them so that they will always do what is best and to their honor. And as to them, I recognize that they have learned their lesson like ambitious students. If there are men in this world who work hard at the rules and deeds of chivalry, these two will be among the best. And, my lady, I will tell you what I understand: Roboán, who is the younger, paid close attention to the counsels and instruction that I gave them, and he took them to heart. He could not refrain from asking me to give him some assistance, and three hundred knights with whom he might challenge the world and win honor. His heart told him that he would attain honor with the grace of God, just as we did, or perhaps even greater. And surely as he spoke the words, my heart told me it was true. My lady, remember that before we left our native land, I told you my plans and what I wanted to do and that we should not tell anyone, for they would think we were foolish. And you answered me that whether it was folly or prudence, as soon as you heard me speak, your heart told you it might be true, and you advised me thus: that we should leave our native land, and we did. and after great trials and hardships, God through His grace guided us and directed us as you see we are now. And surely that same thing could happen to Roboán's proposal."

"I speak the truth before God," said the queen. "The same thing that happened to me when you told me your plans has happened to me with this proposal of Roboán's. It absolutely seems to me that he is to be a great emperor." And breaking into tears, she said: "My lord, although these plans enter a man's heart and he believes he can accomplish them, everything is a risk. If you agree, I think it would be better for him to remain here with you and his brother. You could do much for him and endow him with wealth, for praise be to God you have sufficient to do so. Let him not leave so quickly, even though he has given us some consolation and pleasure for all the loneliness we endured for so long when we were separated. Since God saw fit to bring us together through his mercy, let us not be separated."

178. How the queen and the king granted permission to their son Prince Roboán to leave

"My lady," said Roboán, isn't it better to seek honor early rather than late? And since you are my mother and my queen, you should encourage me rather than hinder me. Surely it is harsh advice from a mother to her son."

"Oh, my son Roboán!" cried the queen. "May misfortune strike me if I do not wish you more success than you do yourself!"

"Well, why are you trying to hinder me then?" replied Roboán.

"I am not trying to," answered the queen, "and wherever you go, my broken heart will go with you. I will be sad and worried always thinking about you. And woe is me! Who will I find to comfort me or tell me news of you and how you are getting along? This will be my pain and sorrow when I can't see you!"

Roboán replied: "My lady, be of good cheer, for I have taken Our Lord God as my guardian and defender. He is all-powerful and with trust in Him and in His aid, I will accomplish such deeds that fame will bring you news of me and will comfort you."

"Well, so be it," said the queen. "Since it pleases your father the king, whenever you are ready, go on your way in the name of God."

179. How Prince Roboán took his leave of the king, the queen, and Garfín, his brother, and of the equipage that he took with him, and of how he departed

Early the next morning, because of Roboán's eagerness, they gave him one hundred beasts of burden laden with gold and silver, and they gave him permission to select three hundred of the best knights of the king's army. He chose those he believed best suited to his needs. Among those, he chose a knight named Garbel, who was a vassal of the king, very intelligent, a wise counselor, and a skilled knight-at-arms.

And he refused to leave the Knight Amigo behind, for he was indeed a very wise, good, and powerful vassal. Roboán gave the knights everything they needed for their homes as well as what they required as personal equipment, and he set a time limit of one week for them to prepare to accompany him. Furthermore, in addition to the one hundred mules laden with gold and silver that he had given Roboán, the king paid for all the equipment for the knights. At the end of the week these three hundred knights came to him ready to go. They took leave of the king and the queen and departed. However, at their leavetaking there was much weeping and wailing, and there was none present in the city who did not lament, and they spoke ill of the king because he had permitted Roboán to go and they could not deter him, since he had already set his plans in motion. And they all truly loved and respected him for his courtliness and the deeds of chivalry he had accomplished, and it seemed to them that the kingdom would be desolate without him.

And as he traveled through the kingdom, he was welcomed with great festivities. All honored him and each insisted on inviting him, thinking to detain him, and that perhaps by staying over he would reconsider this adventure that he had begun. And when he left and they saw that nothing could prevent him from his plans, all their happiness turned to tears and laments; and so he departed his father's kingdom. And no matter what kingdom he traversed, he was welcomed effusively, and the kings gave him some of their wealth and begged him to stay with them.

They willingly offered to share with him what they possessed; he expressed his gratitude and went on his way. Because he and the people who accompanied him were so gallant, the natives of the other cities and villages who had heard of him eagerly desired to see him; and when he arrived there, all closed their places of business just as if their own lord had arrived. However, the young knights who were traveling with him were not inclined to be idle. Some were jousting and others throwing lances and still others as they marched along the countryside challenged each other with shield and lance.

When he undertook to do it, Prince Roboán was the best among all, for he was the best trained young knight that any man ever knew. He was very handsome in appearance, elegant, vibrant of voice and very personable. He was a player of backgammon and chess and an expert hunter of birds, better than any other hunter. He was a skillful raconteur, so that when he went traveling, all wanted to accompany him in order to hear what he was saying. He willingly and generously shared provender where there was need, and was true to his word, wise and experienced, and capable of giving good counsel when it was asked of him. He did not make decisions without consulting others and was a valorous knight, but not reckless, and one who honored ladies and maids. The story clearly states that if a man wanted to relate all the traits and qualities of this knight, he could not write them all in one day. And it was obvious that the fates who brought him good fortune were not the miserly kind, but had been liberal in endowing him with an abundance of good qualities.

And thus it was that Roboán had journeyed one hundred days from his father's land, and had entered another country with a language unlike his own, so that they were able to understand only a few words. However, he had brought his interpreters with him through all the land he had crossed, so that he was welcomed with pleasure. and great honor was accorded him, and his army was under orders to do no harm to anyone.

180. How Prince Roboán reached the kingdom of Pandulfa where Princess Seringa reigned

He had traveled so far that he reached the kingdom of Pandulfa, where the Princess Seringa was sovereign.[1] She had inherited the kingdom from her father, who had no other children. And because she was a woman, the neighboring kings mistreated her, seized her land, and failed to show her the courtesy that every man should show toward ladies. When Roboán reached the city where Princess Seringa lived, he was received warmly. Then he went to call on the princess. She arose and greeted him courteously, showing more courtesy to him than she did for others who came to see her. She asked:

"Friend, are you a knight?"

"My lady," he answered, "yes."

"And are you the son of a king?" she asked.

---

1. The author is describing Asia Minor, not Asia Major.

"Yes," he said. "By the grace of God."

"And are you married?" asked the princess.

"Indeed no," said Roboán.

"What land are you from?" she inquired.

"From the kingdom of Mentón," he said. "You may have heard of it."

"Yes, I have heard," she said, "but I thought it very far away."

"You are right," said Roboán. "It is well over one hundred and thirty days' journey from here to there."

"Are you very fatigued?" she questioned.

"The man who travels because he wants to does not consider fatigue," replied Roboán.

"You mean you come to this land for your pleasure and not to enrich yourself?" she asked.

"For my own pleasure," he said, "and I will gain what God grants me and nothing else."

"May God let you gain everything that is honorable," she replied.

"So be it!" he said.

The princess was greatly pleased with him and asked him to be her guest. She said he would be royally entertained. He accepted her offer, since he never refused any sensible request that a lady or maiden asked of him. He then arose from where he had been sitting with her, in order to take his leave.

181. Concerning the conversation between Prince Roboán and a lady named Gallarda

Thinking that the prince was ready to leave, a very beautiful widow named Lady Gallarda, who was bold of speech, said:

"Sir prince, do you plan to leave without saying goodbye?"

"I am not planning to leave," he said "because I am not saying goodbye to you or to the others. And although I could take leave of the others, I could not say goodbye to you even if I tried."

"Oh, sir," she said, "you have so little respect for me?"

"I don't think," he replied, "that a man shows disrespect to a woman when she professes she loves him a great deal and he finds it difficult to say goodbye to her." And he and his companions departed for their quarters.

The princess began to talk with her maids and ladies:

"Have you ever seen so youthful, so handsome, so elegant and cultured a knight, and one so perceptive in the answers he gave?"

"Indeed, my lady," said the widow Gallarda, "from what I heard, he seems to me very intelligent, soft-spoken, and very pleasant to all listening to him."

"You mean you were pleased with him for what he said to you?" inquired the princess.

"Certainly, my lady," said the widow, "I am very pleased with him for what I heard him say to you. Mark my words, my lady, I would be happy for him to come to see you, for you would be able to talk with him and learn if he is what he seems. And I promise you, my lady, that if he speaks to me, I will test him in conversation by using sarcasm and see if he says anything ugly."

"My lady," said the princess, "do not try your fine speech on him or try to test or badger men more than you should, for while you are trying to ridicule them, perhaps they will make a fool of you."

"I understand, my lady," answered the widow, "but come what may, I am going to do it, because I love you so much, and that is reason enough to speak to him."

"May God bless all the maids and ladies who wish him well," said the princess.

"So be it," they all replied.

The princess then ordered them to take good care of Roboán and to give him whatever he needed. She was easily able to do this for she was very wealthy and possessed vast and abundant riches, not counting the income that she had yearly from the kingdom. After her father, the king, had died, she had inherited all his treasure, which was amazingly large. She was very practical and knew well how to take care of what she owned. And she was much to be praised for how well she had supported herself after the death of her father and how well she had ruled her kingdom. There were wicked neighbors who invaded her country and caused great destruction and for no other reason than the fact that she refused to marry those who were not of her class and who did not hold as much power as she.

182. How Count Rubén told Princess Seringa in the presence of Prince Roboán how the king of Grimalet was making incursions into her country

After Prince Roboán had dined, he saddled up with all his troops and went for a ride throughout the city. All the citizens were as impressed with him as if he were lord of the kingdom. And all together called God's blessing upon him because he truly merited it. After he had ridden a while through the city, he headed for the palace of the princess. When they told her the prince was coming, she was very happy and ordered them to welcome him and all his company. The princess was in the great palace that her father the king had ordered constructed and she was accompanied by more ladies-in-waiting and maidens than the ones Roboán had met when he had visited her in the morning. When Roboán arrived, he sat before her and they began to chat about many things. While they were conversing, Count Rubén, uncle of the princess, entered. Roboán stood and greeted him warmly and asked if he wanted to speak with the princess privately, and if so, he would leave them. "Indeed I do wish to speak to the princess," said the count, "but I don't want the conversation to be without you, for alas! what I have to say is not a secret." And he added:

"My lady, it is necessary for you to pay close attention to the news that now has reached us."

"And what news is this?" asked the princess.

"My lady," replied the count, "the king of Grimalet has invaded your land and is raiding and burning throughout. He has seized six castles and two towns from you, and he said that he would not rest until he had destroyed all your kingdom. On account of this, it is necessary for you to hold a council with your people. Summon them and consult with them, and prepare, so that this danger and destruction go no further."

"Count," stated the princess, "order it done, for you know that when my father died, he left me in your care, for I am a woman and do not know these matters or how to approach the problems. Whatever you consider right to order has my full approval."

183. How Prince Roboán sent his vassal the Knight Amigo with an ultimatum for the king of Grimalet

The count frankly and wisely told the news to the princess in the presence of Roboán, for the count was very intelligent and experienced in many things. He related this news thinking that Prince Roboán would perhaps be influenced to aid the princess with gallant troops. The princess began to complain bitterly:

"O Lord God! Why didst Thou allow me to be born, since I cannot defend myself against those who mistreat me? It would surely be better if I had never been born and someone else who knows how to stand up and fight were in my place!"

The prince, when he heard her lament, felt great pity, and the affronts committed against her grieved him deeply, and he said:

"My lady, have you ever sent a message to this king who mistreats you, that he should not do this to you?"

"Of course, I have," said the princess. "Many times I have sent word to him but I have never gotten a satisfactory answer from him."

"To be sure," declared Roboán, "whoever does not give a courteous answer is not a man; rather I believe he is a devil full of arrogance, for the arrogant never know how to respond properly. I do not believe that such a king as this one you speak of will long endure in his exalted position, for God does not tolerate the arrogant; instead He crushes and casts them down to earth, just as He will do with this king."

"I trust in His mercy," said the princess, "if the king does not repent and cease this madness and arrogance. He has long committed crimes against me in my kingdom since my father, the king, died."

Prince Roboán turned toward the count and said:

"Count, have one of your squires assigned to me to accompany one of my knights to show him the road and the land. I will send a request to that king, counting on his courtesy that while I am here a stranger in your kingdom, through respect to me he will cease his attacks against you. I believe he will be reasonable and will be favorably inclined."

"I agree willingly," replied the count. "Then I will give you the squire to go with your knight to guide him throughout the kingdom of the princess and I'll have him supplied with whatever he needs until he reaches the king."

Then Roboán sent for the Knight Amigo and ordered him to carry a letter to the king of Grimalet. He instructed him to beseech him on his behalf to be tolerant as a king should and, out of respect to him since he was a stranger, to cease committing acts of war in the kingdom of Pandulfa while he was visiting there. Further, he would be grateful, and if by chance he refused his request or said anything rash or arrogant, the Knight Amigo should challenge him on behalf of Roboán.

184. How the widow Gallarda repented of the questions she had asked Prince Roboán

The Knight Amigo took Prince Roboán's letter and, accompanied by the squire, mounted his horse. The count came out to instruct them what they should do. The princess was very grateful to Roboán for what he was doing for her, and she asked all the knights, ladies and maidens present to join her in showing gratitude. All were very appreciative except the widow Gallarda who said:

"O son of a king! How can I be grateful to you for anything considering how you made fun of me today?"

"Certainly, my lady," said Roboán, "I do not believe that you quite understood me, for if you had understood my words and the significance of them you would not have judged me as you did. but if your mistress the princess agrees, I will speak with you and make you understand; for if a person does not understand what a man says once, it is fitting that he repeat it."

"Of course, I am happy for you to speak to whomever you wish to," replied the princess, "for I am certain she will hear nothing but good from you."

Then Roboán arose and went to sit with the widow and said to her:

"My lady, you should be very grateful to God for so much good and mercy as He has done for you. I am grateful to Him because He created you one of the most beautiful, gayest most graceful, ladies in the world, and a most unselfish, sweet-voiced, and elegant lady in every way. And it appears obvious that God took His time in creating you, and He endowed you with so many shades of beauty and kindness that I do not believe a man could find them in any other woman in this world."

The widow tried to incite him to anger, in order to see if he would say something offensive, in spite of the fact that she understood and saw that she could say many good things about him, because he possessed many good traits.

"Really, prince," she said, "I do not know anything good to say about you; but if I knew anything, I would gladly say it."

When Prince Roboán heard this, he was troubled in his heart, and he considered her to be rude and said to her, "My lady, don't you know what to say about me? I will teach you, for it is proper for a person who knows nothing to learn."

"Surely," said the widow, "if I can't take this second insult better than the first one, then I am still dealing with the first one, and we will have to discuss it."

"My lady," said Roboán, "there is nothing wrong with listening to what one has to say and then answering according to what is said."

"Well, instruct me," she said.

"I am happy to," he replied: "lie as I lied, and you will find as much to say about me as you care to."

When the widow heard this statement so loaded with insult, she gave a shout loud enough to split one's eardrums, so that all present were astounded.

"My lady," asked the princess, "What is the matter?"

"Mistress," replied the widow, "whoever speaks to the prince jokingly is unlucky, for I spoke what I thought was in jest, and he replied as though it were a serious matter."

And the princess said, "Did I not tell you that you would try to test him and perhaps you would be tested? Blessed be the son of the king for giving a reply that the widow deserves."

And Prince Roboán turned to speak to the widow as though a little angry: "My lady, I would be happy if you would be more careful in what you have to say, and if you would not talk as much as you do, or laugh at anyone, for it seems to me that you are eager to intrude in men's affairs, which is not fitting for a good man, much less a woman. And it can be that men may involve themselves in your business, since you have the urge to involve yourself in others' affairs. And therefore, they say that 'the magpie on the bridge laughs at everybody, and everybody at her.' Surely it is quite proper for all to laugh at whoever laughs at everybody else. And I believe that this happens to you because of your spirited personality and frankness of speech. The truth is, if I have ever in my life seen a meddling chatterbox, you are that person. Although some men want God to give them the talent of sharp speech, that they may be good speakers, occasionally it is better to listen than to speak. By listening a man can learn much, and by talking he can make mistakes. And my lady, I say these words to you, throwing myself on your mercy, and wishing you only good, for since the first time I saw you, I have been pleased with the good qualities of beauty, poise, and fine manner of speech with which God endowed you, And therefore, I would like for you to be as discreet as possible in everything. But, lady, if I have been wrong in daring to say these things to you that I said just now, I beg you to forgive me. With your best interest at heart, I forced myself to say them, and I could not refrain from saying what I believed would be helpful to you."

"Sir," replied the widow, "I cannot show enough gratitude to God for the favor He has done me today, nor thank you sufficiently for the consideration which you have shown to me by correcting me and instructing me. I have never met a man who has done me such a great favor as you by your conversation with me. And you can well believe that from now on I will behave properly, for I can see that it is not fitting for a man to be so tactless in speech, much less for a lady and rash speech can only be wrong. And you will see that you have made me understand that you have created a student who has the desire to learn everything that you say. Although I cannot render any other service to you, I shall always pray to God for your life and for your health."

"May God reward you for it," replied Roboán, "for it seems to me that I deserve little credit in this matter since I had God's help in my response, which was not a very moderate one at all."

"Good heavens," said the widow, "it was a correct statement rather than just words, for I tried to trick you and you made a fool of me, and as the proverb says: 'I set a trap and fell into it myself.'"

"Truly, my lady," said Roboán, "I am pleased with what I heard and I have to give this some thought, for I really believe that if you were not just as I thought you to be when I first saw you, you would not have responded to me so correctly as you did in all things."

And Roboán was very happy and pleased. To be sure, Roboán's words were not wasted or unheeded, for this lady was from that time on the most prudent, tactful, and virtuous lady in the kingdom. Truly, a prince such as this one ought to be in the palaces of queens and the palaces of highborn ladies, so that when he converses with ladies or maidens, his words would accomplish a great deal, just as did the words of Roboán, and the words would be so effective that they would always be good and watchful of their honor. But, alas! it happens with some that they are encouraged to say more than they should, instead of being instructed and taught the correct ways. Sometimes even their parents do not watch them or impose caution on them in these matters, and there are some who learn willingly and repeat easily the lesson they hear. Of course, the most fortunate one among them is the one who strives to speak prudently and always does her best and is careful to avoid malicious gossips. She refuses to believe or listen to anything they say to her, for whoever makes a point of listening will hear a great deal, and perhaps to her own detriment and dishonor. Since she willingly listens to it, she will thereby suffer from it, even though she may understand that the words are said for her benefit; and since she was pleased to gossip, it is fitting that she suffer for it. If God gave her good sense, she should be ashamed and willing to learn from then on. And the lady who learns from what she sees happen to others is fortunate. Therefore the wise man says that the one who learns from the misfortunes of others is very fortunate; but, alas! we seldom believe that what happens to others is a danger or hazard, but only what happens to us and what we have to suffer. Surely this is foolish, for we should understand that dangers and perils which happen to one person can happen to another, for worldly things are of a common nature, so that what happens to one today can happen to another tomorrow, unless he is a man of such great wisdom that he understands how to shield himself from danger. Therefore every man ought to learn from the experiences—especially those dangerous and damaging ones—of others rather than from his own. When he undergoes the experiences himself, he cannot avoid harm to himself and other men will consider him to be a man of little wisdom. And may God protect you all, for whom God decides to care for, that person will be protected. And considering all this, it is fitting for a man to strive to protect himself, and God will help him. Therefore it is said that God helps those who help themselves.

185. Of how the widow Gallarda praised Prince Roboán to the Princess Seringa

And then Roboán arose from his position near the widow, said farewell to the princess, and went to his lodging. The princess, her duennas, and her ladies-in-waiting remained in conversation about him, praising his good qualities. The widow Gallarda declared:

"My lady, how fortunate the lady would be who had this man as her lord, and how fortunate and noble would be the child born of her womb!"

The princess believed that these words referred to her, since the widow was the speaker, and she blushed and said:

"My lady, let us cease this discussion now, for God will determine who the fortunate lady will be."

Everyone paid close attention to the words of the princess and how she had blushed. They believed by these signs that she was not displeased with him. And surely one can often read in a man's face what he holds in his heart.

186. How the Knight Amigo returned with
the reply of the king of Grimalet

Prince Roboán dwelt in the city until the Knight Amigo returned with the reply of the king of Grimalet. And while Roboán was conversing with the princess privately with gallant words, and not impertinent or vulgar speech, the count approached the princess and said:

"My lady, the knight and the squire that Prince Roboán sent to the king of Grimalet have arrived."

"Come then," said Prince Roboán, "and we shall hear the reply he sends us."

Then the Knight Amigo came into the presence of the princess and Roboán and said:

"My lady, if it were not my duty to tell you, I would be silent and not give you the reply that the king of Grimalet gave me. As God is my witness, in all my life I've never seen such a rash and evil king, or one who gave such a rude welcome to another king's messenger or such a rude and arrogant answer!"

"O Knight Amigo," exclaimed Prince Roboán, "may God grant you His thanks and mine! Tell me exactly all that he told you and leave out nothing!"

"On my word, sir," replied the Knight Amigo, "I will tell you. Before I left, he made me pledge that I would tell you his reply completely, and when I hesitated a little in making the pledge, he ordered my head cut off."

"Surely, Knight Amigo," said Prince Roboán, "you are well now and over your fear."

The Knight Amigo replied:

"You can believe, sir, that I still feel that I am in his presence."

"Don't be afraid," said the prince, "for this behavior is unlike you in matters such as these."

"I still trust in God that I will see him in a similar situation and he will have as great a fear of me as I had of him," replied the Knight Amigo.

"It could be so," said the prince, "but tell me his answer and I will see if he is as arrogant as you say."

"Sir," replied the Knight Amigo, "as soon as I arrived, I knelt before him. I told him you sent greetings and I gave him your letter. He answered not a single word, but took it and read it. And when he had read it he said: 'I am amazed at your daring in coming before me with such a message. I hold that the person who sent you here is very foolish and arrogant, having the gall to send me a letter telling me that I should cease working for my own benefit and profit because he is a foreigner who should be honored!' And I told him that whatever he gained by sin was of no advantage to him. And for this answer I gave him, he almost ordered me killed. Set in his wicked purpose, he said to me: 'Concerning the pledge you made me, I order you to tell that reckless fool who sent you here that to dishonor him, in six days

I will burn the gates of the city where he is, and I will enter it through force, and I will instruct him with my sword, so that he will never commit another such deed as this.' Since he ordered me to tell this to you, I asked him to assure my personal safety and said that I would tell him what you had sent me to say. And he so assured me and ordered me to tell you what he wanted, and I told him that since he was sending such an arrogant reply to you, you would declare war on him, and he answered in this manner, 'Be on your way, you scoundrel, and tell him that there is no reason to threaten me, unless he wants his head cut off.'"

"Certainly, Knight Amigo," said Roboán, "you carried out your mission very well, and I am grateful to you; however, it seems to me that the king is an arrogant, ill-mannered fellow, just as the princess told me the other day. And even though God may still want him to repent of this arrogance, may he gain no advantage from repentance."

"So may it please God," added the princess.

187. How Prince Roboán, Princess Seringa, and their knights agreed on a plan to combat the king of Grimalet

"My lady," said Roboán, "when your troops arrive, decide on whom you consider right to lead us and we will obey him. I will willingly follow him in your service."

"Thank you very much," answered the princess, "I am sure that you are of such estate and lineage that, if possible, you would aid every lady and maiden who might be in trouble, and especially an orphan such as I am, without father, mother, or any other help in the world except the grace of God and the good and loyal service that my vassals render me, and the aid which you now bring me through your kindness. May God show you gratitude, for I am unable to show you as much gratitude as you deserve."

"My lady," said Roboán, "how many knights are there in this kingdom of yours?"

"How many are there?" repeated the princess. "I would say that among the nobles and the citizens who can ride, about ten thousand."

"By Heaven, my lady," exclaimed Roboán, "you have an excellent force of cavalry to defend you against all those who wish to do you harm. And my lady," he added, "can these knights get here quickly?"

"Here in a week or sooner," replied the princess.

"Of course, my lady," said Roboán, "I would be happier if they were already here and had already freed you from your enemies and you were at peace. Then I would be free to go ahead with the plans that I came with."

"And how is that?" asked the princess. "Did you not tell me you had come to these lands of your own free will and not to gain anything else?"

"My lady," replied the prince, "it is true, and I still say the same thing.

I came because I wanted to, and not to accomplish any other matter except what God might wish. When I left my land, I took Him as Guide and Director of my affairs, and I do not want or ask anything else except what He wants."

"This quest of yours is then quite uncertain?" asked the princess.

"Clearly, my lady, what is done with trust and hope in God is not uncertain; rather it is certain, and anything else that is done without Him is not," replied Roboán.

"Goodness," exclaimed the princess, "since you selected such a guide for your plans, I am sure you will finish your quest successfully." Seeing that he did not want to tell for what reason he had come, the princess desisted from her inquiry, for no one should know more of a man's secret than he wants to reveal.

188. Of how Prince Roboán and the vassals of the princess clashed with the king of Grimalet and how they vanquished him

Before the week was over, all the armed forces of the princess were present. All were well equipped and set in their purpose to serve their mistress and get revenge for the wrongs and dishonor being done to her. They agreed with the princess to make Roboán commander of the army and to be led by him, since among them there was no man of as high estate as Prince Roboán, who was the son of a king and stood ready to serve the princess.

The next morning they held an inspection in a large field outside the city, and they found that they numbered ten thousand seven hundred well-equipped cavalry. With the three hundred knights of Prince Roboán they totaled eleven thousand troops. They were eager to set out and revenge the dishonor the princess had suffered from the king of Grimalet. On the signal from Prince Roboán they moved out just as they were.

The king of Grimalet had already advanced into the kingdom of Pandulfa, a distance of six days' journey, with fifteen thousand knights. They were divided into two separate forces traveling in two different areas, burning and laying waste the countryside. Roboán had been informed of this by spies he had sent ahead. God looked on them with favor, for they did not encounter any of the forces of the king of Grimalet. When they were about four leagues from the king of Grimalet, the prince agreed to attack the king directly with all his troops; for if the main force could be destroyed and its troops scattered, the two forces would be separated, and so they would be able to conquer them more easily.

When the king learned that he was near the army of Princess Seringa, he saw he would be unable to summon quickly his troops that were distant. He ordered all those with him, about eight thousand knights, to arm themselves, and then they advanced toward their opponents. When they had approached within half a league they saw each other, and then those on each side began to line up facing the other side. Those on each side were moving so quietly that it seemed as though they were marching in a parade. And great was the misgiving on each side for all were staunch knights and well prepared. As time passed, a hundred or two hundred more knights would arrive to swell the forces of the king of Grimalet. When Prince Roboán saw them, he said to his troops:

"Friends, the longer we delay, the greater harm we are doing to ourselves; troops are swelling the ranks of the enemy still, and we have no hope of help coming to us from anywhere save from God alone and our own inner resolution. Let us attack and we shall conquer them."

"Then lead us in the name of God and we shall follow you," they replied.

"Then, my friends," said Prince Roboán, "here is the plan: when I say 'Pandulfa for Princess Seringa!' strike them in force and I will be in the lead to seek out the king especially; for he is the stake that we have to root out, with God's grace."

They launched their attack, and when they were so close it seemed that the lances on one side were about to touch those of the other, Prince Roboán shouted, "Pandulfa for Princess Seringa!" and they charged fiercely at them. They made a great opening in the ranks of the king, and the battle was very bloody on both sides, for it lasted from the hour of tierce until the hour of vespers. Prince Roboán's horse was killed, and he was on the battlefield dismounted for quite a while and defending himself with his sword. However, two hundred of his noble infantry remained with him. Most of them were those whom he had brought from his own country, and they struggled bravely to defend their lord so that no mounted knights reached him without their horses being killed. As soon as each fell from his horse, they ran their lances under his lower armor and killed him. At least five hundred dead knights were piled around the prince, so that they appeared to be a great wall, behind which they were able to defend themselves easily.

As this was happening, the Knight Amigo appeared attacking the king's troops. Striking marvelous strokes with his swords, he made his way to Prince Roboán, although he did not know that the prince was on foot. As soon as the prince saw him, he called, "Knight Amigo, bring me your horse."

"Surely it is proper," he answered, "for you gave him to me, and even if you had not given him to me, I have to come to your help with him." He flung himself from his horse and hurried to the prince with him, for the horse was very swift and well armored. They helped the prince into the saddle. And then they saw on the battlefield many horses without riders. The squires ran to catch one and gave it to the Knight Amigo and boosted him into the saddle. Then he and the prince rode against the enemy calling out in loud voices, "Pandulfa for Princess Seringa!" thus giving comfort and strength to his own men. Because they had not heard the voice of the prince for some time, they were disheartened for they believed he was dead or captured. So strongly did the prince smite the enemy and such mighty blows did he give with his sword that they all fled before him as from some evil thing, because whoever met him face to face surely died. And he encountered the son of the king of Grimalet who was on a large and well armored horse, and he recognized him by his ensign, which had been described to him, and he called:

"Oh, you son of a reckless and arrogant king! On guard, for I am the prince whose head your father threatened to cut off. And I truly believe that when I meet him, he will not choose to talk so insanely and rashly to me as he did to a knight I sent to him."

"Go on your way," replied the son of the king, "for you are not man enough to talk to my father the king about anything, nor does he have to answer you. You are a stranger and we don't know who you are. You are unwelcome in this land and you would have done better to be satisfied with your own."

Then they charged one against the other and struck great blows with their swords, and the son of the king struck Prince Roboán such a powerful stroke on top of his helmet that his head thundered and he had to hold on to his horse's neck. However, he did not lose his sword, bur rather collected greater strength and lunged against the son of the king and struck such a great blow on his right arm with his sword that he cut through the armor, although it was very heavy and sliced a great piece from his shoulder so that almost his entire shoulder was severed. The prince's squires then killed the king's horse and he fell to the earth. The prince ordered fifty of his squires to step forward and to guard him closely. The prince went to look for the king to see if it were possible to find him, and the Knight Amigo, who accompanied him, said:

"Sir, I see the king."

"And which is he?" asked the prince.

"That one, the tallest one in that battalion," replied the Knight Amigo.

"He stands out over all the others like a king," said the prince, "however, I need to be nearer him in order to identify him and so that he may recognize me." And he began to shout: "Pandulfa for Princess Seringa!"

When his men heard him, they came to him, for they had been on their way when they heard him name the Princess Seringa. He faced one of his knights who had fought his way through almost a regiment hand to hand and still had his lance. The prince asked for it, and he gave it to him. The prince ordered the Knight Amigo to go tell the king of Grimalet that he was seeking him and he should come out to receive him if he wished.

When the King saw the Knight Amigo and had heard the message, he drew aside from his troops and asked him:

"Are you the knight to came to me recently?"

"Yes," said the Knight Amigo; "moreover may the devil take away the fear I have of you now, which is he same I had of you when you ordered me beheaded."

"Let the prince you speak of come here," replied the king. "If not, I will go to him."

"You don't need to go to him, for here he is," said the Knight Amigo. The prince had reached the king almost as quickly as the Knight Amigo had, and he said:

"Arrogant, presumptuous king, had you no courtesy or shame, to send such a rude and foolish message as you sent me? I believe your arrogance will bring you nothing but trouble, without a doubt. I would still forgive your arrogant message if you would cease your mad venture and return to the Princess Seringa all that is hers."

The king replied, "I consider you stupid, prince, for saying that you would forgive me for the folly that you committed in sending word for me to cease for your sake what was to my advantage."

"Let us fight the battle which we have to fight," said the prince. "It is useless to waste the day in argument, especially with a reckless man who refuses reason. On guard, King Arrogance! for I'm going to attack!" added the prince.

Placing his lance under his arm, he charged and struck the king with such great force that it passed through his shield, but because of the strong armor that he wore, it did not harm him but struck the king to the ground. The knights on both sides, who had remained quiet on the order of their lords, then jumped into the fray, some to defend their lord who was being pinned to the earth, and the others in order to kill or to seize him. They attacked each other fiercely, so that many on each side fell dead or wounded to the earth. It was obvious that neither side gave any quarter, so fiercely did they strike and kill. One of the king's knights dismounted from his horse. He ran to him and gave it to his lord. However, the knight survived only a short while on the battleground and then was killed. The king no longer had a taste for that battle. As soon as he climbed on the horse and saw the majority of his troops wounded and dead on the field, he sank the spurs to his horse and fled, with his men following.

But Prince Roboán, who was very courageous, did not allow them to leave unhindered. He pursued them striking, killing, and taking prisoners. There were over six thousand of the king's troops among the dead, wounded, and prisoners. Eight of Roboán's knights were casualties. However, the knights who accomplished most in the battle and struck down most of the enemy were Prince Roboán's troops, for they were elite knights and experienced in many conflicts. For that reason, the king of Mentón had assigned them to Roboán when he had departed.

189. How Prince Roboán consolidated his grasp on the battlefield and then returned to the Princess Seringa

Prince Roboán returned with his troops where the king had his headquarters and there they found a vast treasure. They ripped down the tents and seized the king's son who was wounded, and with all the other prisoners and wounded they set out for the Princess Seringa. And while Prince Roboán and his troops were doing this, Princess Seringa was greatly concerned and afraid. She and her ladies were in the church of Saint Mary, praying and asking our Lord God to aid their troops and protect them from the hands of the enemy.

And while they were thus occupied, a squire arrived and said to her, "My lady, give me a reward for good news!"

"I will if you bring good news," replied the princess.

"My lady," said the squire, "Prince Roboán, your servant, won the battle in a brilliant victory. He brings to you the king's son as a prisoner wounded in the right shoulder. He brings you more dead, wounded and prisoners, but he left more on the battlefield, since they were unable to bring all of them. In addition, he brings a vast treasure they found in the king's quarters. There were over six thousand of the king's knights killed, captured, and wounded."

"Squire, for the love of God," exclaimed the princess, "tell me the truth! Is Prince Roboán wounded?"

"I tell you, mistress, he is not, although his horse was killed and he was afoot on the battlefield fighting for his life bravely for a long time and aided by two hundred of his infantry, who served and defended him loyally."

"Upon my word, squire, you are truly welcome! I promise to give you a horse and weapons and I will make you a knight and arrange for you an advantageous wedding and give you some land." And others arrived after the squire in order to earn rewards but found that he had beaten them to it. Nevertheless, the princess continued to grant rewards to all who brought her the news.

When Prince Roboán and the other soldiers reached the city, the princess accompanied by all her ladies and handmaidens was awaiting them in a church on the outskirts of the city. Everyone in the city was celebrating happily. And when the soldiers arrived, Prince Roboán ordered a squire to unbuckle his spurs. "Sir," said the count, "it is not the custom in our land to remove our spurs."

"Count," answered the prince, "I do not know what the custom of your land is, but according to the custom of ours, no knight should call on ladies while wearing spurs." And then they removed his spurs, and he dismounted and went to see the princess.

"Blessed be the name of God," exclaimed the princess, "for you are alive, well, and of good cheer!"

"Mistress," said the prince, "whoever commends himself to God makes no mistake, and because I commended myself to God, I was successful, for He was my shield and my protector in this struggle, and He granted us success on the battlefield."

"I cannot thank Him enough, or you for what you have done for me," said the princess. Then the princess rode forward and the prince took her horse by the reins and led her to her palace. Afterward, the prince and all the others went to their lodgings to remove their armor, for they had great need of rest. The princess ordered Prince Roboán's needs attended to and baths were made ready for him, for he was sore and fatigued from the blows he had received on his armor. He accepted the hospitality but shrugged off the idea that the battle had had any effect on him.

And at the end of three days he went to see the princess, taking with him the son of the king of Grimalet.

"My lady, I bring you this jewel. I believe that in exchange for him, you should recover all that the king of Grimalet, his father, took from you. He will probably give you a large share of land. Have him guarded well and do not surrender him until the king does all that I tell you. I certainly believe that he will do it, for he has no other son but this one. If he should die, without this son the kingdom would be in turmoil over succession to the throne. I am absolutely positive that he will give you all your property and a great share of his own. And order those other knights whom you hold prisoner, twelve hundred in all, to be well guarded, for each one will give you a great ransom for you to release him from prison. This is the word they sent by their messengers."

Then the princess said: "I don't know how to thank you for what you have done and are doing for me and all my kingdom. I beg you to select towns, castles, and villages which you want in this kingdom of mine, and there is nothing in this kingdom of mine so dear that it will not be granted to you if you want it."

"Mistress," replied the prince, "I thank you, but I have no need of towns or castles now, but only your kindness that will give me permission to leave."

190. How Count Rubén urged marriage between Princess Seringa and Prince Roboán

"Alas, my dear sir," said the princess. "For the love of God, let not your leaving be so hasty, for you can be sure that if you leave here, the king of Grimalet and the king of Brez, who is married to his daughter, will come to destroy me."

And Prince Roboán noticed the affectionate words that the princess had said to him. When she called him "dear Sir," it seemed to him a term fraught with such meaning that it went straight to his heart. As he was confused, he blushed scarlet and could answer her not at all. Count Rubén, uncle and vassal of the princess, was there and noted the words the princess had spoken to Prince Roboán and how he had colored and was unable to reply, and he could see that love was developing between them. He approached the princess and whispered in her ear:

"My lady, it is impossible for me not to tell you what I think, for it is to your advantage, and it is this: I believe if you and the prince want to make a happy marriage that it would be to your honor and the security of your kingdom if you do, for he is certainly one of the best knights in this world. Since he is the son of a king and it is apparent in all his actions, you can have nothing to say against him."

And the princess hesitated, as red as a rose, and said to him: "O count, you have embarrassed me to death!"

"And why, my lady?" asked the count, "for I speak in your interest and to your honor."

"Well, I believe it is just as you say," she replied, "but I cannot give you an answer right now."

"Well, think about it," said the count, "and I will come to you later."

"All right," said the princess.

And while the count and the princess were speaking privately, Prince Roboán was transported, thinking about her comment. He believed she had spoken to him through great love or because she had needed him at that time. When he saw her blush while the count was talking to her privately, he believed absolutely that love had caused her to speak those words and he thought the count was reprimanding her for it. Roboán turned toward the princess and said:

"My lady, in regard to what you said to me about leaving here too hastily because of your fear of those kings, I promise you I shall not depart until I leave you your kingdom at peace. Since I started it, it behooves me to finish it. I have never started anything with God's blessing which I did not complete."

"May God allow you to finish all those things that you begin," said the princess.

"So be it!" added Roboán.

"And I say amen," said the princess.

"Well, God willing, we shall not lose," all said.

191. Of how the Knight Amigo took the message to the king of Brez

Roboán said to her: "My lady, supply me a squire to guide a knight of mine whom I am ready to send to the king of Brez. We shall answer him according to how he responds to us."

The prince sent for the Knight Amigo, and when he came, he said to him: "Knight Amigo, you are among the first knights whom I had as vassals, and you served the king my father and me very loyally, for which I am obliged to pay you and to help you as much as I can. Although you have passed through trying times with me, I want you to undertake a small mission for the princess there." The prince said this thinking he would not want to go because of what had occurred to him with the other king.

"Sir," said the Knight Amigo, "I will gladly do it, and I will serve the princess in whatever way she desires."

"Well," said the prince, "go now with this message of mine to the king of Brez, and tell the king on my behalf that I request that he not plan on committing evil or damage in the country of Princess Seringa, and, if he has done any wickedness here, I want him to rectify it, and I want him to give her and all her land a truce for sixty years. If he does not want to do it or gives a contrary reply, as the king of Grimalet, his son-in-law, gave you, challenge him for me and then return."

"I will return," said the Knight Amigo, "if they give me the chance. But I will tell you this much: if I had not promised it to the princess, I would not go there. It seems to me that I have become a burden to you and you want to get rid of me. The danger that I suffered with the king of Grimalet has not happened to you, and you are sending me to another king who is as wicked and arrogant as the other, and you have so many other good and intelligent knights that you could send who would carry out your order much better than I."

"O Knight Amigo," said the princess, "for the faith that you owe God and your master here, and for my love, take the road where the prince sends you; for I trust in God that you will be very successful in your mission, and you will return very happy and will be praised and honored over all others."

"A great favor!" said the Knight Amigo. "Since I have promised you, I will go this time, for I can do nothing else."

"Knight Amigo," said Prince Roboán, "I have never seen you act the coward in anything you had to do except this."

"Sir," replied the Knight Amigo, "I owe you a favor, but God knows I would refuse this mission now if it could be done without losing face. But this trip will be made although it is a bitter one, since I promised it."

And he took a testimonial letter that the prince gave him for the king of Brez and departed accompanied by the squire they had assigned to guide him.

And when he reached the king he found him in a beautiful and delightful city called Requisita. The queen his wife and their two small sons and many knights were gathered around him. When they told him that a knight was coming with a message from Prince Roboán, he ordered him to enter straightway. The Knight Amigo entered and knelt in front of the king and said: "Sire, Prince Roboán, son of the renowned king of Mentón, who is now with the Princess Seringa, sends you his respectful greetings and this letter through me."

The king took the letter and gave it to a bishop who was his chancellor to read and tell him what it contained. The bishop read it and told him that it was a testimonial letter which Prince Roboán had sent him asking him to believe what the knight should tell him on his behalf.

The king said to the Knight Amigo, "Friend, tell me what you want and I will listen to you with pleasure."

"Sire," said the Knight Amigo, "Prince Roboán asks you through your good grace and out of respect to him, to plan no wrong in the kingdom of Pandulfa where the Princess Seringa lives, and if you or your people have committed any offense, that you prepare to make amends for it; that you may grant her a truce and a sixty-year pact to commit no wrong anywhere in her kingdom in word, deed, or through counsel; and that he will be most appreciative to you for it and will consider himself obliged to spread your fame as far as possible."

"Knight," said the king, "what is the land of Mentón where this prince, your lord, is from?"

"Sire," answered the Knight Amigo, "the kingdom of Mentón is a great, wealthy, and very delightful land."

"Why then did this prince leave there?" asked the king. "Why did he leave so good a land and come to this foreign land?"

"Sire," said the Knight Amigo, "he did not leave his land because of any shortcoming in it, but to seek adventure in the world and to gain honor in deeds of chivalry."

"And how does he support himself in this land?" inquired the king.

The Knight Amigo answered: "Sire, with the vast treasure that his father gave him: one hundred mules loaded with gold and silver and three hundred knights of the finest chivalry. Only eight of them are missing who died in the battle he fought with the king of Grimalet."

"O knight, may God grant you good fortune! Tell me if you were present at that battle."

"Sire," said the Knight Amigo, "yes, I was."

"And was it a bloody battle?" asked the king.

"Sire," said the Knight Amigo, "you can easily understand it was very bloody, for there were well over six thousand knights, prisoners and wounded, on the king's side."

"Then how could it be that no more than eight of those of the prince died?" asked the king.

"Well, sire, no more of the prince's three hundred knights were killed, but there were more than two thousand of the Princess Seringa's troops killed or wounded."

"And this lord of yours, how old is he?" asked the king.

"He is very young," said the Knight Amigo, "for he is just beginning to sprout a beard."

"He set himself a great task for one so young in fighting with so powerful a king as the king of Grimalet and in defeating him."

"Sire, do not be astonished," said the Knight Amigo, "for he has already proved himself in other great deeds, and in his deeds it seems he is trying to be like his father."

"And how good a knight-at-arms is his father?" inquired the king.

"Sire," replied the Knight Amigo, "he is the best knight-at-arms in all the world. And he is a king of great virtue, for Our Lord has demonstrated many miracles through him in deeds of war."

"And do you have more to add on behalf of your lord?" asked the king.

"If your reply is favorable," said the Knight Amigo, "I have no more to say."

"And if it is not favorable, what does he intend to do?" the king questioned.

"What God may desire," said the Knight Amigo, "and nothing more."

"Well, I tell you that I do not intend to give you a reply," said the king, "for your lord is not the kind of man to whom I should respond."

"My lord king," said the Knight Amigo, "since that is the way it is, I ask you please to give me safe-conduct, and I will tell you the message from my lord in its entirety."

"I so assure your safety," responded the king.

"Sire," said the Knight Amigo. "because you do not intend to agree to the request he sent you, which you ought to do for your good if you are prudent, and because you show him so little respect, I challenge you on his behalf."

"Knight," said the king, "this lord of yours scorns kings, for he sends ultimatums to them so readily. But go over there while we discuss this matter."

192. Of the reply that the king of Brez sent to Prince Roboán's request

Then the king asked those who were present what they thought about the request. And the bishop, the chancellor, answered him:

"Sire, whoever can avoid a quarrel, does well in bargaining to avoid it; for frequently he who thinks to gain in it, comes to harm and loss. Therefore I hold that it would be well for you to quit this dispute with this man, for he has no vital interests in this land, but he will not hesitate to engage in any action in which he thinks he may gain renown and knightly honor. Since he was so successful with the king of Grimalet, he will be ready to attack others and prove it without any shadow of a doubt. For whoever is once very successful is encouraged to go in pursuit of other successes as his spirit blossoms."

"What you say now is true," said the king, "but a bucket can go to the well too often and it can leave its handle or its spout there, and this prince wants to undertake so many enterprises that he is bound to fall and to perish. However, bishop," the king continued, "I consider your advice to be good, for since we are at peace, we should not seek a quarrel with anyone; and I think it proper to do as he asks, for we have committed no offense in the kingdom of Pandulfa, nor is there any reason why we should have to make any restitution. Have letters written to him that I promise not to do any wrong in the kingdom of Pandulfa and I give a truce to the princess and to her kingdom for sixty years. Give the letters to that knight and bid him God-speed."

And the bishop then composed the letters and gave them to the Knight Amigo. He told him then to take his leave of the king, which he did. And before the knight could return to the princess, knights representing the king of Grimalet came with a treaty for the Princess Seringa: he would restore the towns and the castles he had taken from her, and in return she would release his son whom she held prisoner. And the princess answered that she would not do anything without Prince Roboán's counsel, for since he was the source of her good fortune, she considered it right that nothing should be approved or carried out except as he should order it. And the king of Grimalet's messengers asked her to send for him, and then she had him summoned.

193. Of how peace was made between the king of Grimalet and the Princess Seringa, mistress of the kingdom of Pandulfa

Prince Roboán then mounted his horse and went to the princess and asked her, "My lady, who are these strange knights?" And she told him they were messengers from the king of Grimalet.

"And what do they want?" asked Prince Roboán.

"I will tell you," said the princess. "They come with a treaty on behalf of the king of Grimalet that I release his son and that he will return the villages and castles that he seized from me."

"My lady," said Prince Roboán, "in my opinion, one ought not to be so willing to give in for so little."

"And what is your opinion?" asked the princess.

"My lady," said Roboán, "I will tell you. I understand that the king of Grimalet holds two large towns and six castles as enclaves in your kingdom, and they always give you great trouble."

"It is true," said the princess, "but those two towns are the richest he possesses in his kingdom. I do not believe he will be willing to give them to me."

"You think not?" asked the prince. "You can be sure, my lady, that he will give them to you, or he will never enjoy the sight of his son again."

"Well, then, you talk with them," said the princess.

"With pleasure," answered Roboán.

And then he called the knights and going aside with them, he said, "Friends, what are you demanding, or what do you want the princess to do?"

"Sir," they replied, "we truly believe that the princess has already told you, but what we are asking of her is this: that she return the king's son whom she holds prisoner here, and we will restore the towns and the castles the king seized from her."

"Friends," said Roboán, "the princess would be making a bad trade."

"And why would she be making a bad trade?" asked the others.

"I will tell you," said the prince. "You know full well that the king of Grimalet is completely at fault in all that he took from the princess, against God and to the detriment of his own soul, and it is only right that he should restore everything to her that he seized, since he had no dispute with her nor was there any just reason for having done so. He sent no justification to her as to why he was preparing to invade her country or to take it from her. But while she and all her country were at peace and holding no fear of him, he invaded her lands and her castles, which were unsuspecting and only desirous of living in peace."

"Sir," said one of the king of Grimalet's knights, "these things that you speak of mean nothing to kings, for the one who is weak suffers and the one who is powerful does as he pleases."

To that the prince replied: "These things are not observed among wicked kings, but among good ones all good rules are observed, for such a one would not commit a wrong against another for anything, unless to demonstrate that he had some complaint against him so that he could rectify it. And if he did not choose to rectify it, he would send him a notice, as is the custom of noblemen, and sue him through the courts of the king. And therefore I say that the princess would be making a bad deal in contracting for what is hers, for by right he should make restitution. Moreover, the prince, son of the king, was fairly captured and made prisoner in open combat. Therefore, whoever wants him can be sure that he must first give for him his true value."

"And what is he worth?" asked the others.

"I will tell you," said the prince. "You will give for him his true value, or more; and I believe a good treaty will give her the two towns and six castles that the king holds within the kingdom of the princess, and everything else that he has seized from her, he will restore. Furthermore, he will assure her safety; and as surety, he will have fifty of the most prominent men of his kingdom pledge that he will not commit any wrong against her at any time, on his own account or through his counsel; and if some other person plans to do her wrong, he will come to her aid."

"Sir," the others replied, "you drive a hard bargain and there is no reason in this world why the king would agree to it." And in this, they lied, for the story tells that the king sent them empowered to contract for as much as half of his kingdom in order to recover his son, for he loved him more than life itself.

The prince told them: "If you do not grant what he is worth, you will not get his release. And if the king loves his son and wants to see him alive, he will have to do all this, for there is nothing in this world that will soften these terms that I have stated. I gave it much thought before I reported them to you, and I cannot find any other way in which he can be freed with honor to the princess except in this fashion."

"Sir," said the others, "with your leave, we shall go aside and discuss it, and then we shall answer you as to what in our opinion should be done."

"Very well," said the prince. And they drew aside and Roboán went to the princess.

And as soon as the knights had reached agreement, they came to the prince and said,

"Sir, do you wish for us to speak with you privately?"

"And is it something that the princess should not know?" inquired Roboán.

They said, "No, for all of it concerns her."

"Well, it is proper to tell me in her presence," answered Roboán.

"Sir," they said, "if you are prepared to ease some of your terms, we think it would be acceptable."

"Friends," said the prince, "do not try to test us through speech, for we shall not relax any of our stated terms."

"Well, since that's final," they said, "let it be done right away, for we bring here the king's letter of authority for anything we might negotiate."

Then they gave him the letter authority and wrote the other letters that were necessary for the agreement in the clearest and best form possible. And then the knights accompanied Count Rubén to hand over to him the towns and castles that they had seized from the princess, as well as others belonging to the king. And he went to receive the homage of the king and the fifty good men chosen from among the counts and noblemen, who were to pledge with the king to guard the princess's land, to refrain from committing any wrong there, and to come to her assistance if it should be necessary; moreover, if the king did any wrong or failed to keep his word in any of these matters, the counts and noblemen would be obliged to aid the princess against the king and to make war on him on her behalf.

And as soon as all these things were done and the towns and the castles were delivered over to Count Rubén, he then went to the princess. The count told her, "My lady, the towns and the castles are now yours, and your troops hold the fortresses."

And he gave her the pledges that the king and the other noblemen had written and asked her to release the king's son to the knights, as was right, since she had recovered all her property.

"With great pleasure," said the princess. and she ordered the king's son brought in. And they brought him in and took him from among the other prisoners, for they took special precautions in holding him. And one of the knights of the king of Grimalet who was present said to Prince Roboán: "Sir, do you recognize me?"

"I do not recognize you," said the prince. "However, it seems to me that I have seen you before, but I don't know where."

"Sir," he replied, "I would recognize you among a large crowd, for in all my life, I will never forget the blow you gave me on the neck."

"You mean that I knighted you?" asked the prince.

"Yes, you did with that sharp sword of yours when you struck me this wound I have on my forehead. The helmet was worthless to me and so was the armor that I wore, for you were so strong and invincible in that fight. None of the king's men dared await you but fled as from death."

"By God, knight, if it is so," said the prince, "it concerns me greatly, for I would rather give you something of mine that would be more welcome. Every knight would prefer you as a friend rather than an enemy."

"And why should I be your enemy on account of this? As God is my witness you can believe me, I would serve you better now than before I was hurt because of the gallant qualities I saw in you. I do not believe there is a greater warrior in all the world than you."

"By Heaven," said the son of the king of Grimalet, "I was the one who best knew him in that battle and observed his actions most. After he wounded me and took me prisoner, he sent me aside from the army and assigned fifty squires to guard me. I saw all the soldiers and how he fared. There was none who passed through the army from one end to the other so many times as he, felling, wounding, and killing, and there was no rank, no matter how deep, through which he did not clear a path. And when he cried, 'Pandulfa for the Princess Seringa!' all his men rallied to him." And speaking as another person who testifies to his own dishonor, the son of the king said:

"May I never leave this prison in which I am, since it was my fate to be conquered and a prisoner, if I don't consider myself honored to be taken prisoner and vanquished by such a great warrior as this one."

"Let's leave off these accounts of things " said Prince Roboán, "for I would be grateful to God if I were half the knight you say I am."

And obviously the Princess Seringa was very pleased with their statements, and it was clear she was delighted. for she never took her eyes off him, laughing lovingly and saying: "May Prince Roboán live all the days of my life, for God has shown me great favor through him."

"By Heaven, my lady," said the son of the king of Grimalet, "yet you do not understand what grace God has shown you through Roboán's coming, as I realize it, for certainly, you can believe that the King, my father, and the king of Brez, my grandfather, would have invaded your land from two directions to raid the kingdom and seize your towns and castles until they would have left you nothing."

"And why would they do this?" asked the princess.

"Because of their will and whim to commit aggression in your dominions," he answered.

"And did I or the people of my kingdom merit it from them?" asked the princess.

"No, my lady, but I know it."

"They were committing a great sin," said the princess, "and God protected me from them through His grace."

"My lady," said Roboán, "let's quit this talk henceforth; for God, who defended you from one. will defend you from another if they plan to do wrong. Have the fetters taken off the king's son and send him on his way; for it is now time for you to relax, and let us think about other things."

And the princess had the fetters taken from the king's son and sent him with the other knights she held prisoner, for they had ransomed themselves for two hundred times one thousand marks, and of this the princess kept one hundred times one thousand and Prince Roboán kept the rest. The princess did not want any of it, but felt that Roboán should have it all, as he had clearly earned it through his bravery and excellent fighting ability.

And all the vast treasure that was found on the battlefield when the king was conquered was divided among the counts and the knights who had participated in the struggle. The treasure was handed over to them and they were well pleased with what Roboán did and how he divided it fairly among them, determining each one's value and why he deserved it, so that there was no one with a complaint. And there they were inspired to serve their lady, the princess, and went to her and asked her not to overlook them or abandon them, for they were equipped to serve her and defend her from all those who wished to do her wrong. And if she wished, they would gladly go to foreign lands on her behalf or whatever she should command, and they would risk their lives in order to carry it out.

"May God bless you," said the princess, "for I am sure you speak the truth and I am sure of your loyalty. You would always stand and fight for anything that would benefit me."

They took their leave of her and each one set out for his own land.

194. Of how Count Rubén at the behest of the princess spoke to Roboán about marriage with the princess

When Prince Roboán learned that the knights had made their farewells preparatory to leaving, he went to the princess and said: "My lady, aren't you aware we sent your message to the king of Brez? And what if by chance he is not prepared to agree to our requests? Isn't it better then for you to have the cavalry here so we may advance against him?"

"It would be better if they so wished," replied the princess, "but because they are tired and worn from this struggle, I believe they would rather refresh themselves and come back later if there is need."

The prince began to laugh heartily, and said. "By Heaven, lady, those who were left on the battlefield are the tired and worn; these men are happy and fortunate, and they could not possibly refresh themselves better in their own land than they have been refreshed in this one; for now they are rested and they've really learned how to use their weapons. Order them to wait, for within three days I believe we will have a message from the king of Brez."

"I agree," said the princess, "and I so order."

And they complied very willingly.

The princess had no inclination to forget what Count Rubén had said to her concerning herself and the prince, so she sent for him and said to him in private: "Count, what did you say to me the other day about wanting to speak to me in regard to the prince? Because we were involved in a grave matter, it is hard to recall."

"You forgot something concerning your own welfare so quickly, that I really believe that if I had spoken to you on my own behalf you could not have more quickly forgotten it," said the count.

"Say what you mean, for God's sake," said the princess, "and do not anger me, for I am not so forgetful as you say I am. It is true that I forgot, but maybe I didn't hear you so well at the time."

"My lady," said the count, "I will repeat it to you, and do understand it better than you did the first time. What I said to you then I say to you now, that since you are to be married, the best marriage that I know of now, and the one that would be most to your honor, would be with this Prince Roboán."

"Count," replied the princess, "I place this matter and all my affairs in your hands, for you are the one among all my subjects whom I most trust and most respect. Since you began this matter, you carry it to completion, for it is not fitting for me to speak on such a matter as this."

Then the count went to Prince Roboán and told him that he wanted to speak with him privately. And the prince willingly withdrew with him to a room and the count said: "Sir, although you have not spoken to me about it or asked me, and wanting only your welfare and your honor, I planned a matter which I will now tell you: if you wish to marry the Princess Seringa, I will make the best effort to discuss it seriously."

"Count," said Prince Roboán, "many thanks. I am sure that through your kind nature you wish only my welfare and my honor; but truly this marriage would be better for an older man of higher estate than I. Such is my business that I cannot marry until we go on from here to where I have to go and do whatever God may ordain me to do. For the love of God, count, do not persist in this matter for it would be a shameful thing for me to say no. She would be dishonored and I could not bear that. Truly I wish her well. I am proud of her and adore her sincerely, and I want to preserve her honor and reputation from harm, and nothing else."

"Well, shall I speak of it?" asked the count.

"No," said the prince. "I beg you."

The count went then to the princess and told her everything that Roboán had told him. When the princess heard it, she turned pale and became so sad that she might have fallen to the floor except for the count who held her by the arm.

"My lady," said the count, "do not take it so hard for what is to be yours, none can take away from you. Perhaps you will make a better marriage if you don't make this one."

"I am not despairing of God's grace," said the princess, "for as he now has said no, perhaps he will yet say that it pleases him. And certainly, count, I want you to know one thing: I counted on this marriage completely, if it were possible. According to what my heart tells me, it will be done. And the only thing that worries me is that he will believe I instigated the whole thing and perhaps he will think less of me for it."

"My lady," said the count, "I protected you well in this matter, for what I said to you, I did not tell him. I gave him to understand that I wanted what was best for him and I advised him to want the same, telling him that when I learned what his wish was, I would work to accomplish it."

"You did well," said the princess, "and don't speak further to him about it, and may God do what He considers proper."

195. Of how the Knight Amigo returned with the reply of the king of Brez to Prince Roboán

And at this moment the squire arrived who had been sent with the Knight Amigo with the message from the prince to the king of Brez, and he said to the princess, "My lady, the knight whom Prince Roboán sent to the king of Brez has arrived."

"And did he get what he went for?" asked the princess.

"By Heaven, my lady," exclaimed the squire, "yes he did, and very successfully too in the manner in which a trained and intelligent knight should, as you will see by the letters and the treaty he brings." Then the Knight Amigo approached the princess.

"On my word, Knight Amigo, I am very pleased," said the princess, "for I see you have successfully returned."

"And how can you tell?" asked the Knight Amigo.

"How can I tell?" said the princess. "By seeing you arrive happy and in much better spirits than when you departed here."

"My lady," said the Knight Amigo, "since God gave you the ability to recognize hidden things, understand what I now will tell you: I believe that God has favored you more than any other lady by your acquaintanceship with my lord Prince Roboán; for I found out at the court of the king of Brez that there were more than a few who were planning to do you wrong and had already divided your kingdom among themselves."

"And who were they?" asked the princess.

"My lady," answered the Knight Amigo, "the king of Grimalet, the king of Brez, and the king of Libia; but since you have the agreement of the king of Brez, you have no reason to fear the king of Libia, for the king of Brez got his agreement to it."

"And how did the king of Brez answer the request that Prince Roboán sent him?" asked the princess.

"You can see by these letters I bring you here," said the Knight Amigo.

The princess took the letters and had them read. They found that the treaty of peace and the truce of the king of Brez were stated clearly and in no way could they have been written more to the advantage or honor of the princess.

196. Of how Princess Seringa requested Prince Roboán to remain until the next day because of some matters she had to discuss with him

Being eager to depart, Prince Roboán said to the princess, "My lady, if you please, the time for me to depart is already past, and since your country is at peace, you have no reason to detain me."

"Dear friend," said the princess, "if it is at peace, it is on account of you and through your efforts; and God knows that if it were in your interests to detain you, I would gladly do it. But anyway, I shall speak with you about some matters that I have to."

"Lady," said Roboán, "do you wish the talk to be now?"

"No," answered the princess, "tomorrow morning, for I need to carefully consider what I am to say to you in such a fashion that I will not say the wrong thing."

"Lady," replied the prince, "you are so perceptive and so careful in everything that it would be impossible for you to err in any way in what you say or do."

The next morning when Prince Roboán came to say goodbye to her, the princess said:

"Stay here now, and let the others go, and I will speak to you about what I told you I had to talk about."

All the others withdrew, but they noticed their gestures and their demeanor, for they clearly understood there was great love between them, although they hid it as much as they could and did not want to reveal to one another the great love that existed between them. But the princess, seeing that she ruled her kingdom in peace and was honored among all her neighbors because of Roboán, thought that if God ordained marriage between them, she would be the most fortunate and elated lady in all the world because of the wisdom, valor, and good fortune of this prince. She could not resist telling him, and not to be mischievous, since she was a wise and virtuous lady, but thinking she could overcome him with sweet talk in order to marry him. She said:

"Sir, your bearing, your good looks, your fine manners, your valor, your good fortune, your wisdom, your kindness, and the service you have rendered me in leaving me rich and feared by all my neighbors, and greatly honored, make me say what I will now say to you. I beg you with love in my heart to forgive me what I am going to say to you, and do not think that I speak to you with any wicked or hidden purpose, but to be more protected and shielded and honored, if it be God's wish. And because I do not know whether some of my subjects would be pleased, or perhaps would want it to happen, I did not want to reveal this proposal to anyone but preferred to risk telling it to you and depending on your generous nature, for it would be better that only we know it, so that if it were refused it would be our secret. Certainly if others were privy to the proposal, it could not possibly be a secret, for they say what three know, every creature knows. And what I have to say to you, although I say it with great embarrassment, is this: if God favors a wedding between you and me, I would be extremely pleased. I do not have more to say, for a word to the wise is sufficient."

Then the princess lowered her gaze to the floor and could not look at him, because she was embarrassed as what she had said to him.

"Lady," replied the prince, "I can not show you my gratitude or repay you for the goodness and kindness you have shown me this day in letting me know of the true love you hold for me and for opening your heart to me. And since I can not show my gratitude or repay you as I would like, I pray our Lord God to be grateful to you for it and give success and honor to whatever you want. But I speak so you may know as much of me: from the day on which I was born until today itself, I have never known the love of a woman of your rank. You are one of the ladies I most love and hold dear to my heart, because of the goodness, wisdom, great character, and virtue I see in you. However I am now ready to go. I ask your indulgence to wait for me a year, unless you find someone else to whom you may give your heart with honor, for if God wishes to give such a one to you, I would not want you to miss this great honor for anything in this world."

"Dear Friend," answered the princess. "I do not know what God ordains for me, but I will wait for you at my risk for three years, if I live."

"Lady," said the prince. "I am grateful to you." And he tried to kiss her hands and her feet but she would not let him, rather she said to him, "The time will yet come when I shall kiss yours."

197. Of how Prince Roboán bade farewell to Princess Seringa and all her household

Then they both arose, and the prince said goodbye to her and to all the other ladies, maidens, and others present in the palace of the princess.

The story tells that man has never seen such grief as struck all the people with the princess, for when Roboán left his father, his mother, his brother Garfín, and all his other countrymen, although there was great grief and sadness there, it could not be the equal of this; for though they did not tear their hair or their skin, nor scream, all felt their hearts would break, sighing and crying aloud and putting their hands over their eyes. Prince Roboán and his troops were doing the same thing, for they had become so attached to all the people that they could not bear to part from them except with deep emotion.

This kingdom of Pandulfa is in Asia Major[1] and is a very abundant and fertile land, and the Tigris River flows through the major part of it. It is one of the four rivers of this earthly paradise, just as you will hear from now on, where they are discussed.

198. How Prince Roboán arrived in the earldom of Turbia

The prince with all his troops had traveled so far from the kingdom of Pandulfa that they had reached the earldom of Turbia. In a city, they met the count who came out to greet them. He received Roboán royally and invited the prince to be his guest for a week. However, this count was not safe among his own people, for they disliked him intensely and not without cause. He had oppressed them in many ways, overtaxing some, executing others without a hearing, and sending some into exile, so that there was none in all his dominion on whom the count had not committed these outrages.

This count, when he saw the prince in his city with such a large number of fine soldiers, was exceedingly pleased and he said:

---

1. The author is describing Asia Minor, not Asia Major.

"Sir, God has done me a great favor through your arrival in this land; for I consider He took pity on me and sent you to aid me against these vassals of mine. They do me a great wrong, and since you are here, I can punish them, if you will aid me."

"Certainly, count," said the prince, "I will willingly aid you against all those who wronged you, if they are not willing to make amends for it, but I want to know from you what they hold against you. I would not want anyone who does not deserve it to receive harm from me or from any one else."

"Know, sir," replied the count, "that you have no reason to ask, for they are the greatest traitors ever a lord had as vassals."

"It is fitting," said the prince, "to know the facts, for it would be a great sin to punish those who do not deserve it. It is fitting that we learn who deserves it. Let us separate the innocent from the guilty, and so we can more easily punish and put to death the guilty, for the more we can segregate them the more their strength decreases and yours increases."

"Sir," said the count, "don't vex yourself over that, for all deserve it."

"All?" asked the prince. "This cannot be true except for one of two reasons: either you mistreated them and spared no one, or all of them are false and traitors by nature. If you want me to aid you, tell me the truth and hide nothing, for if you have done wrong and hide it from me, by chance the fault would be yours and mine, and we would be dishonored, for God does not give the battlefield to any but the one He knows holds to the truth and right."

When the count realized that the prince with his intelligence would eventually find out the truth and that there was no way to hide it from him, he decided to tell why he had a terrible dispute with all his subjects.

"Sir," said the count, "the truth of the matter as to what occurred between me and my subjects is in this fashion that I will now tell you. Truly, I acted cruelly to them in many matters, taking their homes, executing them without hearings, seizing their property, and banishing them without cause, so that there is none, alas! no matter how rich or how poor whom I have not wronged and outraged; so that there is no one in my dominion whom I do not fear. And therefore with your help, I would like to relieve myself of this problem and this fear, for after they are dead and destroyed, I could spend my life without fear and suspicion."

"My God, Count!" exclaimed the prince, "if it should happen as you say, it would be a great mistake, for it should not be that way, for one evil does not justify another. And after having committed so many offenses and atrocities against them as you say, you consider it right to do them even greater harm, instead of repenting for the offenses and asking their forgiveness? Surely if we engage them on the battlefield for such a cause, they would be victorious and we would be defeated, and rightly so."

"Well, sir," said the count, "what can I do about it? I beg you to advise me, for this life is not life, but to me it is the same as death."

"I will tell you," said the prince. "It is fitting for you to deal with this problem of yours as a king once did who had the same trouble as yours and who followed the advice of his wife the queen."

"And how did that happen?" asked the count.

"I will tell you," answered the prince.

199. Concerning the story Prince Roboán told the count of Turbia relative to the trouble that he had with his vassals

"A king acted against his people just as you, by mistreating and killing them without mercy and seizing their property openly, so that everyone was seeking a way to kill him. Consequently he always went armed day and night. He never disarmed, not even in his own home, for there was no one he trusted. And so one night, he went to the room of his wife the queen, and went to bed fully armed. The queen was deeply grieved, for she felt great sorrow over the terrible and miserable life the king led. Her heart could no longer bear it and she said to him:

"My lord, please tell me of your own accord the reason for this terrible life you are leading. Are you doing it for penance or are you doing it for fear of some danger?"

"The king said, 'Surely I would tell you if I thought that you would be able to give me some advice in the matter, but alas! I do not believe that any advice can be given.'

"'My lord, don't talk that way,' said the queen. 'There is nothing in this world so hopeless that God cannot solve.'

"'Well, this is how it is,' said the king. 'I want you to know. Before I married you, and afterward, I never ceased doing wrongs and outrages and cruel things to all my subjects. Because of the wrongs I did them, I am not safe from any of them. And I believe they would cheerfully kill me if they could. And that is why I have to go armed to protect myself from their malice.'

"'My lord,' replied the queen, 'through my advice you will do as good doctors do for the sick whom they care for. They order them to diet, and afterward they prescribe good and wholesome foods for them to eat. If they see that the sickness is so serious and hopeless that it cannot be helped through any medical knowledge they know, they allow them to eat anything they want to, the wrong things as well as the right things. And at times the sick people recover from the serious maladies they have by eating the wrong things. And since the fact is that you do not believe you will ever be cured of your illness and your constant fear, I think that you ought to do the contrary of what you have done up to now, and perhaps you will be freed of this fear with God's help.'

"'And how might this be?' asked the king.

"'My lord, I will tell you,' said the queen. 'Have all your subjects come here in order for you to talk to them. Confess the wrongs and outrages that you did to them and in a humble manner ask them to forgive you. Weep and make them understand that you are heartsick over the wrongs you did them, and feeling sorry for you, perhaps they will forgive you. And really I see no other way for you to escape this danger you face.'

"'Well,' said the king, 'be assured that that is good advice and I plan to follow it, for now I prefer death to this life I have.'

"Then he sent for all his subjects to meet with him in a meadow that was rich and verdant. And everyone met with him on the day that he had ordered them to meet. The king had his throne placed in the middle of the meadow, and placing his crown on his head, he said to them:

"'Friends, until now I have been your king and I have used the power of the government as I should not have. Being intolerant and merciless to you, committing many outrages against you, executing some without hearings, seizing property, exiling some without right or reason, failing to observe or acknowledge the many services you have done for me, I therefore consider myself a great sinner, for I sinned against God and you. Being afraid of you because of the great crimes I committed against you, I have gone armed day and night. And confessing my sin and my mistake, I leave you the crown of the kingdom.'

"He took it from his head and placed it on the ground before him. He took his helmet from his head and stripped off the weapons he wore and standing before them only in his doublet, he said:

"'Friends, I ask you through your goodness to forgive me and I place myself at your disposal to do with me as you wish.'

"And he said this with tears streaming from his eyes, and his wife the queen and his children who were present were also crying. And when his subjects saw that he truly repented of the error into which he had fallen and was asking their pardon so openly, all fell at his feet lamenting and begged him not to say such terrible things as he was saying to them and to stay with his kingdom for they forgave him for the great wrong they had received from him, for he was breaking their hearts. And he was from then on a good king and much beloved by all his subjects, for he was very just and the protector of his kingdom.

"Wherefore it is fitting for you, count, to do the same as that king did, and I trust in the mercy of God, for He will guide you to gain the love of your people, just as He did for that king."

"By Heaven, sir," exclaimed the count, "you have given me new life, and I will do what you advise, for it seems that this is the best way; and even though they kill me when I ask forgiveness of them, I know that God will have mercy on my soul."

"Count," said the prince, do not fear, for if you should die doing what

I advise, you will not die alone. For such a purpose as this I will willingly stand with you to defend you with all my strength, for if you wish to make an apology to them and they refuse to accept it, they will be wrong and not you; for they will be making wrong of your right, and God will aid us and thwart them, because we will have truth and right on our side, and they will have nothing except lies and arrogance on theirs."

Then the count sent for all his subjects, saying that he had to talk with them on matters that were of benefit to them and the country. Then they met with him in a great city. And when they saw the foreign cavalry, they asked what people they were and were told that Roboán was the son of a king who came from distant lands and that he was seeking adventure and was performing deeds of chivalry to gain reputation. They asked if he was a friend of the count and were told that he was.

"And is he a man who is pleased with truth and good and is displeased by evil?" they asked.

"Certainly he is," they replied.

"It is well," was the reply. "Since the prince is a good man, we know he will make the count quit his cruel deeds against us."

The others answered that they were sure of him and that he would do so. And so all the natives were comforted, for it was obvious that fear was equally shared between the count and them, for the count had as great fear of them as they had of the count. Then the count ordered a platform constructed in a wide and pleasant meadow they named the Field of Truth, and all were gathered there. The count seated himself on the dais, armed just as he always was, with the prince on one side, the countess on the other, and their small children in front. The count arose and told how he had wronged them in many ways, and he humbly begged them for compassion and to forgive him, for he did not want to live unless as an honest lord with loyal vassals. He disarmed and knelt before them weeping and asked them to forgive him. At this moment Prince Roboán arose, for they were hardhearted and refused to answer anything, and he said to them:

"Friends, I would not want you to be like spoiled children, who are asked repeatedly to do things for their own good and stubbornly refuse. And afterward they want to be asked again and they would gladly welcome it, and if you did not ask it again, they would be in danger. That is why you have no need to remain silent, but rather you should be grateful to God because what I am saying to you comes to you with good intention."

"Sir," said one of them, "we would gladly do so except that we think he is pretending in order to do us more harm."

"Don't believe that," said the prince; "first he will swear it to you on the Holy Scriptures, and he will pledge homage to you. He will give you assurance of safety in my presence And if he fails you, I promise you I will side with you against him."

And they asked him to receive homage from the count, and so he did.

They forgave the count, and he lived in peace and prospered with his vassals, for he ruled them fairly and with justice. The next day the prince said good-bye to the count and to all those citizens who were present.

200. How the prince reached the land of the emperor of Tigrida

The story relates that Prince Roboán set out on the road to wherever God should guide him. However, he asked the count what land he would find ahead. And the count told him that after thirty days' journey he would enter the land of the powerful and honorable emperor of Tigrida, who had forty kings as vassals. He was youthful, happy, and very hospitable, and would be greatly pleased with a man from a foreign land if he was highborn.

The prince set out for that empire, and as soon as he arrived in the land of the kings, they told him that they could not permit him to proceed farther until they had informed the emperor of him, for so it was their custom. However, they would give him all the things he needed until they had sent word to the emperor.

Then they sent the messengers, and when the emperor learned that a prince, son of the king of Mentón, had arrived in his realm and was leading a strong and handsome troop of cavalry, the emperor was pleased and ordered that he be escorted through his realm and be given everything he needed and that he should be welcomed wherever he went. Since the emperor thought it fitting, all the kings and the citizens obeyed his wishes willingly and courteously wherever the prince passed. And much did he merit it, for God had made him so handsome and gallant that all who saw him took great pleasure in his appearance and held great festivities for him.

201. How the emperor of Tigrida knighted Prince Roboán

And when he approached the emperor he found him walking in the fields on the bank of a great river which is called the Tigris. He dismounted and two kings who were with the emperor in order to honor the prince, dismounted to meet him. He went to the emperor and knelt before him and humbled himself just as those two kings accompanying him had advised. The emperor was pleased with him and ordered him to mount his horse. And after he mounted, the emperor called to him and asked if he was a knight. He told him he was. And the emperor asked him who had knighted him and he answered that it was his father, the king of Mentón.

"Surely," said the emperor, "if a knight could hold a double knighthood, I would knight you again."

"Sire," said the prince, "what can the knight lose if he receives another knighthood from another and greater knight?"

"I will tell you," answered the emperor. "It cannot be, for the knight would side with one against the other, for he could not be against his first lord, since he had received his knighthood from him."

"And don't you see," said the prince, "that I will never stand against the king, my father, nor against you for him, because he would never order me or advise me to break my word of honor?"

"I truly believe it," said the emperor, "but there is another more serious matter which men must weigh: that if he receives two knighthoods he must act as two knights."

"And certainly," said the prince, "he can easily do this with the grace of God, because a man who wants to take God as his companion in his deeds, can do as much as two knights, and even more with His aid."

"Indeed," said the emperor, "it is right for me to make this prince a knight, and we shall make no mistake, for I believe they do it one way in his country and another way here."

And the emperor asked him how they had made him a knight, and he said he had stood vigil in the church of Saint Mary one night, never sitting down, and early the next morning, the king had gone to hear mass there, and when the mass was over, the king came to the altar and smote him on the shoulder with his sword. Then he belted on him the sword he had taken from his older brother.

"Now I say to you," said the emperor to the kings, "that he can receive another knighthood from me, for there is a great difference between the custom of his land and ours."

"In the name of God," said the kings, "knight him, for we trust in God that from what we see and understand about him you will be served well by him."

Then the emperor ordered the kings, the prince, and all the other knights to dine with him, and they returned to the city. The emperor ate at one table and the kings at another, and the prince with two sons of the kings at another, and all the troop of cavalry were seated throughout the room in an orderly fashion. And after they had dined the emperor ordered the prince to be dressed in royal clothing that he had given him and celebrations held as was the custom of the land, and so it was done. Two kings accompanied him, one on one side and one on the other, throughout the town. And all the damsels were standing in their doorways, and according to their custom each of them had to embrace and kiss him, and they said to him:

"May God grant you good fortune in chivalry, and may you do as well as the one who knighted you, or better!"

When the prince heard these words, he recalled what his mother had said when he took leave of her—that she knew in her heart that he would be emperor—and his resolve was strengthened to do well.

Early the next morning the emperor went to the church of Saint John where the prince was holding his vigil. He heard mass and then led him to the door of the church to a large jasper font which was full of warm water. They made the prince undress, shielded by some magnificent curtains of gold, and they put him in the font where the water rose up to his chest. And all the maidens walked around the font saying:

"Long live this new knight in the service of God and in the honor of his lord and to himself!"

And they brought him a lance with a large banner, a naked sword, a princely shirt of serge and pearl, and a wreath of gold rich with precious stones. A beautiful and noble maiden to whom had fallen the good fortune to dress him, helped him into his shirt.

And after she had dressed him, she kissed him and said to him, "May God clothe you with His grace!" and then she left, for this was their custom. And then a king came and gave him the lance with the banner and told him, "May God exalt your honor in every way!" And he kissed him on the mouth and departed straightway. Then the other king came and girded the sword on him and said, "May God protect you with His great power and may none endanger you!"

Afterward the emperor placed the wreath on his head and said to him, "May God honor you with His blessing, and may He sustain you and always increase your honor in every way."

Afterward the archbishop came and said, 'May the Father and the Son and the Holy Ghost bless you, for they are three persons and one God!'

And then the emperor commanded them to dress him in royal raiment, and the emperor girded on his sword, and they mounted their horses and went to the house of the emperor. The prince carried the naked sword in one hand and the lance in the other with the banner and wore the wreath on his head. When they sat down at the table, one knight held the naked sword before him and another the lance with the banner until they had eaten. Then they mounted and returned the sword and the lance to him, and thus he rode through the town that day.

The next day the knights, vassals of the prince, began to joust and duel with short lances according to their custom, so that the emperor and all the others were very pleased, and there was hardly a lady or maiden who was not in attendance. The emperor ordered the prince to show what he could do, for it was the custom of the country for a new knight who the day before had received his knighthood to take arms. The prince mounted a magnificent horse he was leading and, challenging his troops, he jousted and dueled throughout the field. He truly appeared to be a prince among men, for although there were many among them who were jousting very well, there was none who seemed to do as well as the prince. And all those present with the emperor were making merry according to the custom of their land, in a large field on the banks of the Tigris river.

202. Herein is related the location of the empire of Tigrida

This empire of Tigrida took its name from the Tigris river, which is one of the four rivers that originates in the earthly paradise, Eden. One has the name Pison, another Gihon, and another the Tigris, and the last is the Euphrates.[1] Wherefore Genesis relates that a river flows in the earthly paradise in order to water the garden, and it branches into four parts, and those are the four rivers that originate in the earthly paradise. And when they leave Eden, they flow under the earth and each one has its source in that place where it reappears, as you will now hear.

They say that the Pison runs through the lands of India, it seems that it springs from the mountain that has the name of Orcobares, and it flows eastward and empties into the sea. The Gihon is the river they call Nirojanda and it flows through the land of the east and disappears under the earth, and issues forth at the mountain Atlant, which in Hebrew is called Reblantar Mar. Later it flows underground and comes forth and flows around all the land of Ethiopia. It runs through Egypt and there it divides into six parts and empties into the sea which is near Alexandria.

The other two rivers, which have the names of Tigris and Euphrates, pass through another great mountain and flow through the eastern part of Syria and the middle of Armenia. Both curve back toward the town that has the name Abacia,[2] and then they call them the Mixed Waters, for they run more swiftly than any mixed waters in the world, and after they have run a long way as one river, they empty into the ocean sea.[3] And the earthly paradise from whence these rivers flow is called the Fortunate Islands; however, none can enter the earthly paradise, for at the entrance, God placed a wall of fire that reaches to the skies.[4]

And the ancient wise men say that the Pison is the river called the Nile, which in Arabic is called al-Nil and in Hebrew Nilos.[5] And they say that in olden times it used to sink and be lost underground and it made a marsh of all the earth so that none could walk through it, and Joseph made this river flow in its bed and saved the Nile and the land. Consequently they say this is the most abundant land in the world, for this river overflows its banks twice a year and floods all the land. And while the river is out of its bed, the

1. The Spanish in the text is *Fison, Gigon, Trigris* [*sic*], and *Eufatres*. I have used the biblical spelling of *Pison, Gihon,* and *Euphrates*. For the biblical *Hiddekel*, I have used the more familiar form *Tigris*.
2. The city of Abacia is probably the city of Basra, which is below the junction of the Tigris and the Euphrates rivers.
3. The "ocean sea" here is actually the Persian Gulf.
4. Genesis 3:24. "So he drove out the man: and he placed at the east of the garden of Eden cherubim, and a flaming sword which turned every way, to keep the way of the tree of life."
5. *Nilos* is Greek, not Hebrew.

twice a year and floods all the land. And while the river is out of its bed, the people travel by boat from one town to the next, and for this reason the towns and the farmhouses are built on high ground.

And this story was placed here about these four rivers of paradise in order that you may know the empire of Tigrida took its name from this Tigris river, and it runs through a large section of the empire. The Euphrates river curves through another part of the empire and reaches the sea. Another part of the border is adjacent to the lands of Sind and another part is contiguous with Asia Major toward the east, where fine sapphires are found, just as you will now hear in the story of Prince Roboán when he was lord of this empire because of his virtues and because God through His mercy saw fit to guide him.

203. Concerning the advice that Prince Roboán gave the emperor of Tigrida about a physician

Wherefore the story relates that this prince was held in great affection by the emperor of Tigrida because he served him well and loyally in all matters that he could. The emperor made him one of his privy counselors. When all the counselors came to the emperor to advise him, there was none who succeeded so well in giving advice as the prince. Thus one day a physician who was from a foreign land came to see the emperor, and the emperor asked him if he was a licensed physician and he said he was. He showed his credentials and told him that he cured men of every known ailment with three herbs: one to drink, another to make salves, and the other to use in baths. And he showed him in an impressive manner and gave strange names to the herbs, so that the physicians of the emperor's court did not recognize them, but it seemed to them that what he was saying made sense. The emperor asked him where those herbs could be found and he told them on the seashore where the sun sets. The emperor asked his physicians and his council for advice, and they advised him to send for those herbs. Then he called the foreign physician and told him that he wanted to send for the herbs, and that he would send some men of his court to accompany him. And the physician said that he did not want anyone to go with him—that he did not want those that he sent with him to learn in an hour what he had learned with great effort in his entire life. But instead, the emperor should give him everything he needed and thirty or fifty camels and he would return them fully loaded, for he especially needed a lot of the herb to make the baths. And when they computed how much money he needed for a round trip of two years, they found that it amounted to ten thousand silver marks.

And so the advisers and the physicians advised the emperor to do it, for this medicine could not be bought for money. The emperor was inclined to do it, but he asked Prince Roboán to tell him what he thought. The prince told him that he dared not advise him in this matter because he did not want what happened to a Moorish king in a similar situation to happen to him through his advice.

"And how was that?" asked the emperor.

"Sire," said the prince. "I will tell you.

"It so happened that a Moorish king had a good and wealthy alchemist and this alchemist had a son who had no wish to follow his father's trade but was always involved in knight-errantry and was a skilled knight. And when his father died, the king told him that he wanted him to follow the trade of his father, and that he would reward him. He told the king that he knew well that he never practiced that calling, but that he had always spent his time in knight-errantry and that he did not know as much as he should about alchemy. He asked him as a boon to give him a letter of recommendation to another king, his friend, in which he promised to serve him to the best of his ability, and this would allow him to go among his friends without the shame of their knowing he was the son of an alchemist.

"The king considered it proper to have it given to him, and he so ordered his chancellor to give it to him. The knight took the letter and departed and went on his way to the king who was his lord's friend. And when he arrived, he greeted him on behalf of his lord the king and gave him the letter which he had sent. Before the king opened the letter, he made it clear that he was pleased with him and asked if his lord was in good health. He told him that he was. Then the king asked him if he was getting along well with his neighbors. He told the king that he was, but that he was distrustful of them. And he asked if he was rich, and the knight replied that all the neighboring kings together were not as wealthy as he alone. Then the king opened the letter and read it. And it said in the letter that the knight was the son of an alchemist and that he was being sent to serve the king and that the king should reward the knight, for he was a man who would serve him in every way possible. The king asked him what was his trade. When the knight heard this, he was astonished, for he realized that the letter was saying he was the son of an alchemist. And while he was pondering over what reply he would give him, the king again asked what was his trade. The knight answered him:

"'Sire, since you persist and because you are the friend of my lord, I want you to know my secret. Know, sire, that my trade is to make gold.'

"'Truly it is a respectable trade and quite suitable to knight-errantry and your coming pleases me very much. May God grant good fortune to my friend the king who sent you here. I want you to set yourself to the work soon,' answered the king.

"'In the name of God,' said the knight, 'whenever you wish.'

"The king ordered lodging prepared and the best of care for him. And the knight could not sleep that night for thinking about how he would be able to get out of his predicament. And of the coins that he was carrying, he put twenty into a mortar and ground them into powder and went to a druggist near the town and said to him:

"'Friend, I want to make some money for you, and I will also profit.'

"'It is all right with me,' replied the druggist.

"'Well, said the knight, 'take this powder and if someone comes to ask you if you have any alexandrique powder, tell him that a short time ago you had three quintals[1] of it, but merchants came and bought it and carried it away and you do not know if any remains. When you look for it, say that only this little amount remains, and do not sell it for less than ten doubloons. You will give me five and the other five will be yours.'

"And the druggist took the powder and stored it carefully. The knight returned to the palace of the king, who had already sent for him. When the king saw him, he ordered all the others to leave the room and he remained alone with the knight and said to him:

"'Knight, you have aroused my greed. I cannot rest until you set your hands to the task.'

"'Certainly, sire,' said the knight, 'you are on the right path; because when you are rich, you will have anything you desire, and all your neighbors will fear you just as they do my lord the king because of the great wealth I made for him in this way.'

"'Well, what do we need in order to do this?' asked the king.

"'Sire, said the knight, 'order some of your men to go in secret to look for alexandrique powder from the merchants and spice dealers and to buy from them all they find. For the cost of one coin I will make two, and if we had an abundance of the powders to last all year, I could make you so great a treasure you would not have room to store it.'

"'By Heaven, knight,' answered the king, 'if you can do this, your arrival was good for me!'

"Then he sent his chief steward and another man entrusted with his secret to accompany the one who went to search for these powders. And they traveled throughout the town searching for these powders, and they never found anyone who knew or had heard of such powders. They returned to the king and told him that they had never seen them nor heard of them until now.

"'Of course not!' exclaimed the knight. 'In truth they bring so much of it to my lord the king's land that two hundred mules could not carry it all. However, I believe that because you are not familiar with it you don't know what to ask for. I will go there with you and perhaps we shall find it.'

"'The knight speaks sense,' said the king. 'Go there then.'

"They went through all the stores of the spice vendors asking for these powders and did not find any trace. Then the knight asked the king's chief

---

1. A *quintal* is a unit of weight varying in different countries from 100 to 220 pounds.

steward if there were other stores of spice vendors nearby—in which case they should go there, for it was possible that they would find them.

"'Truly,' said the chief steward, 'there are no other stores in all the town, but there are three on the outskirts of the town.'

"They went there, and in the first stores they found no trace; however, in the one which was more distant than the others the vendor said that a short time ago merchants had carried away three quintals of such powders as they were inquiring about. They asked him if any of it remained, and he said that he did not know. He pretended to examine his chests and sacks and showed them the remains of the powder the knight had given him. They asked how much he would take for it, and he answered not less than ten doubloons. The knight said they should pay him for it just to make the test. They gave him ten doubloons and the chief steward took the powder and carried it to the king. They told the king they were unable to obtain more of the powder, although the druggist had told them that a short time past he had sold three quintals of it. And the knight said to the king:

"'Sire, keep this powder. Send for lead the weight of twenty doubloons and have coal brought to melt it. Have your chief steward do as I tell him, and you may be certain you will find me truthful in what I have told you.'

"'May God so wish it to be true!' said the king.

"The next morning the knight arrived and ordered the powder and the lead put into a crucible. When it was melted, he ordered them to throw in calcium made from bones, which dissolved the lead and turned it into smoke. The powder from the twenty doubloons remained as a molten mass. When they took it out, they found it to be the weight of twenty doubloons of the finest and purest gold that could be. When the king saw it, he was jubilant and believed that God had done him a great favor with the coming of the knight. He asked him how he could obtain more of the powder in order to create more gold.

"'Sire,' answered the knight, 'send for it in the land of my lord the king, for there you can easily obtain a hundred mule loads.'"

"'Of course,' said the king, 'I don't want anyone except you to go, for even as my friend the king trusted you, I trust in you also.'

"And he ordered him given ten camels loaded with silver, so that he could buy the powder. The knight took his wealth and departed, holding the intention neither of returning nor of placing himself where he would fall into the power of the king; because what he was doing was not the king's wish and he did not want to leave the slightest trace.

"This Moorish king was so dedicated to justice in his country that almost every night he strolled through the town accompanied by ten or twenty of his men in order to hear what each citizen was saying or doing. So one night a group of Moorish youths were in a house eating, drinking, and having fun, and the king was just outside the door listening to what they were saying. One Moorish youth began by saying:

"'Let each one now say who is the stupidest man in this town.'

"And each one named his choice. Then that Moorish youth said: 'Well, the stupidest man in this town that I know is the king!'

"When the king heard this he became irate and ordered his men to arrest them and hold them there until the next morning, when they were to be brought before him. And therefore it is said that whoever listens too closely will hear things to his own detriment. They began to break down the doors, and those inside asked who they were. They said they were the king's men, and the Moorish youth said to the others:

"'Friends, we are in trouble, for surely the king overheard what we said to each other; for he is accustomed to stroll through the town listening to what is said of him. If the king questions us, do not answer at all, but leave it to me, and I will answer him.'

"Early in the morning they were taken prisoner before the king, and the king in a great anger began to berate them:

"'Dogs, and sons of dogs, what did you have against me to say that I was the stupidest man in the town? I want to know which of you said it.'

"'All right,' said the Moorish youth, 'I said it.'

"'You?' asked the King, 'tell me why you think I am the stupidest.'

"'I will tell you,' said the Moor. 'Sire, if some one loses something or something of his is stolen because of his carelessness, or he speaks carelessly, he is stupid because he does not guard what is his, nor is he careful in what he says; but still he is not as stupid as that person who gives away what is his when he should not and apparently wants to lose it on purpose as you did. Sire, you know that a foreign knight came to you, and because he told you he could make gold from lead—which is impossible—you gave him ten camels loaded with silver with which to buy powder to make gold. And I absolutely believe that you will never again see him in your presence, and if you lose what you gave him, it was a great lack of wisdom on your part.'

"'And if he should return?' asked the king.

"I am certain, sire,' said the Moor, 'that there is no way he will return.'

"'But if he should return?' insisted the king.

"'Sire,' said the Moor, 'if he should return, we shall erase your name in the book of stupidity and we shall place his there, because he will knowingly come at great risk to himself, and perhaps death, for he cannot do what he promised you, and so he will be more stupid than you.'

"And therefore, sire," said Prince Roboán to the emperor, "although you may be rich, and able to expend a great amount of wealth in so noble a cause as this physician tells you, even if it is true, I do not dare to advise you to risk such great wealth. If he fails you, they would say that you did the deed without good advice and with a lack of wisdom, for it reveals a great lack of wisdom for a man to risk great wealth in a doubtful venture, for if he is not successful, he is deceived and suffers a loss."

"Well, said the emperor, "I believe your advice is good."

204. How Prince Roboán asked the emperor why he never laughed

And the emperor found himself so well advised by Prince Roboán in so many matters that he respected his advice highly and did not respect the advice of others at all, and he guided himself by his advice and not by the advice of any other. And thus the other advisers to the emperor became very envious, and they spoke to one another:

"Surely if this man stays long here with the emperor, we will be destroyed, for the emperor cares nothing for us, and we shall lose the honor and benefits to which we are accustomed. It is essential that we all agree on this."

The count of Lan, who was one of the counselors, arose and said:

"Friends, it seems to me that we cannot take another way except this that I will tell you now in order to humiliate and destroy this prince who came to this land to harm and to dishonor us. You know that the emperor never laughs and that he has decapitated whoever asks him why he never laughs. This prince is still not knowledgeable of this nor does he suspect it, and if in some manner he might ask the emperor, I believe that he would have him executed for it, or at least the prince would lose the emperor's favor. Therefore, I will tell you how we may be able to do it. I shall invite him and all of you to dine together at my home, and when we are alone, we shall say how we are amazed at the emperor because he doesn't laugh, and we shall ask the prince if he has ever seen him laugh, and I am sure he will answer no. Since he has the confidence of the emperor, since he goes privately with him to talk quite often, you will ask him to ask in confidence why the emperor does not laugh. Perhaps he emperor will kill him or exile him from this land for invading his privacy."

And so they did and the prince believed them, for he had no reason to be on his guard against them. And one day while strolling with the emperor through the garden and conversing pleasantly of many things, he recalled what the count of Lan and the other counselors of the emperor had said to him, for he saw that the emperor did not laugh at the many amusing things that he should have laughed at, and he said to him:

"Sire, begging your pardon, I want to ask you a question."

"All right," said the emperor, "say what you wish and I will be glad to listen."

"Sire," said the prince, "I see that you like to be entertained, and you know how to talk in a witty fashion so that a listener is pleased, but I see one thing that you lack which all those who love amusement have."

"And what is that?" asked the emperor.

"Sire," said the prince, "I have never seen you laugh, no matter how much you were amused, and I would like to know, if you don't mind, why you don't laugh?"

When the emperor heard this, he was shocked and his complexion paled and for a long time he could not speak. Then he turned, extremely angry, to Prince Roboán and said: "Friend, you were ill-advised to ask me the question you did. May God damn the body of the one who set you to this, for he wanted you killed and wanted me to lose a good friend in whom I trusted and by whom I am well served and supported in all things."

"And, sire, why does this question trouble you so much?" asked the prince.

"It is such a great problem that it could not be greater," said the emperor. "Any man who ever asked me this question lost his head. But up to now, I liked you so that my heart cannot bear to give you the sentence I gave the others for that cause. I don't want the others to know anything about this, so I want you to go with me as though we were just talking, and when we reach the seashore, I shall send you to such a place that perhaps death would be better for you than life. By chance, it may turn out to your benefit and your honor if you are resourceful and prudent. But, alas! there are few who know how to stand good luck, and they fall into bad luck and endure it although they are not willing."

205. How the emperor, as punishment for the question, exiled Prince Roboán to the empire of the Fortunate Islands where he was welcomed, married the empress, and became emperor

Then the prince said, "Sire, now I believe the proverb is true which says, 'Be careful in crossing yourself or you will poke your finger in your eye.' And so it happened to me, for I thought I was saying something and I said nothing, and thinking to gain, I lost, and I could have spoken to you about other things you liked and not have asked you such a foolish question in which no advantage lay. Wherefore, sire, may God show his gratitude to you for not giving me the sentence I deserved, which you meted out to the others who fell into the same error as I did."

At this moment, as they were walking as though in conversation, they arrived at a high wall the emperor had ordered built on the seashore. When they reached a door in the wall, the emperor placed his hand in his purse and drew forth a key and opened the door. They went inside and closed the door behind them. And there was a boat without oars in the water, and it was approaching the seashore and barely touching the sea. It stopped a distance from the bank so that one man could enter and no more. And the emperor ordered the prince to get into the boat, although he felt sorry for him and was weeping copiously. When the boat reached the bank, the prince embarked, and as soon as he got in, the boat pulled swiftly away from shore and reached the high seas, so that he did not have the time to say to the emperor as much as "Sire, by your leave!"

Now however, the emperor repented that he had not pardoned him, and after the boat was lost to view, he closed the door of the postern and rejoined his company. And when the prince's knights saw the emperor alone and did not see their lord, they were surprised and said to the emperor:

"Sire, what became of the prince who was strolling through this field with you?"

"You will know in good time," said the emperor.

"You may believe, sire," they said, "that if you do not tell us where he is, it is our duty to go in quest of him and not to desist until we find him or die in the quest."

"Do not grieve," said the emperor, "for I sent him under my orders to a place where he will obtain greater honor than what I hold, if he is a man of wisdom, and will return to you before the year is up. And rest at ease, for I will have given to you whatever you need until he returns to you."

"Sire," answered the knights, "we shall wait here until the time limit you set for us is up, and if he suffers some wrong or harm, God will hold you and not us responsible; however, we will be miserable, lonely, and unhappy without him."

And the emperor began to comfort them and reassure them, telling them that the prince their lord would receive no harm or injury whatsoever. And with this they were presently reassured.

206. Of Prince Roboán's title, of how he entered the Fortunate Isles, and how he married Nobility, who was mistress there

After the prince had gone away in the boat that the emperor had thrust him into, he did not know where he was going nor could he understand who was guiding it; and thus the boat traveled as fast as the wind. And the next morning when the sun was rising, he arrived at the coast on the far side of the sea at some mountain peaks so high it seemed they touched the sky. There was no exit or entrance, except for a single postern that had iron gates. And as quickly as he arrived in front of the postern gates, the doors were opened just as quickly, but no one appeared to open or to close them. The prince stepped from the boat and entered through the postern, and then the gates were closed. And in the rocks there was a tunnel dug by hand, through which an armed knight on horseback could enter, and there were lighted lamps hanging from the ceiling, which illuminated all the tunnel. The prince was amazed because he saw no one with whom to talk or whom to ask where he was. He would gladly have returned if he could have, but the gates were so tightly closed and so well built in the rock, that he was unable to move any part of them. He went through the tunnel as far as he could, so that it was the hour of tierce before he reached the other end. He had covered at least six miles in the tunnel from one end to the other. When he reached the postern at the other end, the iron gates were opened, and he found two elegantly dressed maidens each on a palfrey and leading a handsomely saddled and bridled palfrey by the reins. They dismounted, kissed his hands, and had him mount the palfrey. They rode away with him telling him their mistress the empress sent greetings, that two kings, her vassals, were coming out to welcome him accompanied by many knights-errant, that they would kiss his hands and receive him as lord, that all the citizens of the empire would then pledge homage to him at the time the empress arrived, that he should know for certain that the empress had sixty kings at her command in her domain, and that all would be at his service and command.

"Ladies," said the prince, "how is this possible, for I have never been in this land, nor do they know who I am, nor did they send for me. I just arrived here, and I do not know whether my fortune will be good or bad."

"Sir," said the ladies, "it was your destiny that goes with you, protecting you, directing and guiding your affairs from good to better. And our Lord God, whom you took as your guide when you bade farewell to the king your father and the queen your mother, saw fit to direct and guide you to this place where you are to be lord, and He will give you the empress as your consort. She is very rich and powerful, and the most beautiful and most cultured lady who was ever born in the world. And although her mother was one of the most beautiful women in the world, her daughter is much more beautiful."

"Ladies," asked the prince, "who was the mother of the empress?"

"Sir," they said, "the Lady Parecer who rescued and protected Sir John, son of King Orian, from great danger as is told in his story. Sir John told Queen Guinevere that he had a lady more beautiful than she as his mistress, and if he could not prove it, according to the custom of the kingdom, he had to face the punishment the law of our land required."

"And who was her father?" asked the prince.

"Sir," they replied, "Sir John, who was married to the Lady Parecer, as you can learn by the book about his life if you want to read about him."

"And is he in this country?" asked the prince.

"Yes, sir," they answered.

"Ladies," said the prince, "was this lady of yours ever married?"

"Yes, she was," they said, "married to an emperor who lost her through his bad fortune and his lack of resourcefulness. You must be careful not to lose her through the wrong advice some one might give you, and that way, you will be the most powerful and fortunate lord in all the world."

"Ladies," said the prince, "from where does your mistress get such power as to know and recognize things that she has not seen? And I say this to you because of what you said to me earlier—that I took Our Lord God as my companion when I left my father, the king, and my mother, the queen. And it is true that I did so."

"Sir," said the maidens, "the empress her mother left her and all her kingdom enchanted, so that none can enter here without her permission, and her kingdom is completely surrounded by high mountains, as you saw when you entered by the postern gate where the boat brought you. And there are only four postern gates for leaving and entering like the one where you entered. May you know that as soon as you got in the boat, at that moment, she knew all your business, who you were, and all the things you have done since you were born. But she cannot foresee the future."

And the prince was amazed at the strange things the maidens were telling him, and he considered the words the emperor had said when he left— that he would send him to a place where perhaps he would prefer death to life, or perhaps if he were resourceful, great honor and benefits would be his. And he knew that this was the place where one of these two things would happen to him, as mentioned before. And the prince asked them:

"What is the name of this mistress of yours?"

"Sir," they answered, "Nobility."

"And why do they call her that?" he asked.

"Because her father so named her, and rightly so, for this is the most virtuous lady in all the world. Nobility cannot exist without virtue."

The maiden was carrying the book of the story of Sir John and began to read it. She read well, elegantly and precisely, so that the prince clearly understood all she was reading and took great pleasure and enjoyment in it. Surely there is no man who hears the story of Sir John who does not enjoy the beautiful words in it. Every man who likes to have amusement and pleasure and to be well informed ought to read the book of the life of Sir John. And as the prince was in the company of the maidens in this diversion, one on his right and the other on his left, they saw a large group of armed knights coming together with those two kings of whom the maidens had spoken to the prince. When the kings reached him, they dismounted and went to kiss his feet as was the custom of the land. The prince was reluctant to allow them to until the maidens told him not to forbid it, for it was absolutely necessary to allow it. Then they mounted, and with the prince between them they went to the city where the empress lived. Thirty kings from among her vassals were there. The empress was in a large room on an imposing dais. When the prince entered the room, the kings went to him, knelt before him, and kissed his feet. When the prince approached the empress, he tried to kiss her hands and she refused to let him. Instead, she took him by the hand and led him to a seat beside her, for this was their custom. And there she accepted him as hers; he accepted her as his, and an archbishop who was present blessed them and gave them his benediction. And then the kings, the counts, the viscounts, and all the noblemen and the leaders of the cities and towns pledged homage to him and accepted him as lord and emperor. The empress placed a magnificent crown of great price on his head with her own hands and blessed him:

"Long live this lord of mine and may God increase his honor in his lifetime. May the empire endure, and may he protect everyone fairly and not be remiss in service to God."

And then all said, "Amen."

Then the tables were set in an orderly fashion for the room and the kings' tables were placed to the right and left of the table of the emperor and the empress. The tables of the counts and the noblemen were set a short distance from the tables of the kings, and the tables for the knights were placed in another room. And know that the table placed before the emperor and the empress was the most magnificent that man has ever seen in the world, for it was made of gold, with many precious jewels. There was a ruby inset at each of the four corners, and each was as large as a playing ball, so that even the smallest was worth a large kingdom. In the middle of the room a large round table was set with the table service of gold, and there was not a cup or plate which was not made of gold studded with precious jewels. Two kings brought dinner to the emperor and the empress, and two other kings carved the meat placed before them. The two maidens who had led the palfrey to the emperor at the edge of the sea served them wine in individual cups of beautifully ornamented beryl. This tableware was easily worth as much or more than that which was placed before the Bold Knight when he entered the lake with the Mistress of Treachery, except that was pretense and a lie and this was the real thing. After they had eaten, a group of beautiful and elegantly dressed maidens came before them with wreaths of flowers in their hands singing harmoniously and sweetly, and there does not exist a man in this would who would not be eager to be present to hear them sing. And after the maidens had sung, the emperor and his company went to rest. And after they had slept, the emperor and all the kings mounted their horses and went for a ride through the city. The city was draped with rich curtains of gold and silk, and through all the streets they found the people celebrating joyously in many ways and saying in loud voices, "Long live the emperor and the empress in peace and happiness!"

In this way the emperor lived in that empire twelve months less three days, and everything he asked for or wanted was placed before him. But the devil, who never fails to deceive man as much as he can, did not want the emperor to stay a year there, for if he completed a year he would not lose the empire as he did. By appearing in an honorable and pleasing shape, the devil made him leave the path of righteousness and the honorable life in which he lived and to seek vanity and nothingness. He tried to make him lose his soul which is the most valuable possession a man has. And it happened in this fashion.

207. How Prince Roboán asked the empress for the mastiff

It happened that one day the emperor was going to the forest, and the devil saw him away from his companions in pursuit of a stag; so he appeared before him in the shape of a woman—the most beautiful one in the world. When the prince saw her, he reined in his horse and stopped and said to her:

"Friend, who brought so beautiful and attractive a woman as you here? I believe that I have never seen a lady so beautiful as you!"

"Sire," she said, "I heard how you came to this land and that you were a man of high position and talented in everything and that you had married the empress. So I came here through the wish to see you and since my good fortune was to find you here alone, if you will do something for me, I will do something for you. Since you like hunting, I will show you a dog you can easily obtain, for there does not exist a deer in this world that he cannot overtake and pull down if he sees it."

And through greed for the dog, he lay with her and afterward he asked her how he could obtain the dog. She told him to ask the empress for the dog which she kept in a small closet in her bedroom. And she showed him through certain signs in which room she kept it.

The emperor returned to the city, and during the night while he was with the empress, he said:

"My lady, you know well I am yours and am in this land through your kindness. I cannot presume to ask you, who have done me as many favors as you have, for some things that I need and would cost you little."

"And why do you doubt that I would give what you ask of me?" asked the empress. "You do me a great wrong, for you should understand that who gives you the greatest gift would not hesitate to give you the smallest. I gave myself to you, so you shouldn't doubt I would give anything I have to you, no matter how valuable it might be. The day that I accepted you as my lord, I dispossessed myself of whatever I owned and I made you lord of it."

"Lady," said the emperor, "since that is true, have the mastiff given to me that you keep in that closet."

"Of course, sire," she replied, "I am pleased to. Take this little key, and in the morning, open it, and although you may not see the dog and it may not come out, call it by name and it will come to you."

"Lady, what is its name?" asked the emperor.

"Pleasure," answered the empress.

"May you have pleasure all the days you live!" said the emperor.

"Amen!" said the empress, "but with you, nevertheless, and not without you."

And when day came, the emperor arose, and opened the closet and entered. He looked everywhere and did not see the dog. When he called it by name, it came affectionately and jumped on him. It was whiter than crystal and wore a collar made of a golden sash inlaid with the finest mother-of-pearl and gold made like a plaited rope. He took it by the leash and mounted his horse and went to the forest. No matter how large the boar, deer, or stag that appeared, the dog overtook it and dragged it down and would hold it still until the emperor came and killed it. Many knights and squires accompanied on foot, as their palfreys were used to carry the dead deer.

The emperor took great pleasure and happiness in the mastiff, and when the empress arrived he took her hands and kissed them. She tried to kiss his and could not.

"Sire," she asked, "what do you have against me, that you upset me and make me look foolish in front of these people?"

"My lady," said the emperor, "you gave me great pleasure, and I think I could not show my gratitude to you in any other way, for on my word, I believe that I would be the foolish one if I had not done this in return for such a favor as you do me. I do not know any man in the world, no matter how great or powerful he might be, who would not consider himself the richest and most fortunate man if he had such a gift to take pleasure in as this one you gave me. May God reward you, for I cannot express my gratitude enough."

The empress was very happy because she realized the emperor was elated and pleased with the mastiff. And the emperor stayed a long time with her talking of the good qualities of the mastiff and how it never hesitated to attack anything, no matter how fierce it might be. And when four days had passed, the emperor went to the forest and took the mastiff with him, and he kept his knights and squires some distance away from him.

208. How the prince went to hunt with his mastiff and the devil appeared to him

With his mastiff he hurried into the forest, and as he was going through a dense thicket, the devil appeared before him in the form of that lady who had appeared the other time. However, it seemed to the emperor that she was much more beautiful than before.

"Sire," said the lady, "is this the mastiff I told you about?"

"Yes," replied the emperor.

"And is he good?" she asked.

"By Heavens, lady," said the emperor, "I do not believe there is in all the world a dog as good as this one, and you may believe it is worth a kingdom for a man to have pleasure."

"Truly, sire," she said, "if you retain the love you shared with me I will tell you how you can obtain another gift better than this in which you will take greater pleasure."

"And what could that be?" asked the emperor, "for I know nothing in the world that could be worth more than this mastiff."

"I know something," she said.

"I promise you," said the emperor, "I will always hold the love I pledged to you and will do whatever you wish."

She told him to ask the empress for a hawk that she kept in the closet near where the mastiff was kept, for the hawk was the best in the world.

The emperor's men were surprised that they did not see him come out anywhere, nor did he blow his horn as he was accustomed. While the emperor was conversing with the devil, a large stag crossed before them. The mastiff barked and went and seized it, and the emperor arrived and killed it. The devil went away, and later a large fierce boar crossed his path. The dog pursued it and the emperor came to attack the boar, but as he entered the fray, the boar wounded the horse in the right leg and made the emperor fall. However, he was not hurt, and he quickly regained his feet and began to blow his horn. His people came to his aid and killed the boar. The emperor, eager to obtain the hawk, was in a great hurry and headed directly for the city. As soon as he reached the empress, he began to beguile her and amuse her so that he could obtain the hawk from her. He seized her hands and kissed them over and over again. She became angry because he did not allow her to kiss his hands and told him that if he did not allow her to kiss his hands, she would never give anything he might request from her. In order to appease her, he said he did not let her kiss his hands because he felt he would be doing her a wrong. However, he pretended that he was not on his guard, and relaxed his hands. When she saw he was off guard, she seized his right hand and kissed it more than one hundred times. The emperor was unable to make her release his hand, although he was pretending to make a great effort to do so.

And they shared a great happiness because of what each did for the other. And when such things as these happened to them, judge in your heart how great is the pleasure shared by those who love each other truly.

And when it was nighttime, the emperor said to the empress while they were enjoying themselves: "My lady, whoever gives a gift freely is never bothered by giving and in fact is pleased to give, but so little time has gone by since you gave me a gift—the best in the world—I cannot presume to ask for another so soon."

"Heavens, sire," said the empress, "you are mistaken in thinking such a thing and in worrying that you would not get from me what you request. Don't you know that it is inherent in nobility to continue to increase her giving, and if she does not, she considers that she has given none? Consequently, do not fail to ask, for what you want will never be refused you."

"My lady," said the emperor, "you are giving me liberty to annoy you again."

"Truly, sire," she replied, "it would not be trouble but a pleasure."

"Well then, my lady," said the emperor, "give me a hawk that you keep in that closet."

And she took a small key from her alms purse and gave it to him, telling him to open the closet in the morning and get it.

"Moreover, sire," she said, "I wouldn't want you to be devious in these requests, for at times he who thinks to deceive another is himself deceived. Do not fail to request what you want. for you can be sure it will never be refused you, for since the first day I accepted you as mine, I resolved in my heart never to refuse anything you requested, but God knows that I want you to be circumspect and that no disgrace would fall on you or your soul. And since I am in your power and you hold me, guard me well and do not let me go and do not lose me, for I will stick to you with truth and loyalty, for if once you lose me and I leave your hands, know that you will never regain me, just as Truth spoke to the Water and the Wind."

"And how was that?" asked the emperor.

"I will tell you," answered the empress.

209. Concerning the parable the empress told the emperor at his request about the Water, Truth, and Wind

"I heard that Water, Wind, and Truth swore brotherhood to one another and Truth and Water made a request of the Wind and said, 'Friend, you are very clever and go rapidly anywhere in the world, and therefore we need to know from you where we will find you when we need you.'

"And Wind said, 'You will find me in the highest places in the land, and if you do not find me there, you will find me in the valleys between the mountains, and if you do not find me there, go to a tree called the aspen and you will find me, for I never leave there.'

"And Truth and Wind asked Water where they could find it when it was needed. 'You will find me,' said Water, 'in the rivers. And if you don't find me there, you will find me in the green rushes. Look there, for you will always find me, without fail.'

"And Water and Wind asked Truth, 'Friend. when we need you, where shall we find you?' And Truth answered them: 'Friends, while you have me in your hands, guard me well so I do not get away, for if I once get away, you will never recover me, for my nature is such that I despise anyone who once leaves me, for I hold that whoever once considers me of little merit is not worthy to possess me.'

"Wherefore, my lord," said the empress, "pay attention to these words and do not forget them if you wish to keep me, and thus you will keep us together."

Surely, all men should understand these words so that they will be prudent and not lose the friend they have won and the property they hold, for no one can foretell the danger and trouble that may come as well as the friend who sees and senses in his friend such things as may drive them apart. For if deep love existed between them, great dislike and hatred will remain, for a small wrong from a friend makes a greater wound in a man's heart than a great wrong from an enemy, and it hurts more, for instead of support, you are betrayed. And she said this to him because she knew who had advised him to do wrong, and that he was committing folly out of greed for those things he was asking for.

The emperor paid no attention to the words of the empress, and the next morning he arose and opened the closet. He saw a hawk, which after many moultings was whiter than snow, sitting on a perch. His eyes were as red and brilliant as hot coals. He wore shackles ornamented with gold and pearls, and the strap to the shackles was made of golden threads pulled from the hair of the empress, which seemed to be fine gold, and there was no difference between it and gold, except that her hair was finer and more delicate than threads of gold. The emperor grasped the hawk and took him from the closet, and the hawk was so beautiful and so large that every man in the world who sees him would be exceedingly pleased to look at him. You can really believe the pleasure the emperor took in him was not small, for his heart could not bear to be parted from him, and he wandered through the palace carrying him on his hand and studying him. He came to the empress many times, thanking her excessively for the present she had given him.

The next day he went hunting with his hawk on his hand and the mastiff, which he led by a leash, tied to its collar. When he reached the river bank, he loosed the hawk, which never made a mistake. He loosed him at ducks, as well as herons, ostriches, and other birds, and no matter how large the prey, it never escaped being captured. And he did not release his prey when he saw eagles, for they fled from him as if he were lord of all the birds. And even the golden falcon that appeared at that time did not dare await the hawk and fled for its life.

"O Lord God!" said the emperor, "how fortunate am I among all the fortunate lords in the world! I don't know any one—no matter how rich or powerful he might be—who would not value it more than all the riches of the world if he possessed even one of these gifts! Surely it is true that a man takes delight and great pleasure in wealth, but this is a pleasure above all pleasures. And furthermore, I am lord of a great land, and am wealthy, and lord over so many kings, and I possess above all this the most beautiful, the most graceful, the most intelligent, the best spoken, the most composed and wisest, the most modest, the friendliest, and the happiest and best woman who was ever born in the world! Lord God, I cannot tell You how grateful I am for the favors You have shown me and there is no way I can repay You properly."

He returned to the city and was so elated that he seemed like a man bereft of his senses. He went to the empress with his hawk on his hand and leading his mastiff on the leash. As soon as he reached her, he kissed her hand with great happiness.

"Oh, my lord!" said the empress, "you still have not learned from the other times you made me angry? Surely you hope to lose me."

"And how will I lose you?" asked the emperor.

"You will lose me if you don't let me kiss your hands," responded the empress.

The emperor gazed at the floor thoughtfully, and the empress took his hands and kissed them many times. Afterward the emperor placed the hawk on his perch and the mastiff in his closet and turned to the empress. They spent some time conversing about the good qualities of the hawk and the mastiff. She talked about the good that God had done for her in his coming and her knowing him, saying that God through his grace was shielding her from trouble and injury. And they spent at least two weeks together enjoying each other's company, and he did not leave her, or go riding or hunting, for it seemed to him that he was missing none of the good and pleasurable things of this world.

And it was certainly true, for there was no reason for worry since his kingdom was at peace and in absolute harmony. Everyone was friendly to his neighbor and led a restful and serene life. There was no one to invade the land by force, for it was walled completely around. And I truly believe this was the greatest love that ever anyone knew between two persons who loved each other so much, but because of the unfaithfulness of the emperor his happiness turned to grief, and so the word of the wise man was fulfilled which said that great sadness often follows great happiness. And as a man of ill destiny, paying no heed to the great mercy God had shown him and not knowing how to preserve or enjoy the good fortune in which he found himself, the emperor fell into ill fortune, which he had to endure, although he did not want to, as you will now hear.

210. How Roboán asked the empress for the horse, on the advice of the devil

And so it happened that at the conclusion of many days of sharing pleasure with the empress, he mounted his horse and went hunting with his falcon. And traveling through the forest, he met that accursed devil who had deceived him on two other occasions. He appeared before him in the form of a lady even more beautiful than the other times, and said to the emperor, "Lord, you have to tell me from now on that you love me greatly and that you will do for me whatever I desire, for I have made you owner of the two most wonderful things in the world."

"It is certainly true," said the emperor, "and you have placed me in your debt to do always what you wish, and do not doubt that I will do so."

"My lord," replied the devil, "since you are so grateful and remember so well the advantages you receive, now I want to show you another gift that you can obtain from the empress that is more wonderful than the other two you have, and more worthy of a knight."

"And what gift would be worth so much?" asked the emperor.

"My lord," answered the devil, "it is a horse whiter than snow and the swiftest in the world, for there is no other in the world, no matter how fast he may be, that can run so fast as this one."

"I am very grateful to you," replied the emperor, "and you may be certain that you have won me forever." Then he left the forest and went home to the empress, taking a great catch of game.

And after night fell and they went to her private chamber, he became affectionate and did all kinds of pleasant things for her. However, she knew very well what he wanted to ask her, and she could not refuse him, for when she first married him she had promised never to deny anything that he might ask of her. And truly, the empress was prudent and always kept her word, and she never failed any man in what she had promised him, for she considered that the greatest fault a man could have was to break his word and the promises he made. And with these thoughts, the empress fell asleep. And the emperor could not sleep and he turned and tossed frequently in bed, not daring to awaken her and ask for the horse. And the empress felt this, took note, and wondered why he was troubled and sighing and unable to sleep, and she said to him:

"My lord, what is worrying you? Sleep and rest, for anything you want you may have, and for Heaven's sake, do not try to kill yourself through so much worry. And if you stop this worrying, you will save yourself and me; and if you do not, you may be sure it will result in great harm to you and great anguish for me."

"Lady," said the emperor, "since you so assure me, I will sleep and rest, for I trust in your kindness that you will agree to whatever I want."

"And may you agree to whatever I want, as I agree to what you want," replied the empress. "And then, minds and wills and hearts will be as one; but God made the nature and hearts of men different, and so they can never agree completely."

"Lady," said the emperor, "may God always keep our hearts together, and may whoever plans to come between them never share the beneficence of God!"

"And so be it," said the empress.

And the emperor fell asleep, and God made him so sleepy that he slept well until after mid-morning. And the empress did not dare to turn or move in bed for fear of awakening him, thinking that he would then want to make the request that he had been planning. When he awoke, he believed it was quite late in the day. He sat on the bed and said to her, "My lady, are you sleeping? It is late in the day."

"Well," said the empress, "you slept and rested and may God help me if I do not take greater pleasure in your resting than you do. But you are troubled in your heart and do not know how to contain what you feel. Certainly, it is not good. I see you are quite moderate in all things except this. If you are not careful in this matter, it will bring you great harm. For goodness' sake, from now on restrain yourself."

And when the emperor heard this, he restrained himself and did not attempt to ask of her what he held in his heart. He arose and was served something to eat, and they rested all the day. When the emperor strolled through the palace and reached the closet where the devil had told him the horse was kept, he stopped and listened to see if he could hear anything. He heard nothing nor did he see anything that had been given to the horse to eat or to drink. Therefore he was surprised, but the horse was of such a nature that he neither ate nor drank, because this was the horse that Belmonte, son of king Trequinaldus, won from Vedore when he left his father, as is related in the story of Belmonte, and the empress had it in her possession and her control through magic.

And when night fell, the emperor and the empress prepared to go to bed. However, the empress did not go to bed right away, but instead she delayed much of the night hoping the emperor would fall asleep and forget to make the request. But the emperor was obsessed by that accursed horse and could not sleep, nor would he fall asleep. When the empress went to bed, she found him awake, and the emperor said to her, "Lady, why are you so late?"

"My lord," she replied, "I had to distribute silk, gold, and pearls to the maidens to make a pretty banner. It will be finished in three days, and I truly believe that no man has ever seen one as beautiful as this one will be."

And she continued to delay by talking, so that he would tire and fall asleep. And so it happened, for he quickly fell asleep and did not awaken until the next day when the sun rose. He arose from bed suddenly, like a man surprised. The empress was started and said to him, "My lord, what happened? Why did you arise so suddenly? What is the matter with you?"

"Lady," answered the emperor, "I was dreaming just now that I was riding on that horse of yours that I planned to ask for, and he was rapidly overtaking a large stag which I was pursuing, and I hurled my spear into him. The mastiff quit chasing the stag and the stag charged toward me. The horse turned and ran from him so that he could not harm me. However, he ran into a large body of water and began to swim with me, and with fear of the water, I awoke in fright."

And the empress felt deep sorrow in her heart because he mentioned the horse, for she felt that since she had deceived him, he was bound to request it from her. And so it was, for then he asked her to give it to him as a favor. She put her hand into her purse and took out a key and gave it to him and made him promise that he would not open the door until the third day when the pennant would be finished. So he promised, and on the morning of the third day he opened the door of the room where the horse was kept and saw it brilliant white and beautiful, bridled and saddled. He took it by the reins and led it away, saying that he planned to go hunting.

And when the empress saw him, she felt grief the equal of death. She entered the room where the maidens were. They had the pennant finished and had fastened it to the staff of a stout lance. The empress went out with the pennant in her hand and said to the emperor: "Lord, you are going hunting, and I can do nothing but fulfill your request completely. I beg you to carry this pennant with my love, and you will never enter any place in the world with it in which you cannot accomplish successfully whatever you undertake. Lead the horse by the reins until you are outside the door, and then mount and ride."

And so he did.

211. How the empress fervently entreated Prince Roboán not to depart

After she gave him the pennant and told him to lead the horse by the reins and to ride outside, the empress finally realized that he was leaving. Her heart was troubled and she wanted to detain him if possible. But the power that controlled him was no longer hers, but the horse's. But she went with him to the door of the castle and said these words to him, hoping to make him stay:

"My lord, don't you remember the oaths and the pledge you made me the day that you married me? Never to leave me and to be loyal and true to me? But I see that you have no compassion for poor wretched me and I am left alone without the things I most love and the person for whom my love will never die until my death. And since it is not in my power to make you stay, my lord, may it be in yours. However, the weather is turning foul and you can already see that the winds are blowing fiercely and will not allow you to do as you plan. Moreover, I truly believe that you want to go, so that you will never see me again nor I see you again. Would to God that you and I had never seen one another! I am sure that in some future time you will love me, and I you until I die, but since I can not stay you, nor do you wish to stay, I shall beg the winds to impede your leaving, and I will pray to the god of the sea not to sustain you on it, and I will pray to Venus, the goddess of love, to make you remember the love that we had as one and the vows we promised one another and that they may never permit you to fail the love and the promises you made me. However, I do not believe that your heart, knowing the true devotion I hold for you above all else, can in any way bear for you to abandon me, since I do not deserve it, having loved you truly and granted you your every whim. And although I knew you were sinning against me, I did not choose to tell you, because I did not want to hurt you or shame you. But you did not esteem poor wretched me, nor did you respect me as you should have—nor yourself—although I warned you and told you that you should hold on to me while you had me in your power, for if I once slipped away from your hand, you would never hold me again. And I am sure that if you do not stay, you will lose whatever honor, pleasure, and good you have, as you know, and you will lose me who was your true mistress in love and made everything pleasurable for you and desired to make your life happier than my own. But I say this much to you—that whenever you find yourself in danger you will see my image before you and know that those dangers come to you because of the wrong you have done me, and you will try to return and will be unable to, and you will have no pleasure or happiness, nor will you laugh as you used to, and you will desire me and be unable to have me! Oh, my lord, is the cruelty in your heart so great toward me that you would risk placing yourself in danger of death by preferring to abandon me and leave me sad and heartbroken? For certain, one has a cruel heart who ceases to love the one who loves him. And since you refuse to remain for my sake, stay because I believe I am pregnant by you, and so you will receive pleasure from what you have done; and without you, I would not know how to choose a name for my son when he is born."

And she knelt before him on the gound. He was already on his horse and she said, "My lord, what is your answer?"

He answered her, "Let him be named Fortunate."

And thus they named him after he was born, and there is a book in Arabic of the numerous deeds of chivalry and other good deeds he accomplished after he came of age and went in quest of his father.

The empress remained there kneeling before him and with tears streaming from her eyes, she said: "My lord, for the sake of mercy, I ask you to stay. Dismount and I will welcome you with open arms, for in no other way will the horse allow you to dismount for he is eager to go. You should not leave what you have gained for what you might gain, or what is done for what you might do, nor should you trade delight for misery, for I am sure that after you are gone you will want what you had and will be unable to have it. May the one be cursed who deceived you thus and inspired you to ask for what you could have avoided. And it seems to me that he was truly your enemy and not your friend, and you should realize that the enemy gives the appearance of good and of love, but puts man in danger and dishonor. And therefore they say that the one who is not pleased to love you, really hates you."

When the emperor heard these words and was preparing to turn in order to dismount, his spurs lightly touched the horse and he sped off like the wind, so that he had not the time to say to her, "By your leave, my lady."

212. How Prince Roboán went away on his horse and of the lamentation of the empress

Whereupon the story relates that he who enjoyed such great pleasure and power and did not know how to keep it was born under an evil star, for this empire is one of the most delightful and bountiful in the world, for it is called the Fortunate Islands. It borders on one side the islands of Sind and on the other touches the sea of the empire of Tigrida, and the other two borders are to the east. The empress and her ladies and maidens were very disconsolate and sad, and she lamented at the top of her voice like a person who despaired of ever again seeing him in whose power she had desired to end her days. She loved him more than anything else in the world, and she paced through the palace like a crazy woman, shouting and saying: "Oh, wretch, it was an evil day on which I was born and a dreadful hour in which I saw this man who has abandoned me and hurt me so! O evil Fate! Why did you give me pleasure which led me to such great sorrow? You are like the snake that makes his track with his head and erases it with his tail. You are always fickle and are like the sea that swells and falls and is never still. And you do not know how to stay with the man you begin with, for if you cause him to rise high, you make him fall from on high. That is why a man ought never to trust you, for when expectations are highest, you are accustomed to fail, just as you did me, for when I believed I could trust in the greatest pleasure and the greatest happiness in which I could be, you crushed me and took from it with no pity, having no compassion or feeling for me, and I had great faith that you would not abandon me. And rightly do they call you Fortune, for you are never constant. And since you abandoned me, from now on I will not look for you or have any hope in you, and so I will remain an unhappy woman. And even though you gave me pleasure and happiness, I have no reason to be grateful to you for it, for though you gave it to me, you took it away and left me in despair and sadness. And I do not deserve it from you. And henceforth, I will have the doors and the walls of my domain locked, so that no one can leave or another ever enter again, and I will live alone without pleasure like the turtledove when it is widowed, for it does not know how to find another mate or how to perch on a green branch, but sits on the driest one it finds. So I will dress in mourning robes and I will wear sackcloth for the rest of my days, and this will be my song each day:

Alas, miserable abandoned wretch,
I am left without consolation!
Alas, wretch, robbed
Of all my worldly gains!
Death, be welcome, come for me.
For such bitter grief I cannot bear.

And so the empress was disconsolate and never again wanted to marry.

As soon as the emperor reached the postern gate where he had entered, the horse left him there at the boat, and he was carried across to the other side of the sea to the same place where he had embarked. When the boat reached land, he did not want to go ashore, hoping that it would yet return him to the postern gate through which he had entered when he had first departed this shore. And through greed for things he could easily have done without if he had wanted to, the wretch lost the good fortune and honor he had obtained. And therefore they say that he who does not plan ahead may fall backward. And this prince, although he was very clever and very perceptive and had great courage, did not know how to guard against the tricks and the deceptive crafts of the devil, who is always striving to deceive men in order to make them lose their souls and honor in this world.

213. How Prince Roboán arrived in the boat at the empire of Tigrida and found the emperor sad and lamenting

And with the heartfelt grief over what he had lost, the prince began to lament:

"Woe to me, wretch!
Woe unto me, miserable me!
And woe unto me, stupid me!
And woe unto me, disconsolate wretch!
Where is my delight?
Where is my triumph?
Great wealth I owned,
And now I live in poverty.
I was surrounded with friends,
And now I live alone.
My power is vanished
And of no advantage to me,
All through my folly
I have lost all I possessed.
I lost everything here
As did Aeneas in Carthage,
When he spoke and went away
With none to bid him farewell."

And while he was sitting in that boat sad and sorrowing, the emperor of Tigrida arrived at the postern gate and opened the door, as was his custom every day since he had taken the prince there. He saw him in the boat holding in his hand a lance with a beautiful banner. He approached and said, "Friend, how goes it with you?"

And Roboán could answer not a single word.

"My friend," said the emperor, "come ashore, for there is no remedy for what has happened, and comfort yourself and be careful from now on, and since you did not have the wisdom to protect yourself in the first place, be wise if it happens to you again."

They left through the postern gate, and the emperor asked for a palfrey. They brought it to him, and the prince mounted with his banner in his hand. There lacked only two days until the year would have been over. And the emperor went privately with the prince and asked how things had gone with him, and he said, "Sire, good and bad."

"I can already see that," said the emperor, "it went well with you at first and badly later. But you must take comfort and laugh with me now, if you feel that you can."

"Well," replied the prince, "In no way can I laugh, and if someone else had said that to me, I would gladly have killed him."

"Well, why?" asked the emperor, "why did you ask me why I did not laugh? I went through what you did, and I was the first to have that pleasure and I lost it all through my lack of prudence just as you did." However, the emperor continued consoling him as much as he could. The news reached the city, and when the prince's soldiers heard it, they were very happy and went out to welcome him. They kissed his hands and gave thanks to God because they saw him alive and well. They had given up hope of ever seeing him again and had been on the verge of going in quest of him. There was great rejoicing throughout the emperor's kingdom when all learned the news, except by those who had advised Roboán to ask the emperor the question. They were not pleased by the coming of the prince, but instead were very apprehensive for they believed they would be punished for it. And when the prince entered the city accompanied by the emperor, great festivities were held, and there was not a single knight, lady, or damsel who did not go out to meet them, crying, "Welcome to the loyal friend of the emperor!"

Truly the emperor gave everyone to understand that he was greatly pleased with Roboán, for he held him by the arm saying many agreeable things to him in order to cheer him. He said to him with great happiness: "Friend, now I consider you my son, since God did not choose for me to have one, and I want to do for you what I never thought I would do for any man in the world, and I want you to do for me what I will tell you."

"Sire," said the prince, "I will always be obedient to whatever you wish."

"Well," responded the emperor, "I want you to laugh and be happy, and I will laugh with you."

"Sire," said the prince, "since it pleases you, I will do all in my power."

214. How the devil in the form of a maiden appeared to Roboán and the emperor in a garden

And when they entered the palace of the emperor, they went to a beautiful garden that was near the emperor's room, and they saw a lovely lady bathing in a beautiful and clear fountain in the middle of the garden. This was the lady who had deceived them by advising them to request the three gifts from the empress, so that they would lose her. And the emperor said to the prince: "My friend, do you recognize somebody over there?"

"To my sorrow I recognize her," said the prince, "for that lady is the one who through great deceit made me take leave of my good sense and intelligence and made me lose what pleasure and honor I had, and may God curse her for it!"

"So be it," said the emperor.

And she began to laugh and to mock them. She put her head in the bottom of the fountain and began to tumble in the water, so that they could not help but laugh. However, the prince could not laugh wholeheartedly; but from then on, the prince and the emperor laughed and took great pleasure and enjoyment together.

"It's an ill wind that doesn't blow some good," said the emperor. "This one cheers the unhappy and gives a man wisdom to be more prudent in the future, for this accursed devil has changed us into wise men who can be on guard against error and careful not to believe everyone who comes to us with flattering and deceitful words, just as this one did to me and to you. But if she had not deceived me first, she would not have been able to trick you in this affair; and thus, I would not have had a companion by my side with whom to share sorrow. Since we were companions in misfortune, we shall be companions in good fortune and comfort each other the best that we can. Certainly a stout heart overcomes ill fortune, and there is no man, no matter how courageous, who can well endure the weight of misfortune if he is alone, but if he has a companion he can endure misery better. And therefore they say that misery loves company."

215. How the emperor died and Prince Roboán became lord of all the empire of Tigrida

And this emperor, after he lost the enchanted empress, married again, but never had any children, and his wife died. And as the prince was with him, the emperor thought that if he should die, the kingdom would lack strength and would be lost and destroyed. Recognizing the good traits and qualities of knight-errantry in the prince, he selected him to become lord and emperor of the empire after his death. He adopted him in the presence of all his subjects and had him pledge allegiance. They accepted him as their lord at the death of the emperor. The emperor lived only a year longer, and the prince reigned in his place, loved by all the subjects of the prince's native land and of the empire and welcomed as their emperor.

And the new emperor was pleased to rule them in fairness and peace, and he defended and protected them well. All the neighboring rulers were envious, for he was well served and supported by all his vassals, except the seven counts, counselors to the late emperor, who had advised him to ask why the emperor did not laugh. And through envy they strove to stir up as much trouble in the empire as they could among their relatives and friends, because they were afraid of what they had done against him. However, the emperor preferred not to remember it but instead ignored it. He did not desire to talk about it, nor did he allow anyone else to talk about it. Instead he always welcomed the seven counts and honored them as much as he could. He tried to please them, doing good and favoring them with special kindness. All his courtiers were amazed at him for doing so many favors for those who he knew would try to arrange his death if they could.

216. How the king of Garba and the king of Safira and the seven counts rebelled against the emperor Roboán

But the emperor, as one who always did good as much as he could, took the word of the Gospel in which it says that man ought never to return evil for evil. And this is true for those who repent of this sin in which they fall. But these unfortunate men were unwilling to acknowledge the wrong they had committed against the emperor when they tried to arrange his death, and would not repent of it. They would not recognize the great kindness the emperor had done them by forgetting the scheme they had hatched against him and his favoring all of them the same as the others, for he gratefully acknowledged the services each one did for him and rewarded them all alike. They spoke with two kings, vassals of the emperor, one the king of Safira and the other the king of Garba, both rich and powerful rulers, and they made them believe that the emperor was plotting to do them harm and was planning to send for them in order to kill them, because he was not a native of their land and did not like the natives of the empire, especially the powerful ones; and so they instilled them with a great distrust of the emperor. And alas! man is of such a weak nature that he is more easily frightened than emboldened, and through fear he will make great efforts and his heart will inspire him to do what he ought not to do. Wherefore the old proverb says,

"Whatever the ear hears, the heart believes." And furthermore, the man of faint heart is always fearful and ready to do wrong, and these two kings were in a state of fear instilled in them by those seven counts. The emperor wanted to see his father and his mother and his brother and to go on a pilgrimage to the monastery his father, the king, had built and where our Lord God performs many miracles. He had decided to leave the country in the charge of those two kings together with two other kings who were from another part of the empire. He commanded these two kings by letter to come, each accompanied by only a small force of soldiers, for he wanted to save them great expenditures. And when the king of Garba and the king of Safira saw the letters from the emperor in which he ordered them to come immediately, accompanied by a few soldiers, the doubts the counts had instilled in them came to mind, and the two kings conferred at a tract of land lying between the two kingdoms, which was to be divided between them. One of those counts who had inspired this distrust in them held this land in fief. They sent for the other counts and showed them the letters. And after they read the letters, one of them arose and said: "My lords, whoever is filled with ill will can not forget it, and whoever wishes to do ill looks for a way he can do it without danger to himself. And don't you see that for the emperor to carry out his will, and to be able to complete the plot he has against you, he is ordering you to go accompanied by just a few soldiers? I tell you it is my advice not to go there now. Now that you are warned, prepare with as many troops as you have—and the best armed—and you will be able to defend yourselves, and you will see that he plans to attack if you do not flee."

And they believed him and did as he suggested.

217. How the Emperor Roboán prepared troops to fight against the two kings and how he sent word to them again to visit him

The emperor learned that those two kings were rebelling, and further that those wicked counts had sent men to make the emperor understand that the two kings were refusing to obey him and planned to invade his territory. Also, they paid bribes to the emperor's subjects to turn against each other. And the emperor's people let him know how the king of Garba, the king of Safira, and the counts were plundering his land. And the emperor heeded the word of the wise man that says, "Take the trouble to get advice at the beginning of a sickness, for if it comes late, the medicine is of no advantage when the sickness has grown and seized control because of long delay." He did not delay in summoning all his subjects and setting out against those two kings. The opposition was well prepared to defend themselves; however, they sent word to the emperor by a knight that they were puzzled as to why he had committed troops against them, for they truly believed that they had done nothing against him for which he would wish them ill or would do ill to them. When they received him as their lord, they were the first who went to kiss his foot, and they both had placed the crown on his head after the archbishop of Frecida, his chancellor, had blessed him when he sang the new mass on the altar of Saint Spiritus, where the emperor had held his vigil that night.

The emperor said to the knight who had brought the message:

"Knight, it is true that everything happened just as they have sent word. I always loved them and honored them above all the kings of the empire, and I trusted them just as a lord should trust loyal vassals who wish him well. But I do not know why they refused to come when I sent for them in my letters. Trying to save them high costs, I sent for them to come to me with only a few knights. And they were so imprudent that they refused to send a reply nor did they want to know what I wanted with them, and furthermore, they invaded my country and killed a large number of my people. I think they have made a big mistake, and I did not deserve it from them. However, considering all this, if they would come to hear me out as they should, accompanied by just a small force, and ask me to forgive them, I know they would not find anything else in my heart but mercy and compassion, for no man exists who lacks compassion for those who repent and ask forgiveness."

"My lord," replied the knight, "I will go with this message of yours to those kings your vassals, and I trust in the grace of God that they will then come here to receive your judgment. I will need a time period of about a month."

And the emperor agreed and ordered him to leave without delay. And the knight went to the kings and told them what the emperor had replied to what they had sent him to say.

"Well then, lords," said a count, "since these words follow those that we said in our message, you can understand the ill will that the emperor holds toward you. It is obvious that he has not changed his mind, for he still sends you word to visit him accompanied by a small force of soldiers. And when he sees you with a small force, he will do with you whatever he wants. And henceforth, be on your guard, for if you do not take care to protect yourselves, you will suffer great harm."

When the kings heard these words, they were apprehensive, and, as they were ill-advised men, they refused to send a reply to the emperor and instead sent for all their friends to come to their aid.

218. How the emperor sent the Knight Amigo with his message to those two kings who had rebelled against him

The emperor waited out the time limit, and without knowing all the foregoing, he ordered the Knight Amigo to take a message to the king of Garba and the king of Safira to learn from them why they had rebelled and to inform them that they ought not to do so. Seeing that this errand was very dangerous, the Knight Amigo said:

"Sire, if it suits your pleasure, you ought to excuse me from such orders and errands as these. In order to speak intelligently before great lords, every man ought to have six qualities: first, he ought to be of sound basic intelligence in order to understand the things he has to tell; second, he should be eloquent in order to relate them well; third, he should be educated in order to know how to arrange his message logically, so that the end is in accord with the beginning and does not contradict it; fourth, he should be of noble blood, so that he will not be afraid to tell what he has been charged to tell; fifth, he ought to be wealthy, for all men willingly listen to and follow the rich; sixth, he should be well liked by men, for the man who is not well liked is not listened to although he may possess all the other good traits. Furthermore, in order for all these things to be useful in a rational man, he ought to be trustworthy and truthful, so that no lie may be found in what he says nor may there be any reason to reprimand him. And although, my lord, I may be obliged to serve you, and you truly respect me, I do not believe that I hold any of these good qualities, except trust and truth, which are the things I most value in this world. Therefore, it seems to me that it would be better for you to choose one of your vassals in whom you may find all these traits, or most of them, and he would be able to serve you better than I on this mission."

"By Heaven, Knight Amigo!" exclaimed the emperor, "realizing that God endowed you with good sense, and knowing of your logic, your faith, your truthfulness, and the fact that you never fail to speak the truth through fear or shame, and how you are loved and respected by one and all on account of these good qualities of yours, I place all my actions in your hands, and so I hold that I am well served. And I still trust in God that the other two things that you lack—being rich and a nobleman—you will soon gain, and I will work as hard as I can to help you attain them."

And the Knight Amigo went with the emperor's order, and he found the two kings together in a large field near the city of Paludes, and the counts were with them. This city is named Paludes because it is surrounded with lakes that are formed by the Mixed Waters. He handed them the letters of safe conduct that the emperor had sent them.

And Count Farán began to laugh when he saw the Knight Amigo and he spoke to the kings: "My lords, now you can see the arrogance and treachery of the emperor, for in this man lie all the plans of the emperor, for this is the adviser who guides him! And he will not speak to you except with subterfuges, deceit, and arrogance."

And the Knight Amigo heard him and said: "You missed a chance to be quiet, count, and you could have avoided these words if you had chosen: 'Whoever lives by treachery may die of treachery.'"

And the count said, "Amen!"

"And I say 'Amen' also," spoke the Knight Amigo.

"Knight Amigo," said the kings, "say whatever you wish and we shall listen and have done with these words."

"My lords," said the Knight Amigo, "although I may not be so clever or so gifted with wisdom as you are, nor as wise as is necessary to relate the message from my lord the emperor to such noblemen, I shall take the risk, counting on your kindness and fairness, for if I am lacking in something, your greater wisdom will understand it and improve it better than I know how to say, and I will tell it the best that I know how." And he said thus:

"My lords, my lord the emperor sends you greetings, and sends word to you that when he first achieved his great office you were the most zealous of those who did the most then to extol his honor, and you were the first to place the crown on his head. He has always respected you and honored you over all the others of his empire. Therefore he is amazed that you invade his territory and are ravaging it. Wherefore he sends word to you as people he truly loves, requesting you to cease doing it, and then to go to him. And if you find that he has failed you in some way, he will rectify it as you want; however, he believes that he has not wronged you in any way. And if he has wronged you, he considers it fitting to go to you, since he would make amends. And if you do not intend to accept this offer, you will be doing wrong on your part, for the one who is not willing to accept an honest apology is more to blame than the one who committed the wrong."

219. How the Knight Amigo was taken prisoner and a merchant purchased him

And before the kings could answer, Count Farán stood and said: "My lords, if you pay heed to the words that this knight spoke to you, you will see something of the arrogance I told you about earlier, for he was sent to influence you with the carrot and the stick.[1] And for Heaven's sake, my lords, tell this knight that you will come to an accord and send your reply to the emperor, but do not be in such a rush to answer."

And so they did. They sent the Knight Amigo with this reply to the emperor. And as the Knight Amigo was returning along his way with their reply to the emperor, he encountered a company of Count Farán's soldiers which was making a raid in the emperor's territory. They captured the Knight Amigo and all those who were accompanying him, and they took them to a city that has the name Altaclara. And they call it that because it is on a high place and seems to be quite large. And as they were being held there as prisoners, they were taken out to be sold, and a rich merchant went to

1. The Spanish translates literally "with the bread and the stick."

inspect them in order to purchase them. And when he saw the Knight Amigo, he was pleased with him and his witty speech, and said to him, "Amigo, tell me what you would like to be?"

"Well, good sir," he replied, "who told you my name?"

"How's that? Is your name Amigo?" asked the merchant.

"That's what they call me," he answered.

"I like that," said the merchant. "But tell me what would you like to be?"

"To be free," said the Knight Amigo.

"I realize that," replied the merchant, "but tell me if you want me to buy you."

"And why ask me for advice about your property?" asked the Knight Amigo, "for it is up to you to buy me or not, since I am here ready for sale."

"Friend," said the merchant, "I see you are so clever that I believe I will buy you."

And then he bought him.

"Oh, my lord," said the Knight Amigo, "since you bought me, I beg you to buy those who were captives with me. You can be sure we will serve you well and you will gain great wealth through us."

And the merchant did so. They were sold to him with the stipulation that as soon as he had taken them across the sea they would be his.

220. How the Knight Amigo defeated Count Farán and wounded him seriously in the face

Having purchased them, the merchant was leading them away when they encountered Count Farán, who did not know that his soldiers had captured and sold them. When the merchant saw Count Farán coming, accompanied by a small force of soldiers, he ordered the Knight Amigo to mount up, and he gave each of the others a horse, for he was leading quite a number of horses to be sold. When the count reached them, he recognized the Knight Amigo and said to him: "I well believe, sir, that you will not answer me now so impudently as you did in the presence of the kings ten days ago."

"Count," responded the Knight Amigo, "if you choose to say something, you will get a reply that I could not give ten days ago while I was in the power of your soldiers who held me captive. But God be praised, I am now in the power of this good man who bought me."

"He shall not buy you!" exclaimed the count, and he prepared to charge and seize him. The Knight Amigo drew his sword and all the others with him did the same, and they wounded the count with two blows and killed ten of his men.

"Well, well, sir count," said the Knight Amigo, "you had quite an answer here. And you could very well have avoided this if you had chosen to. Now rest here a short time while we go to prepare something for you to eat."

"Knight Amigo," said the merchant, "what shall we do now? For I am sure that the count's soldiers will not be amused when they learn of this and will come in pursuit of us."

"I will tell you," replied the Knight Amigo. "Near here is a castle belonging to the emperor, and let us go there for I am carrying maps, and I am sure they will welcome us and entertain us."

"Let us go," said the merchant, "but be careful that I don't lose what I purchased."

"I give you my pledge and homage that I shall not leave you until you collect all yours and more, for I swear by God that I will give you great rewards for it," said the Knight Amigo.

221. How the Knight Amigo captured the wife and daughter of Count Farán

As they were going along their way, they met the young daughter of Count Farán, accompanied by her mother and four men on horseback. And when the Knight Amigo saw them he recognized them and was very pleased. And he said to the merchant, "My lord, now I have pledges that I give you for me and my companions."

And they took the countess and her daughter and seized the four men who were accompanying them. The countess thought that she had fallen into evil hands, but the Knight Amigo was courteous and very gentle, and especially toward ladies, and he said to her: "Countess, do not be afraid, for there is no man here who will do you harm, bur rather render you honor and courtesy. However, you are in this trouble because of the arrogance of your husband the count. This much I shall do for you: I shall keep your daughter safe from all dishonor and harm. You will go to your husband the count who is lying wounded in the field at Tebres, where he showed his arrogance as much as he could, without God and without any cause. Prepare something better for him to eat than what we have already prepared for him, and give thought to redeeming your daughter, for by redeeming her, you will be ransoming me and these companions of mine who were sold by your soldiers to this good man who bought us. Know that the payment for us is five hundred half-drachmas of gold, and it is necessary for the merchant to have one thousand half-drachmas of gold in exchange for the trouble he has taken and as a reward for the good that he did for us in rescuing us from the power of the count."

222. How the countess found her severely wounded husband Count Farán, and of the things she told him had happened to her with the Knight Amigo

The countess departed and found the severely wounded count in that field as the Knight Amigo had told her, and she related to him the misfortune that had happened to her and their daughter and how the Knight Amigo had been courteous to her and what he had told her. "Well, then, count," she said, "I am afraid that these treasonable affairs you are involved in will bring you great danger unless you quit them and turn to God, for you neither hear mass nor take communion, which every Christian ought to do every day and commend himself to God. You do not kneel as you should when you take communion, and you know that dumb animals in which there is no intelligence do reverence to God, just as occurred with your nephew Jorán in Altaclara yesterday.

"And how was that?" asked the count.

"I will tell you," said the countess. "You know that Jorán was a youthful knight, high spirited, and given to the pleasures of this world, and a dissolute fellow who respected nothing in this world or anything religious. So it happened that four days ago today, he was on his horse in a street in Altaclara. A priest passed by carrying the Host in his hands. He was going to administer communion to a sick man, and hearing the bell and seeing the crowd that was escorting him to honor the Host, Jorán refused when everyone told him to move aside. The horse was trying to move aside from there and Jorán was jerking viciously on the reins. And when the horse saw that the priest was coming near with the Host, it knelt on the ground, and Jorán hurt it with the bit of the bridle and made it stand up. And the horse did this many times until the priest had passed by with the Host. Jorán began to mistreat the horse, with everyone telling him not to, for it had given a good example to everybody to do honor to the Host. And while he was beating the horse, it reared and threw him to the ground, so that he was killed without confession or communion. Then the horse went to the church where the priest was going to give communion to the sick man. The horse was doing no harm, and they were unable to get it to move anywhere. And because they realized that it was a miracle of God, they ordered it left there, and it is still there and will not leave. And it is obvious that Our Lord God demonstrates His miracles on those who do not show reverence for Our Lord Jesus, because today I heard that a rich man sent one of his servants on an errand in a great hurry, and that servant met a priest who was going to give communion to a suffering man, and the servant accompanied the priest on his trip coming and going. Afterward he went on his journey. And because he was late, his master ordered him thrown into a flaming furnace that was in his house. The youth, when he saw himself in that danger, knelt on the ground and begged God to have mercy on him. And while the furnace was flaming, they threw him inside, and Our Lord Jesus Christ took him in His hands, and all who were present saw Him in the middle of the furnace and how He held the youth in His hands so that no harm was done to him. When the furnace was cold, his master ordered him taken out, and they removed him unhurt. And if we esteem our earthly masters, the more we ought to worship Our Lord Jesus Christ who graced us in taking us from the power of the devil, redeeming us by His precious blood and suffering death and torment for our sake. Therefore, I ask you, my lord, please keep and heed these words and God will protect you and us."

"Countess," said the count, "let us go and free our daughter, and afterward, let us think about what we have to do in these matters."

And so they went and made arrangements to have their daughter released, and they did not think of anything else. And after they had paid the one thousand half-drachmas of gold to the merchant for the count's daughter, the merchant accompanied the Knight Amigo to the emperor, for he already had learned how the Knight Amigo had been a captive, and he was very pleased with the merchant and gave some of his wealth to him and let him go.

223. How the emperor fought the kings and conquered them

The kings did not send any reply to the emperor, and after the emperor saw that they were not sending him a reply, he set out against them and found them on a great expanse of level terrain near the banks of the river, the Mixed Waters, with a great host of well-armed soldiers. And the emperor saw them all quite clearly, for he was descending through a high pass and they were at his feet. As soon as the message reached the kings that the emperor was coming down the pass with his retinue and his army, they armed themselves, and their ranks of soldiers stood like those who are determined to defend themselves and die. The emperor was busy descending that day with all his troops to the plains, so that they rested that night. The next morning they donned their armor and mustered their ranks and advanced one against the other. Soon they clashed and the battle was extremely violent, so that all the battlefield was full of dead and wounded. So great was the noise . . .[1] and the screams of the wounded, lamenting because of their wounds, that they could not hear one another, and the emperor moved among them striking amazing strokes, so that whoever encountered him did not easily escape from his hands, for they fell dead or badly wounded from their horses. And then he came upon the king of Garba, and attacking him with his sword, he cut off the king's right arm, and in addition, turned again to him and struck a blow on the crest of his helmet which split his head down to his eyes, so that he fell dead.

1. At this point there is a break in the sense of the text.

When the king of Safira heard this news, it grieved him to his heart. However, he began to encourage his troops and to inspire them, and they began to attack the emperor's soldiers fiercely. Suddenly a host of knights came to the aid of the king of Safira and forced the emperor from the field of battle. Only a few more than three thousand knights left the battlefield with him, while all the rest remained on the battlefield dead or wounded.

When the emperor realized that he was alone and all his soldiers dead except for the three thousand knights who were left of the thirty thousand that he had led, he considered himself most unlucky. He withdrew into the mountains by that pass through which he had entered. He began to comfort those knights the best he was able. They stripped off their armor and arms, for they were very tired, and the enemy remained that night on the battlefield, taking the weapons from the dead knights. They killed those who were wounded, leaving not a single one alive. They took the clothing and everything else they found on them.

224. How the emperor returned to battle the day after, won it, and controlled the whole battlefield

The emperor arose at midnight and withdrew some distance from his soldiers and began to pray, asking God's forgiveness if he had wronged Him in some way, and if He felt that he was not intended to be the ruler, that He should take him wherever He considered proper and that He should place another there who was more deserving.

"But Lord God," prayed the emperor, "I believe I am a great sinner for losing so many troops who died today for me, and for which I beg You for mercy and that it may please You to forgive me."

While the emperor was at prayer, he heard a voice from heaven that said to him: "Roboán, friend of God, do not despair for God is with you. And you well know that the king of Mentón, your father, never despaired of the mercy of God no matter what misfortune happened to him, and God aided him in all his deeds. Therefore, be encouraged in the mercy and power of God, for He will aid you. Remember the pennant that the empress, daughter of the Lady Parecer, gave to you that the seven holy maidens made. Take it and put it on a long lance staff, and be assured that as soon as your enemies see it, they will give up and you will take them all prisoner."

When the emperor heard these words, he remembered what the empress had said when she gave him the pennant—that wherever he went with it, he would conquer. And it pleased God that the chest which held the pennant remained in the emperor's storeroom above the mountain pass. Then he returned to his soldiers and sent for that chest containing the pennant, which was well protected among many relics. And as soon as they brought it to him, he opened the chest, knelt, and took out the pennant with great devotion, tears streaming down his face, for he believed that great virtue resided in it, since that voice from heaven had spoken and reminded him of the pennant. And so it did, for those seven maidens who had made it were seventy years old, and all were born in a multiple birth in the time of the empress's grandmother and she had reared them. And the maidens led such virtuous lives that they rejected marriage, swore chastity, and maintained it in a pure and saintly manner, so that God did many miracles for them in that empire, and God placed His special virtue in anything they made with their hands.

When the morning broke, the emperor took out the pennant with its large and stout staff and said to the knights: "Friends, yesterday you were very fortunate at the beginning and in the middle of the battle, but the end was not good for us, as you see, and I believe this was because of my sins. But Our Lord God, taking pity on us, as a powerful Lord who did not think it right for us to remain in despair, ordered us to attack them. They will not be expecting us and we shall capture them all, and I am absolutely sure that it is to be so."

"Certainly, lord," said the knights, "we are delighted, for death is better for us than for you and us to survive, for that way we can escape the dishonor for the loss we caused our friends and relatives here." And they set out in good spirits to die or conquer, and launched their attack.

And as soon as those troops of the king of Safira saw the pennant, they immediately turned their backs and began to retreat, with the emperor and his soldiers in pursuit, killing and wounding, so that none of them remained who was not dead or a prisoner. The king of Safira was taken prisoner along with the count who had stirred up the dissension between the emperor and the two kings. The emperor and his soldiers thanked God profusely for the grace He had shown in allowing them to win without harm to themselves, for none was wounded or hurt at all. They believed this was a miracle of God, for they were outnumbered ten to one, and according to logic, the others should have vanquished them, and especially since there were just as many good knights on one side as on the other. But our Lord, aware of the goodness of the emperor and the great services he had done Him on many occasions, could not do any less for the prince and considered it well to maintain his honor and to allow the others to be conquered and for Roboán to be the conqueror. Wherefore, he who has God on his side is very fortunate, for such as he has no reason to fear anything. And therefore the Holy Gospel says, "If God be with us, who can stand against us?"

Thus as it is said, "No one!" For it would be madness and a lack of wisdom for anyone, no matter how powerful he might be in this world, to try and stand against the power of God who is almighty.

225. How the emperor ordered Count Farán to be decapitated and pronounced him a traitor

After the emperor saw that all the battlefield was won, he ordered his soldiers to disarm and to rest, although they had labored little in that battle, for God had fought for them. He ordered them to bring to him the king of Safira and Count Farán whom they held prisoner. The emperor asked the king of Safira why he and the king of Garba had rebelled against him. And the king of Safira told him: "My lord, I do not know any other reason except through our great misfortune and because we did not know to guard ourselves from bad advice, and especially from Count Farán here who was the instigator of all this trouble. He and the other counts who died here instilled in us a great fear and distrust of you, saying that you planned to kill us. They especially convinced us it was so because you had ordered us both to come with just a few soldiers, so you could kill us more easily, and also because you were a foreigner who did not respect the subjects in your empire. And the count will not deny this, for if he wishes to say otherwise, I will debase myself and lay hands on him and make him say it is true."

The count did not dare to deny the truth, and said that all had happened just as the king of Safira said.

"It is true, count," said the emperor, "that you have done me a great wrong, for I never deserved this, and therefore you had no cause to stir up rebellion against me in my realm. Moreover, I now believe that the old proverb is true which says that feet which are accustomed to walking cannot stand still. And whoever is accustomed to doing evil does not know how to quit. And you, count, remember that you were the one who advised me, along with the count of Lan, when I first approached the emperor to ask him why he did not laugh. And you advised me to do this so that the emperor would have me decapitated, for this was his customary way of treating whoever asked him that question. Considering that your purpose had not been accomplished in that way, you tried to stir up rebellion in my domain in order to overthrow me. And I do not want you to try it a third time, for the wise man says, if your friend betrays you once, may God curse him, and if twice, may God curse you and him, and if three times, may God curse you for trusting the friend too much. And therefore, I prefer that you be cursed the second time, instead of myself for the third time."

He ordered him to be decapitated, and the count deserved it for trying to overthrow his lord by advising his subjects to rebel and make war against him. And certainly the one who gives evil counsel deserves this sentence, just as the one does who does wrong on the advice of another.

"Well then, count!" said the Knight Amigo, "it is only right on account of the arrogance you assumed on the day that you said I was dealing in deceit, and I told you that whoever lives by treachery would die from it, and you responded, 'So be it.' And surely you should have realized that these efforts and this wicked union between you and the kings would only bring disaster to you. Therefore it is obvious that you are wearing the fetters you deserve."

"In the name of God," said the count, "it's easy for you to talk, but if I had you as you have me, I would treat you even worse."

"Then try to surpass this!" said the Knight Amigo, and he lopped off the count's head. And therefore they say that whatsoever a man soweth, that shall he also reap.

Afterward, the emperor ordered the king of Safira to have all the towns and castles in his kingdom surrendered to him. The king told him that he should travel through the realm and the king's subjects would accept him in the towns and castles of the kingdom without any hesitation. The law of the land was such that, if the emperor should come to visit the country, the king who was a vassal of the emperor had to welcome him whether he liked it or not, and the people had to accept him whether he inherited from the king or from his father, for their lord had to come to terms with the emperor. And he said that he would go then to the largest city in his kingdom, which they called Montecaelo. And it took this name because the land is the color of the sky, and all looks like sapphire, and all the fine oriental sapphires are found in that land. And that land is the very last inhabited land toward the east, and there Asia Major borders on the lands of the cold north, whereby it is fitting that something should be said here about the three kingdoms of the world that Noah created, and where he began each one and where he finished, and why it is called Asia Major.

It is found in the ancient histories, that after the language was divided into seventy languages, as you have heard, the gentiles were scattered and Noah began to unite them and to advise them. He divided the world into three parts and established the boundaries of each third, and he apportioned them to his three sons. He called one Europe, the second Asia, and the third Africa. Europe is the third that is the part to the north, and Africa is the third that is to the south. Asia is in the middle of these two sections. And Noah gave Europe to Japheth his oldest son, Asia to Shem his middle son, and Africa to Canaan his youngest son. Europe is the part to the north if you face east, and it begins at the top of the world, near the east, over the empire of the Fortunate Islands, and extends through the land of the Turks and through the lands of Gog and Magog, and through the lands of Germany and Slovakia, Greece, and Rome, and through the lands of the Welsh, the Picards, and the Burgundians, and through the land of Brittany, and through the lands that are called Portugal, which means "the large land," and through the land of Gascony, and from the Alps to Bordeaux, and through the lands of Spain. It terminates on the island of Calis which Hercules settled, in a church which serves as a landmark, which is on the seashore about two leagues from the castle of Calis. And those who came later gave the church the name of San Pedro and it never lost this name, and they call it Saint Peter, for thus the Moors ordered them to do.

And the third part, Asia, is divided into two segments: one is the part to the east and begins with the river Euphrates up to the lower part of Spain, and they call it Asia Major. And on the right hand of this Asia Major is the sea that is called the Sea of India, and in this Asia Major are the lands of Hazes, Germany, and al-Fares, and it borders India. The part to the north of it is the lands of Sind and the part to the south, the lands of Agas and Almus, which are the share of the Ethiopians who are called cannibals, because they eat white men whenever they can get them.

And the river Euphrates divides Asia Major and Asia Minor. And at the other end of this Asia Minor are the plains and the desert, and between the land of Africa and the desert there are some mountain ranges called Gameldaron, and those lands have some sandy areas of fine sandlike powder. The winds move and raise that powder from one place and cast it to another across the width of the desert, and at times, create a great mound that seems as though it was always there. And the sons of Israel wandered forty years to the end of this desert until the time limit that God allotted was reached, and they entered the land of Canaan, and the sons of Israel settled the land of Shem, son of Noah, which is Asia Major toward the west. And the sons of Israel settled the land of Arabia, which is in the realm of Mecca and the others dwelt in the land of Canaan, which is in the province of Jerusalem.

And the other third, Africa, begins at Alexandria with a division of the kingdom of Egypt, and it stretches in length from the city of Barca, which is in the eastern part, up to Tangier[1] which is in the western part, and which is called in Latin Mauritania, and it stretches in width from the sea to the sand areas that exist in the land of the Ethiopians, and there are vast deserts and great mountains, and they go from west to east.

This explanation of the three parts of the world was placed here so that those who plan to travel through the world may learn of it, especially those who plan to explore and evaluate the lands, so that they will be able to find them and live better, just as this emperor did, who wandered through the lands doing good and whom God raised to high position, as you heard.

226. How the emperor traveled through the land accompanied by all the counts and the others on whom he bestowed lands

The story relates that the emperor went to the city they call Montecaelo and was there welcomed with great festivities befitting his rank, although the

---

1. The text says *Tanjat-ally-adia.* My guess here is *Tangier.*

people realized their lord, the king, was a prisoner of the emperor. The people of the city were very wealthy, noble, and cultured, and they lived in peace, justice, and happiness, the great and the poor as one. Two days after the emperor entered the kingdom, the bishop of the town, who was chancellor to the king, and all the citizens asked the emperor to have mercy on the king. And the emperor, with the great compassion he felt for him, pardoned the king, for he realized that the king was a good and wise man, and the emperor did not want to disregard the laws of that land. The emperor commanded the citizens to accept the king again as their lord, for the people were not going to recognize him without the order of the emperor, since the king had broken his trust and had failed the emperor in the loyalty he should have shown him. They welcomed the king, as one loved by all, and they held a great celebration for the emperor, showing how much they appreciated the favor he had done them.

Early the next morning, they took the emperor to a garden surrounded by a high wall inside the town in which a very high and arched room was built. The vault was executed in Moorish style with some beautiful sapphires, and in the middle of the room was a sapphire shaped like a ball, octagonal, and so large and heavy that two camels could not carry it. And it has such great medicinal power that any men or beasts who have some swelling and are taken there and placed near that stone are straightway healed. And it does the same thing to blood, for a person who is bleeding and is placed before that stone will cease to bleed. The emperor himself had a test made of it. He had the throats of some cattle slit near that sapphire, and no blood flowed from them, and they breathed through the wound and did not die until their appointed time to die. They neither ate nor drank, as all mortal beasts of this world must do, for they are unable to sustain themselves without eating or drinking. And all may believe that there are no other virtues in the sapphire but these two—one against swelling and the other against the flowing of blood. And truly this is the land where the perfect and potent sapphires are found, and they especially come from the kingdom of Safira, which took its name from the sapphire.

After the emperor had traveled through that land and restored it to tranquillity, he went through the kingdom of Garba, which has an abundance of everything and is very bountiful, and all of it is irrigated by the waters of the Tigris and the Euphrates. He bequeathed this kingdom to Garbel, one of his vassals, a very wise old knight and great warrior, because he thought his name was in keeping with the name of the kingdom. He was a very good king and well liked by all his subjects. And this knight was the same one the king of Mentón, his father, had given to him as his adviser when he left home. Furthermore, he gave the earldom of Count Farán to the Knight Amigo and the earldoms of the other six counts who were killed in that battle to some of his other knights, whom he judged to have served him best and who deserved them. Very few of his knights remained of the three hundred he had taken with him. However, he favored those who had escaped unhurt by endowing them with property and rewarding them as much as he could, so that there was none whom he did not reward and honor for the good services they had rendered. Therefore all his subjects praised the emperor because he had rewarded the knights so well who had served him so much, and consequently all were eager to serve him, believing he would reward them for the services they might supply. Surely it is only right that whoever does well should have a good reward for it.

The emperor, having traveled throughout the land with all these counts and with all the others to whom he had bequeathed property, settled them in their possessions, granted them all the special favors they requested, and left them at peace, each in his own realm and with the esteem of all their subjects.

All the citizens of the empire were happy and content because they had a lord who truly loved them and respected their traditions and customs. He was very faithful in attending their religious services, and with no evidence of scorn, and he granted many favors to the churches, and endowed them with towns and castles, and furnished them with princely accouterments according to their need. Among all the good qualities the emperor possessed was this—he dealt out justice fairly to all, and he never revoked a concession he had given nor any that the former emperors had granted, but instead, he reaffirmed them by his letters and charters, endorsed with authorizations in gold. And no man was ever known to violate them who did not become a personal enemy of the emperor, for the emperor judged that none should violate the agreements he made nor the ones made by the other emperors, and he held it his duty to uphold them. Surely it is madness and folly for anyone to act against the will of his lord, and especially to deny the things that he does which bring aid and comfort to those who need them.

The one who grants favors not only honors whoever receives the favor, but himself as well, for he is honored and praised by God and man for the good that he does. Therefore they say that honor does not reside in that person who receives, but in the giver. And so whoever rejects the favors and services of his lord and denies them in speech, in deed, and in counsel, should be despised by God and man. He should suffer cruel and merciless punishment, for he feels no remorse for the evil and hurt to his brother. As all men are brothers, we should love one another according to the faith of Jesus Christ which we share.

227. How the emperor sent the Count Amigo to Princess Seringa

The story relates that the emperor, being on good terms with his people, asked their permission to take a wife, so there would be some one of his lineage who could rule the empire after his death. Some of them nominated the daughters of emperors, and others, the daughters of kings. And while he was considering these, he recalled the words that he had had with the Princess Seringa, and he sent the Knight Amigo—whom they now called the Count Amigo—there to learn if she was alive or if she was married, and if he found her alive and not married to give her an affidavit that he was sending, which told her on his behalf that he wanted her to comply with her promise to marry him, if it suited her. Count Amigo then went without delay, and he found the Princess Seringa in that city where he had left her, and he asked if she was married, and his host told him that she was not.

The next morning he went to see her, and as he entered the door, she recognized him although she did not remember his name, and she said to him, "Knight, what is your name?"

"My lady," he replied, "Amigo."

"Oh, Knight Amigo!" she cried, "you are so welcome! Tell me by the faith you owe God, how is my friend the prince?"

"Very well, my lady," said the Knight Amigo.[1]

"Blessed be the name of God!" she exclaimed. "What I most loved and most wanted to hear of all the things in this world is this. And does he ever recall what he did for me and my country?"

"Of course not, my lady," said the Count Amigo, "if he did any good here, he has forgotten it, for he never remembers the good he has done, but what he is to do, and he sends you this letter he wrote in his own hand."

The princess opened the letter and read it, and she found inside a ring with a small and beautiful ruby that she had secretly given to the prince when he said goodbye to her. When she saw it she alternately blushed and paled, for she received the ring with pleasure and concern. She was delighted, thinking that he sent it to her by that knight because Roboán believed what she had said to him; and she felt concern, thinking that he had died and the ring had been returned to her.

"My lady," said the Count Amigo, "if you want to hear the message for which I came here, I will relieve you of your great worry."

"Knight Amigo," replied the princess, "may God allow you to tell the good news."

"Amen," he said, "and so it will be. My lord the emperor sends you greetings."

"What emperor?" asked the princess.

"Roboán, your friend," answered the count.

"What is he emperor of?" asked the princess.

"Of the empire of Tigrida," he answered.

"And how could he have forgotten what he loved most in this world while God was favoring him and making him emperor?" she asked.

---

1. The text here alternates between the use of "Knight" Amigo and "Count" Amigo.

"In no way, my lady, did he forget," said the count, "because the reason he sends me here is to find out if you are married and if you are not, may it please you to marry him."

"Are you bringing letters for my uncle Count Rubén?" she asked.

"Yes, my lady," he said.

"Well, I beg you talk with him, and tell him what you have to say, and do not tell him that you spoke with me on this matter.

And so he did. When the count heard this news, he was extremely pleased and went to the princess and said, "My lady, will you give me a reward?"

"I will," said the princess, "if you tell me good news."

"Upon my word, my lady," said the count, "it is so good that I am sure you will be pleased with it."

"I will gladly listen if you so wish," said the princess.

"My lady," said the count, "Prince Roboán, your champion and protector, is the emperor of Tigrida and he sends word for you to marry him."

"Oh, count!" she cried, "will you advise me?"

"By heaven, my lady," said the count, "I will."

"And, count," said the princess, "do you consider it right that I should leave my kingdom unprotected?"

"My lady," said the count, "it cannot be unprotected when it has an emperor as powerful as that one as its defender."

"Count," said the princess, "I have guided myself by your counsel up to now and I will guide myself henceforth. Do what you think is right and it will be to my credit and to yours."

The count ordered letters prepared on behalf of the princess to all her subjects to come to the meeting that the princess planned to convene in order to talk with them about things that would be to her honor and of great benefit to the nation. And when they had gathered together a week after Easter as she had commanded, the count, uncle of the princess, spoke on her behalf to all the citizens who had arrived there. He told them that Prince Roboán, son of the king of Mentón, who had fought for the princess and had regained for her the towns and castles that she had lost, and had made all the nearby kings who had tried to seize her property promise to leave her lands in peace, was emperor of Tigrida, and that he had sent a request for the princess to become his wife, and that they should state their opinions, for she would not do anything without the counsel of her countrymen.

They considered it a great honor for her, but some said that if she abdicated, perhaps their former enemies would rise up again to wrong them and ravage the kingdom. But in conclusion, they all agreed to advise her to marry, for an honor to her was an honor to themselves. And they sent word to ask the king of Bran, brother of the queen who was mother of the princess, to go with her, escort her, and honor her on that day. And the king agreed to do so, and he accompanied her with a large force of cavalry in full dress. And the princess took with her many ladies and maidens, daughters of hidalgos, who were the most refined in all the kingdom. There were one hundred in all, dressed in garments of gold and silk according to the fashion of that country. They began their journey so that they entered the empire of the emperor on the celebration of Pentecost, and there they awaited the command of the emperor. The Count Amigo, who had gone in advance, told the emperor that the Princess Seringa had left her country and was coming to meet him, and the king of Bran was escorting her with a large force of cavalry and that she was accompanied by one hundred highborn ladies and maidens who were elegantly dressed. When the emperor heard this, he was very happy, for he had been unable to rest easily after he had sent the Count Amigo to the princess for worrying whether she would be married, for the three-year time limit that she had promised to wait for him had expired. Everyone could see that he was elated, and he sent for all the kings who were his vassals to come out to welcome her. He commanded that they be given everything they needed, and he accorded them great honors, for they were vassals who hoped to see their lord make a good marriage. When the emperor learned for certain that she was coming, he went out to welcome her two days' journey from the Tigris river, at a city named Ledica. He took her horse by the reins and went directly to a convent on the outskirts of the city. His chancellor, the archbishop, was there with the emperor, and they entered the church. He kept vigil with them and then they left. They went to the city, where she was welcomed as befitted an empress. And this marriage was solemnized on Saint John's Day.

228. How they had a son at the end of a year who was named Blessed Son

The story relates that this was the most beautiful ever reared in that region and that God had chosen to combine beauty with beauty and gentleness with gentleness and goodness with goodness, so that all who saw them on their thrones never tired of seeing them, nor did they have the desire to eat, drink, or sleep, but were like people in a daze who could not remember anything except when the emperor and the empress arose from the dais in order to go to their bedchamber. The populace considered themselves very fortunate, for that marriage was equal in honor, attractiveness, and in true love. Truly it was so, for what pleased one pleased the other, and nothing they saw displeased them. And so God joined them together and blessed them, and there was never a need for a mediator in any matter in which they were involved. At the end of a year they had a son such as you might suppose would be born of such a union as that of the emperor and the empress, and this son was named Blessed Son. And truly he was blessed above all other men in this world, and he honored his mother and father and was obedient in everything they wanted. He was compassionate and an adherent of fairness, and very generous with his gifts to the needy, so that no one in his domain was poor or lacked for anything unless it was due to his own wickedness. And as soon as the boy reached the age of seven, the gave the empire into his charge.

229. How the Emperor Roboán and the Empress Seringa visited the kingdom of Pandulfa and went to visit his father, his mother, and his brother Garfín

The emperor and the empress went to visit the kingdom of Empress Seringa, and afterwards went on a pilgrimage to the monastery of the Holy Spirit, which the king of Mentón had ordered constructed where he had first met the Count Amigo. And they went to see his father the king, and his mother, and Prince Garfín, his brother. Truly no one should doubt that there was great happiness and pleasure among these, for the story relates that in the seven days they visited with the king of Mentón, there was no night that was not as bright as day no matter how dark it seemed. They never got sleepy but gazed at each other as though they were natural stone images, and they did not move. In truth this happened through the grace of God, who loved them for their natural goodness. And afterward they returned to their empire, where God performed many miracles through them throughout all the lands they ruled, so that it is called the Blessed Land today. It took its name from the son of the emperor and empress, for he had the name Blessed Son, just as you have already heard, and of whom they say a book is written in Arabic in which is told all his life and the many good deeds he accomplished.

Wherefore the translator says that the one who gives himself over to good works is very fortunate and always strives to do his best, for by doing good, a man can attain the love of God and men, and advantages and honor in this world and the next, never getting angry or despairing of the favor of God. And one ought not to worry or be anxious. For whoever wants to travel a long road and plans to reach the end of it with Him, it is fitting to walk at His pace and not be worried, for if he worries, he will tire, and if he tires, he will slacken, and perhaps be unable to complete his journey. Therefore, the philosopher says that the harder part of a journey is the first steps, and the completion is not easily accomplished, and natural movement is the contrary of that done by force, for nature begins leisurely and goes steadily gathering strength unto the end, and thus the work is more completely fulfilled. And therefore we should beg God that He, through His holy grace, may help us to begin our work with a natural movement and complete such works as may be in God's service and to the advantage and honor of our bodies and to the salvation of our souls. Amen.

The End